COFRESTRI PLW

PARISH REGISTERS OF WALES

COFRESTRI PLWYF CYMRU

PARISH REGISTERS OF WALES

Cynullwyd gan: Compiled by

C J Williams
&
J Watts-Williams

LLYFRGELL GENEDLAETHOL CYMRU
a GRŴP ARCHIFYDDION SIROL CYMRU
mewn cydweithrediad â
CHYMDEITHAS YR ACHYDDWYR

NATIONAL LIBRARY OF WALES &
WELSH COUNTY ARCHIVISTS' GROUP
in association with the
SOCIETY OF GENEALOGISTS

2000

Mabwysiadwyd y llyfr hwn gan Gymdeithas yr Achyddwyr fel rhif 13 yn y gyfres *National Index of Parish Registers*
This book has been adopted by the Society of Genealogists as volume 13 of the *National Index of Parish Registers*

Mae cofnod catalog i'r llyfr hwn ar gael o'r Llyfrgell Brydeinig.
A catalogue record for this book is available from the British Library.

Clawr Caled: ISBN 1-86225-020-0
Clawr Meddal: ISBN 1-86225-022-7

Argraffiad cyntaf 1986
Ail argraffiad 2000

First edition 1986
Second edition 2000

Argraffwyd gan / Printed by: Y Lolfa

RHAGAIR

Y mae argraffiad cyntaf y gwaith hwn a fu mor werthfawr i lawer, yn arbennig i'r rhai sy'n ymwneud â hanes eu teuluoedd, allan o brint ers peth amser. Pleser arbennig felly yw cael croesawu ymddangosiad yr argraffiad diwygiedig ohono. Seiliwyd yr ail argraffiad hwn ar adolygiad trylwyr o ddaliadau'r archifdai er mwyn ymgorffori'r cofrestri ychwanegol a adneuwyd oddi ar yr argraffiad cyntaf yn 1986. Y mae hefyd yn adlewyrchu'r gwaith a wnaed i ficroffilmio'r cofrestri, a gweithgareddau'r cymdeithasau hanes teulu yn eu trawsysgrifo a'u mynegeio. Diolchaf i bawb a fu â rhan yn nwyn y gyfrol i fodolaeth, yn enwedig ei golygyddion John Watts-Williams, Ceidwad Cynorthwyol yn Adran Lawysgrifau a Chofysgrifau Llyfrgell Genedlaethol Cymru, a Christopher Williams, cyn Archifydd Sirol Clwyd; rhaid diolch hefyd i Isadran Argraffu'r Llyfrgell Genedlaethol a Gwasg y Lolfa am waith nodweddiadol lân.

ANDREW GREEN
Llyfrgellydd

FOREWORD

The first edition of this work, of such great value to many, especially those who study family history, has been out of print for some time. It is a particular pleasure therefore to be able to welcome the appearance of this, its second edition, which is based on a thorough revision of the holdings of the archive repositories to incorporate additional registers deposited since the publication of the first edition in 1986. It also reflects work done on the microfilming of the registers, and the activities of the family history societies in transcribing and indexing them. I thank warmly all those who had a part in bringing the project to fruition, particularly its editors, John Watts-Williams, an Assistant Keeper in the Department of Manuscripts and Records of the National Library of Wales, and Christopher Williams, former County Archivist of Clwyd; I have to thank also the Printing Section of the National Library and Y Lolfa for characteristically skilful work.

ANDREW GREEN
Librarian

CYMRU - YR HEN SIROEDD
WALES - THE OLD COUNTIES

MÔN
ANGLESEY

Y FFLINT
FLINTSHIRE

CAERNARFON
CAERNARFONSHIRE

DINBYCH
DENBIGHSHIRE

MEIRIONNYDD
MERIONETH

TREFALDWYN
MONTGOMERYSHIRE

ABERTEIFI
CARDIGANSHIRE

MAESYFED
RADNORSHIRE

PENFRO
PEMBROKESHIRE

CAERFYRDDIN
CARMARTHENSHIRE

BRYCHEINIOG
BRECKNOCKSHIRE

MYNWY
MONMOUTHSHIRE

MORGANNWG
GLAMORGAN

0   10   20   30

CYNNWYS

CONTENTS

LLUNIAU

ILLUSTRATIONS

Cydnabyddiaeth
Archifdy Gwent 3
Archifdy Morgannwg 6, 11
Archifdy Sir y Fflint 1, 8
Archifdy Ynys Môn 2
Gwasanaeth Archifau Gwynedd 7
Gwasanaeth Archifau Sir Gaerfyrddin 9
Llyfrgell Genedlaethol Cymru 4, 5, 10, 12

Acknowledgements
Anglesey County Record Office 2
Carmarthenshire Archives Service 9
Flintshire Record Office 1, 8
Glamorgan Record Office 6, 11
Gwent Record Office 3
Gwynedd Archives Service 7
National Library of Wales 4, 5, 10, 12

CYDNABYDDIAETH

Mae'r golygyddion yn ddyledus i staff yr archifdai sydd â gofal dros y cofnodion a ddisgrifir yn y gyfrol hon am ddarparu rhestrau ac am ateb eu hymholiadau mor amyneddgar; i Mr Dafydd Hayes, Cymdeithas Hanes Teulu Clwyd, a Mrs Yvonne Edwards, Cymdeithas Hanes Teulu Gwynedd, am eu cymorth; i aelodau isadrannau Argraffu a Ffotograffiaeth y Llyfrgell Genedlaethol am baratoi rhannau o'r testun; ac i'r Lolfa am orffen y testun a'i argraffu.

Dylid diolch i Fainc Esgobion yr Eglwys yng Nghymru ac i swyddogion ei Chorff Llywodraethol am gymeradwyo'r egwyddor o ddiogelu cofnodion plwyfol, ac i'r ymgynghorwyr ar archifau ymhob esgobaeth am eu hymdrech i'w gwireddu. Ond ni allesid bod wedi cyflawni dim heb gydweithrediad yr offeiriaid. Rydym yn hynod ddiolchgar iddynt hwy am roi hen gofrestri plwyf Cymru ar gadw yn ddiogel mewn archifdai a, thrwy hynny, wneud y gyfrol hon yn bosibl.

ACKNOWLEDGEMENTS

The editors are grateful to the staffs of the repositories which hold the records described in this volume for supplying lists and patiently answering enquiries; to Mr Dafydd Hayes, of the Clwyd Family History Society, and Mrs Yvonne Edwards, of the Gwynedd Family History Society, for their assistance; to the staff of the Printing and Photographic Sections of the National Library, who prepared parts of the text; and to Y Lolfa for completing and printing the text.

Thanks are due to the Bench of Bishops of the Church in Wales, and the officials of the Governing Body, who approved the proposals for the preservation of parish records, and to the advisers on archives in each diocese who encouraged their deposit. However, little could have been achieved without the co-operation of incumbents; particular thanks are due to them for depositing the ancient parish registers of Wales in safe custody in record repositories, so making the present volume possible.

RHAGYMADRODD

Cofrestri plwyf ar adnau

Rhydd y gyfrol hon fanylion am gofrestri plwyf gwreiddiol ac adysgrifau'r esgob, ac am ficroffilmiau, adluniadau, a chopïau eraill ohonynt a gedwir gan archifdai yng Nghymru a'r gororau, a chan Gymdeithas yr Achyddwyr. Mae'n cynnwys y tair hen sir ar ddeg, gan ddisgrifio cofrestri tros fil o blwyfi a chapeli anwes a oedd mewn bodolaeth cyn 1812, a chofrestri tua 400 o eglwysi a godwyd wedi 1812 y mae eu cofnodion ar adnau mewn rhyw archifdy neu'i gilydd.

Yn 1944 arwyddwyd cytundeb rhwng Llyfrgell Genedlaethol Cymru a Chorff Cynrychiolwyr yr Eglwys yng Nghymru i roddi cofnodion esgobol, cabidylaidd, esgobaethol, ac eglwysig eraill ar adnau yn y llyfrgell.[1] Yn unol ag estyniad i'r cytundeb hwnnw, dechreuodd y Llyfrgell ar y dasg o gasglu'r cofrestri plwyf a chofnodion plwyfol eraill yn 1950. Trwy gytundeb pellach yn 1976 rhwng y Corff Cynrychiolwyr a phob un o gynghorau sir Cymru (ac eithrio Powys) penodwyd yr archifdai sirol hefyd yn gadwrfeydd addas ar gyfer cofnodion plwyfol eglwysig.[2] Mewn cylchlythyr a ddosbarthwyd yr un flwyddyn yn enw Cofrestrydd Archesgob Cymru anogwyd pob periglor i roi ei gofnodion eglwysig ar adnau mewn lle diogel, a phenodwyd ymgynghorydd archifol ymhob esgobaeth i arolygu'r gwaith. Mae llwyddiant yr ymgyrch yn amlwg pan sylweddolir fod pob un o hen blwyfi Cymru wedi rhoi eu cofrestri ar adnau naill ai yn y Llyfrgell Genedlaethol neu yn un o archifdai sirol Cymru erbyn hyn. Staff y sefydliadau hynny sydd wedi paratoi'r arolwg hwn.

Terfynau'r esgobaethau

Tan ei datgysylltu yn 1920 roedd yr eglwys Gymreig yn rhan annatod o Eglwys Loegr. Anwybyddid ffiniau Cymru a Lloegr gan yr esgobaethau (a oedd yn wir yn eu rhagflaenu). Ymestynnai'r pedair esgobaeth Gymreig hynafol ar draws ffiniau'r siroedd fel a ganlyn:

Bangor	Môn, y rhan helaethaf o sir Gaernarfon, rhannau o Feirionnydd a Threfaldwyn, ynghyd â deoniaeth Dyffryn Clwyd yng nghanolbarth sir Ddinbych
Llandaf	y rhan fwyaf o siroedd Morgannwg a Mynwy
Llanelwy	y rhan fwyaf o siroedd y Fflint a Dinbych, ynghyd â rhannau o siroedd Caernarfon, Meirionnydd, Trefaldwyn, a'r Amwythig

| Tyddewi | siroedd Caerfyrddin, Aberteifi, Penfro, Brycheiniog, y rhan fwyaf o Faesyfed, a rhannau o Drefaldwyn, Morgannwg, Mynwy, a Henffordd |

Nid oedd yng Nghymru ond un priodoriaeth yn rhydd oddi wrth awdurdod esgobaethol, sef Penarlâg yn sir y Fflint.

Roedd hefyd rannau o Gymru yn perthyn i esgobaethau Seisnig:

Caer	rhannau o siroedd y Fflint a Dinbych
Caerlwytgoed	plwyf Llannerch Banna, sir y Fflint, a rhan Gymreig plwyf Llanymynech, Sir Amwythig
Henffordd	rhannau o siroedd Trefaldwyn, Maesyfed, a Mynwy

Trosglwyddwyd amryw o'r plwyfi hyn o'u hesgobaethau Seisnig i rai Cymreig yn 1849. Bu cryn newid yn y ffin rhwng esgobaethau Bangor a Llanelwy yn 1859 pan roddwyd deoniaeth Dyffryn Clwyd i Lanelwy yn gyfnewid am ddeoniaeth Cyfeiliog a Mawddwy. A chafwyd ad-drefnu pellach ar y gororau yn sgîl Deddf Eglwys Cymru 1914 a ddaeth i rym yn 1920. Roedd y plwyfi a arferai berthyn i esgobaethau Cymreig ond a safai yn gyfan gwbl ar dir Lloegr i'w trosglwyddo i esgobaethau Seisnig, ac i'r gwrthwyneb. Roedd pob un ond dau o'r pedwar plwyf ar bymtheg a safai yn rhannol ar dir Cymru ac yn rhannol ar dir Lloegr, i'w trin 'yn unol â dymuniad cyffredinol eu plwyfolion,' fel petaent yn Lloegr. Yn y ddau achos arall, bu'n rhaid cynnal pleidlais, a dewisodd pobl Llansilin fod yn rhan o Gymru. (Mae cofrestri'r plwyfi Cymreig sydd yn dal i berthyn i Eglwys Loegr wedi eu rhoi ar adnau yn yr archifdy sirol priodol dros Glawdd Offa — Caer, Amwythig, neu Henffordd). Crewyd dwy esgobaeth newydd yng Nghymru — Mynwy o esgobaeth Llandaf yn 1921, ac Abertawe ac Aberhonddu o esgobaeth Tyddewi yn 1923.

Terfynau'r siroedd

Mae testun y gyfrol hon wedi ei drefnu yn ôl hen siroedd Cymru fel yr oeddent cyn eu diddymu gan y mesur ad-drefniant llywodraeth leol yn 1974 a'u ffurfio, trwy rannu rhai ohonynt ac uno eraill, yn wyth o siroedd newydd. Yn 1996 ad-drefnwyd llywodraeth leol drachefn ac, er bod rhai o'r hen siroedd wedi ailymddangos, nid ydynt i gyd yn meddu'r un ffiniau ag yr oeddent cyn 1974. O ganlyniad, y mae ambell archifdy wedi newid ei enw ers argraffiad cyntaf y llyfr hwn. Ond nid yw'r cofrestri wedi eu symud o'r naill archifdy i'r llall. Yn ne Cymru y mae gwasanaethau cyfun — Gorllewin Morgannwg, Gwent, a Morgannwg — yn darparu archifdai yn hen siroedd Morgannwg a Mynwy. Sefydlodd rhai o'r awdurdodau newydd — Castell-nedd Port Talbot (yn enw Gwasanaeth Archifau Gorllewin Morgannwg), Conwy, a Wrecsam — gyrchfannau archifol sydd yn dal copïau microffilm o gofrestri plwyf eu hardaloedd.

Cofrestri plwyf

Hyd yn oed yn y siroedd lle y maent wedi goroesi yn well na'r cyffredin, nid yw cofrestri Cymru i'w cymharu ag eiddo'r siroedd Seisnig ar y gororau. Thomas Cromwell yn 1538 a orchmynnodd gyntaf y dylid cadw cofrestri plwyf, ond un gofrestr yn unig sydd ar gael heddiw yng Nghymru yn dyddio yn ôl i 1538, sef cofrestr Gwaunysgor, sir y Fflint. Nid y gofrestr bapur wreiddiol mo honno ond copi memrwn a wnaethpwyd ar ryw adeg wedi'r cadarnhad yn 1598 o gyfansoddiad y flwyddyn flaenorol a orchmynnai gadw'r cofrestri plwyf yn fwy gofalus. Eithr y mae gan sir Amwythig bump o gofrestri yn dechrau yn 1538, a chan swydd Henffordd saith.[3] O'r ychydig dros fil o blwyfi a chapeli anwes hynafol sydd yng Nghymru, nid oes ond saith deg â chofrestr yn cychwyn cyn 1600 ac y mae ymhell dros eu hanner hwy heb gofrestr cyn 1700. Yn wir, mewn llawer o blwyfi, yn enwedig yn ne Cymru, nid oes cofrestr cyn 1754 pan ddechreuwyd cadw cofnodion priodas ar wahân, neu hyd yn oed 1813, pryd y defnyddiwyd y cyfrolau printiedig ar gyfer bedydd a chladdu am y tro cyntaf ar eu gwedd bresennol. Yn y plwyfi hyn, mae'r cofrestri cynharaf (o femrwn fel rheol) a gynhwysai gofnodion bedydd, priodas, a chladdu rhwng yr un cloriau, wedi diflannu'n llwyr.

Mae'r cofrestri wedi goroesi yn well mewn ambell esgobaeth na'i gilydd. Llanelwy sydd â'r cyfartaledd uchaf o gofrestri cynnar, a chan Dyddewi (lle y mae dros hanner y plwyfi heb gofrestr gynharach na 1754) mae'r isaf. Yn gyffredinol, mae cofrestri gogledd Cymru yn fwy cynnar na rhai'r de. O ran siroedd, y Fflint sy'n rhagori. Mae ganddi'r unig gofrestr sy'n dechrau yn 1538; mae deunaw o'i naw ar hugain o blwyfi hynafol (62%) yn meddu ar gofrestr sy'n dechrau cyn 1660, ac mae gan bob un o'i phlwyfi gofrestr cyn 1754. O'u trefnu yn ôl cyfartaledd y plwyfi sydd â chofrestr cyn 1660, siroedd gogleddol Trefaldwyn (49%), Dinbych (33%), a Meirionnydd (29%) ddaw nesaf i'r Fflint. Yn ne Cymru, sir Fynwy (20%) sydd agosaf at y cyfartaledd a geir yn y gogledd. Ar waelod y rhestr gwelir Aberteifi (4%) heb un gofrestr gynharach na 1653; bron dwy ran o dair o'i phlwyfi heb gofrestr cyn 1754; a chynifer â thri ar ddeg ohonynt heb gofrestr cyn 1813.

Dengys manylion dau arolwg arall a wnaethpwyd pan oedd y cofrestri yn dal i fod yn y plwyfi, pa gyfrolau sydd wedi eu colli yn ystod y can mlynedd a hanner diwethaf. Seiliwyd y cyntaf ar atebion clerigwyr i holiadur a ddosbarthwyd yn adeg Cyfrifiad 1831.[4] Cafwyd manylion, gyfrol wrth gyfrol gan amlaf, am y cofrestri cyn-1813 a oedd ar gael y pryd hwnnw, ac ambell waith cynigiwyd rheswm da am golledion diweddar o'u plith. (Mewn ambell esgobaeth, mae'r atebion gofwyol tua diwedd y ddeunawfed ganrif a dechrau'r bedwaredd ar bymtheg yn cynnig manylion am oed cofrestri hefyd.) Er gwaethaf ei aml feflau a'i ambell wall dybryd, bu arolwg 1831 yn ffynhonnell werthfawr i awduron.[5] Yn nes at ein dyddiau ni, gwnaeth y Llyfrgell Genedlaethol arolwg o gofnodion plwyfol fesul esgobaeth rhwng 1933 a 1940.[6] Ar ffurf holiadur i'r clerigwr y lluniwyd yr arolwg hwn hefyd, ond fel rheol mae'r atebion yn ddigon manwl i hwyluso cymhariaeth bellach. Yn fwy diweddar fyth gwnaeth rhai o'r archifdai arolwg o'r sefyllfa yn eu siroedd gan archwilio'r cofrestri eu hunain. Mae'r wybodaeth am unrhyw gofrestr sydd wedi mynd ar goll ers ei gofnodi gan y naill arolwg neu'r llall wedi ei hymgorffori yn y testun.

Collodd 136 o blwyfi o leiaf un o'u cofrestri er 1831, ac mewn 51 o achosion eraill mae cofrestri a nodwyd yn y 1930au wedi diflannu erbyn hyn. (Mewn ambell blwyf daeth i glawr gofrestr gynharach na'r rhai a nodwyd ar ei gyfer gan y naill arolwg a'r llall, ac ers cyhoeddi argraffiad cyntaf y llyfr hwn yn 1986 ailddarganfuwyd cofrestri mewn sawl plwyf. Ar y llaw arall, yn ystod yr un cyfnod dygwyd cofrestri un o blwyfi'r gogledd ac ni chafwyd hwy yn eu hôl). Bu'r colledion yn drymach yn ne Cymru; mae tua un o bob pedwar o blwyfi Caerfyrddin a Phenfro wedi colli cofrestr er 1831, a thua un o bob tri o blwyfi Aberteifi, Brycheiniog, Maesyfed, a Morgannwg.

Collwyd cofrestri yn ddamweiniol trwy dân (Llanddeusant, Llangynog, a Phentywyn, sir Gaerfyrddin; Llansannffraid Glan Conwy, sir Ddinbych; Hanmer a Llanfynydd, sir y Fflint; Diserth a Phyllalai, sir Faesyfed; Rhodogeidio, sir Fôn; Eglwys y Drindod a Saint Arvans, sir Fynwy; Angle a Chastellmartin, sir Benfro); a thrwy lifogydd (Llechryd, sir Aberteifi). Yng Nghilymaenllwyd, sir Gaerfyrddin, a Llangatwg, sir Forgannwg, fe'u rhoddwyd o bwrpas ar y tân er mwyn cynhesu trigolion y persondy. Fe'u dygwyd gan swyddogion y plwyf (Nantglyn, sir Ddinbych), gan offeiriaid (Caerau a Threlái, sir Forgannwg), a chan ladron (Trefesgob, sir Fynwy). Yn sir Gaerfyrddin, cyhuddwyd curad Llan-gain o werthu'r gofrestr am ddeugain punt; yn sir Aberteifi, haerir bod cofrestr gynnar Llanfihangel Genau'r-glyn wedi ei dwyn ymaith i'w harddangos mewn llys barn ac na ddychwelwyd mohoni; ac yn sir Benfro tybir bod y Ffrancod wedi difa cofrestri Llanwnda a Threletert yn adeg y glaniad yn 1797. Fe sonnir hefyd am fuwch yn cnoi cil ar gofrestr plwyf (nas enwir) ym Môn.[7]

Ychydig sy'n rhaid ei ddweud am gynnwys y cofrestri, oherwydd yr un yw eu hanes a rhai Lloegr sydd wedi cael sylw tra helaeth.[8] Yn Lladin mae'r cofnodion, gan fwyaf, tan tua 1732. Mae cofnodion Cymraeg yn hynod o brin, ond fe'u gwelir o bryd i'w gilydd yn ystod y ddeunawfed ganrif mewn cylch cyfyng iawn o blwyfi. Ambell waith gwelir plwyf tlawd yng nghefn gwlad yn ymwrthod yn llwyr â'r gorchwyl o gadw cofrestr ei hun gan roi'r cofnodion yng nghofrestr y plwyf agosaf ato. Er enghraifft ni cheir cofrestr ar wahân ar gyfer plwyf Llanfaelrhys, sir Gaernarfon, tan 1811, ond ceir y cofnodion perthnasol am y cyfnod cyn hynny yng nghofrestr Aberdaron. Rhoddir croesgyfeiriad at achosion o'r fath yn nhestun y llyfr hwn. Mae amryw o blwyfi bychain yn dal i ddefnyddio'r un gofrestr brintiedig ar gyfer bedydd neu gladdedigaeth ag a ddechreuwyd yn 1813, ac oherwydd hynny mae'r cofrestri a roddwyd ar adnau ganddynt yn gorffen gyda'r flwyddyn 1812. Caewyd yr hen gofrestri priodas trwy orchymyn y Cofrestrydd Cyffredinol yn 1971 pan ddaeth y cyfrolau dwyieithog i gymryd eu lle, gyda'r canlyniad fod y cofrestri priodas a roddwyd ar adnau gan blwyfi gwledig yn fynych yn llawer mwy diweddar eu cynnwys na'r rhai bedydd a chladdu. Dewiswyd y lluniau i'r gyfrol hon gyda'r bwriad o ddangos cynifer â phosibl o'r amrywiol fathau o gofrestri gan gynnwys enghreifftiau o'r cofrestri priodasau a ddefnyddiwyd ar wahanol adegau er 1754, ac o'r cofrestri bedyddiadau a chladdedigaethau er 1813.

Adysgrifau'r esgob

Mesur 1597 oedd man cychwyn effeithiol y drefn yn Eglwys Loegr o yrru bob blwyddyn at yr esgob gopi o'r cofnodion a roddwyd yn y gofrestr plwyf yn ystod y deuddeg mis blaenorol — copi a adwaenir wrth yr enw adysgrif yr esgob, neu yn fyr A.E. (B.T. – bishop's transcript). Cadarnhawyd y mesur gan ganon 1603.[9] Er bod gan lawer o blwyfi Lloegr adysgrifau sy'n mynd yn ôl mor bell â 1597 a chyn hynny, nid oes gan blwyfi Cymru nemor ddim ohonynt cyn 1660. Yn hynny o beth cydymffurfiant â phatrwm cyffredinol cofysgrifau'r esgobaethau Cymreig. Yn wir, yr unig blwyfi Cymreig sydd ag adysgrifau'r esgob cyn 1660 yw'r dwsin neu ragor ar y gororau a arferai berthyn i esgobaeth Caer neu Henffordd.[10] Hyd yn oed wedi 1660, nid yw adysgrifau esgobion Cymru wedi eu cadw'n gyflawn a pharchus bob amser. Yn achos Tyddewi, er enghraifft, daeth rhai o adysgrifau coll y ddeunawfed ganrif i'r golwg yn gymharol ddiweddar fel labedi ar fwndeli o ewyllysiau sydd yn awr yn y Llyfrgell Genedlaethol.

Gellir crynhoi dyddiadau adysgrifau'r esgobion Cymreig fel a ganlyn fesul esgobaeth:

Bangor	1662–1917	(1675–1880 gan fwyaf)
Llandaf	1696–1916	(1725–1870 gan fwyaf)
Llanelwy	1661–1898	(1661–1850 gan fwyaf)
Tyddewi	1671–1911	
archddeoniaethau:		
Aberhonddu	1685–1874	(1700–1850 gan fwyaf)
Aberteifi a Thyddewi	1673–1911	(1799–1880 gan fwyaf)
Caerfyrddin	1671–1902	(1671–1870 gan fwyaf)
Gŵyr	1671–1910	(1671–1880 gan fwyaf)

Sylwer bod prif gorff yr adysgrifau ar gyfer y rhan fwyaf o esgobaethau Cymru yn fwy cyfyng eu cyfnod nag y mae'r terfynau eithaf yn ei awgrymu. Tua naw deg o blwyfi oedd yn parhau i anfon eu hadysgrifau at yr esgob wedi 1900; un Llangoed, Môn, am y flwyddyn 1917 yw'r diweddaraf ohonynt i gyd, mae'n debyg. Mae dyddiad rhoi'r gorau i'r arfer yn amrywio'n fawr o ardal i ardal. Cystal ychwanegu na cheir gan unrhyw blwyf gyfres gyflawn o adysgrifau'r esgob sydd yn cyfateb yn union i'r terfynau eithaf a nodir uchod.

Mae'r trwch pennaf o adysgrifau i'w cael ymhlith yr archifau esgobaethol a roddwyd ar adnau yn y Llyfrgell Genedlaethol yn 1944.[11] Yn swyddfeydd y cofrestryddion esgobaethol y cedwid hwy gynt, ac roeddent yn gyffredin, gydag un eithriad, wedi eu trefnu y pryd hwnnw mewn bwndeli fesul blwyddyn. Yn ystod y cyfnod rhwng tua 1870 a'r dyddiad y trosglwyddwyd yr archifau esgobaethol i'r Llyfrgell, rhoddwyd adysgrifau archddeoniaeth Aberhonddu yn nhrefn y plwyfi a'u rhwymo'n gyfrolau. Aildrefnwyd adysgrifau gweddill Cymru yn yr un modd wedi iddynt gyrraedd Aberystwyth, a'u cadw'n rhydd mewn bocsys. Yn ddiweddar ffeiliwyd adysgrifau Llanelwy a'r gweddill o rai Tyddewi rhwng cloriau caled. Aros yn eu bocsys mae adysgrifau Bangor a Llandaf am y tro. Rhestrwyd yr adysgrifau yn rhan o'r archifau esgobaethol y maent yn perthyn iddynt. Mae'r rhestrau i'w gweld yng nghatalogau teipysgrif Cofysgrifau'r Eglwys yng Nghymru sydd ar gael yn y Llyfrgell Genedlaethol a'r archifdai sirol, sef: Bangor, cyfrol 2, 1–58; Llandaf, 3, 1–29; Llanelwy, 1, 312–35; a Thyddewi, 2, 162–252. Ar y rhestrau hynny y seiliwyd y wybodaeth a geir yn y gyfrol hon gyferbyn â'r pennawd BT.

Nid oes cysondeb nac unffurfiaeth yng nghyfnod cyfrif yr adysgrifau esgobol cyn 1812. Amrywia o blwyf i blwyf, ac o adeg i adeg mewn llawer plwyf unigol. Gall y dyddiad olaf fod yn sefydlog — Gŵyl Fair (25 Mawrth) neu'n symudol — Y Pasg, neu ddyddiad llys yr esgob (neu'r archddiacon). Hyd yn oed wedi mabwysiad swyddogol y calendr Gregoraidd yn 1752, ni ollyngwyd yr hen arferion gan nifer fawr o blwyfi hyd nes i Ddeddf Rose ddod i rym ar Ddydd Calan 1813. Wedi hynny, mae'r adysgrifau, bron heb eithriad, yn rhedeg yn rheolaidd o 1 Ionawr hyd 31 Rhagfyr. At ddibenion yr arolwg hwn, ac er dangos yn eglur y bylchau mewn cyfres o adysgrifau, dynodir pob un sydd ar gael gan ddyddiad ei flwyddyn gychwynnol, hyd yn oed pan fo'n cynnwys misoedd cyntaf y flwyddyn ganlynol. Er enghraifft, mae adysgrif Abergele, sy'n cynnwys cofnodion am y cyfnod o 7 Ebrill 1670 hyd 21 Mai 1671 wedi ei restru yn syml fel 1670.

Dogfennau memrwn yw'r rhan fwyaf o'r adysgrifau, rai ohonynt wedi eu defnyddio cyn hynny i bwrpas arall, e.e. adysgrifau Llanddoged, sir Ddinbych 1702–3 a ysgrifennwyd ar ddail a dorrwyd o'r gofrestr wreiddiol gyda chofnodion bedydd a chladdu tua 1638 braidd yn aneglur weladwy arnynt o hyd. Yn aml bydd yr adysgrif yn cynnig gwybodaeth ychwanegol i'r hyn a geir gan y gofrestr wreiddiol.[12] Fel rheol ni chofnodir priodasau yn adysgrifau'r esgob wedi dechrau cofrestru sifil ym mis Gorffennaf 1837.

Ceir rhai o adysgrifau'r esgob mewn archifdai heblaw'r Llyfrgell Genedlaethol, sef a) ambell strae ymhlith y cofnodion plwyfol a roddwyd ar adnau mewn archifdy lleol (pob un ohonynt yn fwy diweddar nag 1820, mae'n ymddangos); b) y rhai sy'n perthyn i'r eglwysi ym mhriodoriaeth Penarlâg; ac c) y rhai sy'n perthyn i'r plwyfi sydd neu a fu ar un adeg mewn esgobaeth Seisnig, lle y mae'r adysgrifau yn rhan o'r archif esgobaethol a roddwyd ar adnau yn yr archifdy sirol priodol dros y ffin, Caer, Henffordd, neu Gaerlwytgoed. Am yr un rheswm, ceir yn y Llyfrgell Genedlaethol nifer fechan o adysgrifau sy'n perthyn i ambell blwyf Seisnig a fu ar un adeg mewn esgobaeth Gymreig.[13]

Copïau microffilm o adysgrifau'r esgob
Ffilmiwyd adysgrifau pob un o esgobaethau Cymru gan Eglwys Iesu Grist Seintiau'r Dyddiau Diwethaf yn y 1950au cynnar. Ond ni ffilmiwyd yr adysgrifau cynharaf oll yn eu cyfanrwydd oherwydd nad oedd y dogfennau wedi eu llwyr drefnu yr adeg honno. Mae copïau o'r microffilmiau hyn ar gyfer esgobaeth Llanelwy ar gael gan Archifdy Sir y

Fflint ym Mhenarlâg ac Archifdy Sir Ddinbych yn Rhuthun. Mae archifdai wedi sicrhau microffilmiau o adysgrifau plwyfi unigol, yn bennaf pan fo'u cofnodion llawer yn gynharach na'r cofrestri.

Microffilmiau ac adluniadau o'r cofrestri plwyf
Paratoir adlun rhwymedig o bob cofrestr plwyf a ddaw i ofal yr archifdai. Trosglwyddir yr adlun i'r periglor i'w gadw yn y plwyf. Ambell waith pan fo'r gofrestr yn dal i gael ei defnyddio fe geidw'r archifdy'r adlun ac anfonir y gwreiddiol yn ôl i'r plwyf. Dyna oedd y drefn yn y 1930au pan anfonwyd nifer o gofrestri cynnar i'r Llyfrgell Genedlaethol i'w hatgyweirio a'u hailrwymo. Tra oeddent yn y Llyfrgell copïwyd y mwyafrif ohonynt ar ficroffilm neu ffotostat. Doeth o beth oedd hynny, oherwydd mae'n ymddangos fod rhai o'r cofrestri gwreiddiol hynny wedi diflannu ers eu hanfon yn ôl i'r plwyfi: e.e. Llandanwg, Llandeilo Fawr, a Llandysul (Aberteifi).

Bu'r archifdai yn cydweithio fwyfwy yn ddiweddar i gyfnewid microffilmiau ac adluniadau. Mae llawer wedi ei gyflawni yn y cyswllt hwn yn barod ac mae'r gwaith yn mynd rhagddo wrth i'r gyfrol hon fynd i'r wasg. Fel y sonnir uchod, nid yw'r cofrestri gwreiddiol wedi eu symud o'r naill gadwrfa i'r llall yn sgîl ad-drefnu llywodraeth leol 1996, ond y mae gwasanaethau archifau newydd Bae Colwyn, Llandudno, a Wrecsam wedi cael cofrestri rhai o blwyfi eu hardaloedd ar ficroffilm. Mae ambell archifdy yn cymell darllenwyr i ddefnyddio microffilm neu adlun er mwyn arbed traul ar y gofrestr wreiddiol, mesur sy'n debyg o gael ei fabwysiadu gan eraill yn y dyfodol agos.

Copïau
Defnyddir yr ymadrodd 'copïau' er mwyn gwahaniaethu rhwng adysgrifau cyffredin ag adysgrifau'r esgob. Ceisiwyd nodi hefyd pa gopi sydd yn bigion *(extracts)* o'r cofnodion gwreiddiol yn hytrach na chopi cyflawn, ond y mae'n bosibl mai pigion yw rhai o'r copïau cynharaf, er enghraifft y rhai a ddelir gan Gymdeithas yr Achyddwyr. Gwnaethpwyd cryn ymdrech i grybwyll pob copi lled helaeth ei gynnwys y gwyddys amdano, heb anghofio'r ychydig a gyhoeddwyd a'r llawer a gopïwyd mewn llawysgrifen a theip gan selogion yn ystod y can mlynedd diwethaf. Yn ystod y cyfnod diweddaraf y mae'r cymdeithasau hanes teulu wedi gwneud llawer o adysgrifo systematig. Yn fwy na heb, y mae'r copïau hyn oll ar gael i ddarllenwyr gan yr archifdy lleol, y Llyfrgell Genedlaethol, a Chymdeithas yr Achyddwyr.

Nodiadau

1 J Conway Davies, 'The Records of the Church in Wales', *Cylchgrawn Llyfrgell Genedlaethol Cymru,* IV (1945–6), 1.

2 A G Veysey, 'Ecclesiastical Parish Records in Wales', *Journal of the Society of Archivists,* VI (1978–81), 31–3. Yn 1976 Powys oedd yr unig sir yng Nghymru heb archifdy sirol. Penodwyd archifydd sirol yno yn 1984. Nid yw'r Mesur Cofrestri a Chofysgrifau Plwyfol 1978, sydd yn rheoli diogelwch cofnodion plwyfol yn Lloegr, yn weithredol yng nghyswllt Eglwys ddadsefydliedig Cymru.

3 D J Steel, *National Index of Parish Registers,* V: *South Midlands and Welsh Border Counties,* 3ydd arg (Llundain, 1976), 75–92 *passim,* 146.

4 *Abstract of the Answers and Returns made pursuant to an Act for taking an Account of the Population of Great Britain. . .: Parish Register Abstract* (Llundain, 1833), 198–203, 416–85.

5 Er enghraifft, A M Burke, *Key to the Ancient Parish Registers of England and Wales* (Llundain, 1908).

6 Cedwir yr atebion gwreiddiol mewn cyfrolau rhwymedig, fesul esgobaeth, ymhlith papurau'r Eglwys yng Nghymru yn Llyfrgell Genedlaethol Cymru. Mae copïau serocs rhwymedig ohonynt ar gael yn Ystafell Ddarllen y Llawysgrifau yn y llyfrgell.

7 R M & G A Benwell, 'Interpreting the Parish Registers and Bishop's Transcripts for Anglesey and Llŷn' *Trafodion Cymdeithas Hynafiaethwyr a Naturiaethwyr Môn* (1975), 77.

8 Y mwyaf cynhwysfawr yw D J Steel, *National Index of Parish Registers,* I (Llundain, 1968). Ceir astudiaeth fanwl ynghyd â dyfyniadau o gofrestri o bob rhan o Gymru gan R W McDonald, 'Cofrestri Plwyf Cymru', *Cylchgrawn Llyfrgell Genedlaethol Cymru,* XIX (1975–6). Sonnir am gofnodion plwyfol yn gyffredinol yn ogystal â'r cofrestri gan W E Tate, *The Parish Chest,* 3ydd arg (Caergrawnt, 1969). Rhydd J C Cox, *The Parish Registers of England* (Llundain, 1910) lu o enghreifftiau, ond o Loegr yn unig.

9 Dorothy M Owen, *The Records of the Established Church in England* (British Records Association, 1970), 26–7.

10 Daeth adysgrif strae o blwyf Nyfer, sir Benfro, 1634 i'r golwg yn gynharach y ganrif hon mewn bwndel o bapurau yng nghofrestrfa brofiant Caerfyrddin (Llsgr Francis Green, cyf 8, t 175). Ffeiliwyd ef gyda'r adysgrifau eraill yn y Llyfrgell Genedlaethol erbyn hyn.

11 *Adroddiad Blynyddol Llyfrgell Genedlaethol Cymru 1944,* 32–4; *1945,* 34.

12 Benwell, *op cit,* 87–9.

13 Steel, *op cit,* V, 65–92 *passim,* 143–83 *passim.*

FFURF Y COFNOD

Plwyf neu eglwys

Trefnir enwau'r plwyfi a'r eglwysi yn ôl yr wyddor o dan yr hen siroedd. Defnyddir y ffurfiau Cymraeg gan ddilyn sillafiad Elwyn Davies, *Rhestr o Enwau Lleoedd* (Caerdydd, 1967). Os oes enw Saesneg cyfatebol neu fersiwn Saesneg o'r enw, fe'i rhoddir ochr yn ochr â'r enw Cymraeg gyda strôc letraws rhyngddynt. Rhoddir ffurfiau hynafol neu amrywiol mewn cromfachau. Lle bo gwahaniaeth mawr rhwng y ddau enw, ceir ail gofnod o dan yr enw Saesneg hefyd, a dynodir mai ail gofnod ydyw trwy roi seren o flaen yr enw.

Dilynir enw'r eglwys gan fyrfodd sy'n dynodi'r esgobaeth *fodern* y perthyn yr eglwys iddi. Yn achos y pedair hen esgobaeth, dynoda hefyd ym mha archif esgobaethol y ffeiliwyd adysgrifau'r esgob ar gyfer yr eglwys honno. Yn achos y ddwy esgobaeth newydd, ceir adysgrifau Mynwy ymhlith papurau Llandaf, a rhai Abertawe ac Aberhonddu ymhlith papurau Tyddewi.

Lle bo'r plwyf neu'r eglwys yn sefydliad modern, rhoddir ar linell nesaf y cofnod enw'r hen blwyf y tardd ohono, gyda'r symbol < yn dynodi'r ymadrodd 'a ffurfiwyd o'. Rhoddir hefyd, pan ellir, ddyddiad codi'r eglwys neu flwyddyn creu'r plwyf newydd, pa un bynnag sy'n ymddangos yn fwyaf priodol, er mwyn cynorthwyo'r darllenydd i chwilio cofrestr am y cyfnod cyn sefydlu'r eglwys fodern.

Cofrestri
Cymharwyd pob cofnod â'r atebion i Gyfrifiad 1831, arolwg y Llyfrgell Genedlaethol yn y 1930au, ac archwiliadau mwy diweddar yr archifdai lleol, a nodwyd pob cofrestr a aeth ar goll ers hynny.

Sylfaen y wybodaeth a roddir ar gyfer bedyddiadau (C), priodasau (M), a chladdedigaethau (B) yw catalogau'r archifdai o'r cofrestri sydd o dan eu gofal. Gan amlaf, dyddiad cyntaf ac olaf pob cyfrol a geir yn y catalogau hynny. Felly oni bai bod catalog yr archifdy'n manylu ynglŷn â bylchau oddi mewn i gyfrol, ni noda'r llyfr hwn ddim ond y bylchau sydd rhwng y naill gyfrol a'r llall. Yn y mannau priodol nodir pa gofrestri sydd yn dal ym meddiant yr offeiriad.

Adysgrifau'r esgob
Nodir pob bwlch yng nghyfresi adysgrifau'r esgob. Adlewyrchiad yw hynny o'r ffaith fod yr archifdai sydd â'r cyfryw ddogfennau yn eu gofal wedi eu rhestru'n fanwl. Cofier yr hyn a esbonnir uchod am anghyfatebiaeth yr adysgrifau cynnar i'r flwyddyn galendr.

Adlun, microffilm, a chopi
Ar ddiwedd y llinell sy'n rhestru dyddiadau'r cofrestri gwreiddiol neu adysgrifau'r esgob, nodir pa adlun (Fac), boed ffotostat, ffotocopi, neu ficroprint, neu ba gopi microffilm (Mf) o'r deunydd sydd ar gael. Ym mharagraff olaf pob cofnod y dylid chwilio'r manylion am gopïau printiedig, teipysgrif (ts), neu lawysgrif (ms).

BYRFODDAU

B	claddedigaethau	Mf	microffilm
BT	adysgrifau'r esgob	Mfc	microffis
C	bedyddiadau	ms	llawysgrif
Cop	copi	nd	heb ddyddiad arno
Fac	adlun	PR	cofrestr plwyf
M	priodasau	ts	teipysgrif

ESGOBAETHAU

B	Bangor	M	Mynwy
C	Caer	SA	Llanelwy
H	Henffordd	SB	Abertawe ac Aberhonddu
L	Caerlwytgoed	SD	Tyddewi
LL	Llandaf		

YR ARCHIFDAI

ACRO Archifdy Ynys Môn, Neuadd y Sir, Llangefni, Gwynedd, LL77 7TW. Tel: 01248 752080 Ffacs: 01248 750365

CACB Archifdy Conwy, Pwynt Cyswllt Archifau Llyfrgell Bae Colwyn, Woodland Road West, Bae Colwyn, LL29 7DH. Tel: 01492 532358 Ffacs: 01492 534474 Ebost: cblib@dircon.co.uk

CALL Archifdy Conwy, Pwynt Cyswllt Archifau Llyfrgell Llandudno, Stryd Mostyn, Llandudno, LL30 2RP. Tel: 01492 574020/574010 Ffacs: 01492 876826 Ebost: tudnolib@dircon.co.uk

Carm RO Gwasanaeth Archifau Sir Gaerfyrddin, Neuadd y Sir, Caerfyrddin, Sir Gaerfyrddin SA31 1JP. Tel: 01267 224184 Ffacs: 01267 224104 Ebost: archives@carmarthenshire.gov.uk

Cer RO Archifdy Ceredigion, Swyddfa'r Sir, Aberystwyth, Ceredigion, SY23 2DE. Tel: 01970 633697/633698 Ebost: archives@ceredigion.gov.uk

Ches RO Cheshire Record Office, Duke Street, Chester, CH1 1RL. Tel: 01244 602574 Ffacs: 01244 603812 Ebost: recordoffice@cheshire.gov.uk

DRO Archifdy Sir Ddinbych, 46 Heol Clwyd, Rhuthun, Sir Ddinbych, LL15 1HP. Tel: 01824 708250 Ffacs: 01824 708258 Ebost: dcc_archives@denbighshire.gov.uk

FRO Archifdy Sir y Fflint, Yr Hen Reithordy, Penarlâg, Sir y Fflint, CH5 3NR. Tel: 01244 532364 Ffacs: 01244 538344 Ebost: archives@flintshire.gov.uk

GASC Gwasanaeth Archifau Gwynedd, Archifdy Caernarfon, Doc Fictoria, Caernarfon, Gwynedd (llythyrau i'w cyfeirio at: Swyddfa'r Sir, Stryd y Jêl, Caernarfon, Gwynedd, LL55 1SH). Tel: 01286 679088 Ffacs: 01286 679637 Ebost:archifau@gwynedd.gov.uk

GASD Archifdy Meirion, Cae Penarlâg, Dolgellau, Gwynedd, LL40 2YB. Tel: 01341 424444 Ffacs: 01341 424505 Ebost: archifau.dolgellau@gwynedd.gov.uk

Glam RO Archifdy Morgannwg, Adeilad Morgannwg, Coedlan Brenin Edward VII, Parc Cathays, Caerdydd, CF10 3NE. Tel: 029 2078 0282 Ffacs: 029 2078 0284 Ebost: glamro@cardiff.ac.uk

Gwent RO Archifdy Gwent, Neuadd y Sir, Cwmbrân, NP44 2XH.
Tel: 01633 644886 neu 01633 644888 Ffacs: 01633 648382
Ebost: 113057.2173@compuserve.com

HRO Herefordshire Record Office, The Old Barracks, Harold Street,
Hereford, HR1 2QX. Tel: 01432 260750 Ffacs: 01432 260066
Ebost: shubbard@herefordshire.gov.uk

Lichfield RO Lichfield Record Office, Lichfield Library, The Friary, Lichfield, Staffordshire, WS13 6QG. Tel: 01543 510720 Ffacs: 01543 510715
Ebost: lichfield.record.office@staffordshire.gov.uk

NLW Adran Llawysgrifau a Chofysgrifau, Llyfrgell Genedlaethol Cymru,
Aberystwyth, Ceredigion, SY23 3BU. Tel: 01970 632880 Ffacs: 01970
632883 Ebost: ymh.lc@llgc.org.uk

PCAO Swyddfa Archifau Sir Powys, Neuadd y Sir, Llandrindod, Powys, LD1
5LG. Tel: 01597 826088 Ffacs: 01597 827162
Ebost: archives@powys.gov.uk

Pemb RO Archifdy Sir Benfro, Y Castell, Hwlffordd, Sir Benfro, SA61 2EF.
Tel: 01437 763707

Soc Gen Society of Genealogists (Cymdeithas yr Achyddwyr), 14 Charterhouse
Buildings, London EC1M 7BA. Tel: 0171 251 8799
Ebost: genealogy@sog.org.uk

SRR Shropshire Records and Research Centre, Castle Gates, Shrewsbury,
SY1 2AQ. Tel: 01743 255350 Ffacs: 01743 255355
Ebost: research@shropshire-cc.gov.uk

WAS Gwasanaeth Archifau Wrecsam, Llyfrgell Wrecsam, Heol Rhos-ddu,
Wrecsam, LL11 1AU. Tel: 01978 292622 Ffacs: 01978 292611

WGAS Gwasanaeth Archifau Gorllewin Morgannwg, Neuadd y Sir, Heol
Ystumllwynarth, Abertawe, SA1 3SN. Tel: 01792 636589
Ffacs: 01792 637130 Ebost: archives@swansea.gov.uk

INTRODUCTION

The deposit of parish registers
This volume provides details of original parish registers and bishop's transcripts, and of microfilm, facsimile, and other copies of them held by record repositories in Wales and adjoining border counties, and by the Society of Genealogists. It covers all thirteen ancient counties in the principality, describing the registers of over 1,000 parishes and chapelries in existence by 1812, and of about 400 post-1812 churches for which records are held by a repository.

The task of collecting parish registers and other records into safe custody was begun in 1950 by the National Library of Wales under an extension of an agreement made in 1944 between the library and the Representative Body of the Church in Wales, by which episcopal, capitular, diocesan registry and other records of the church were deposited in the library.[14] In 1976 agreements between the Representative Body and all the Welsh county councils (with the exception of Powys) designated county record offices as additional repositories for ecclesiastical parish records.[15] In the same year a circular letter to incumbents from the Registrar of the Archbishop of Wales urged the deposit of ecclesiastical records in safe custody, and diocesan advisers on archives were appointed to supervise this work. The success of these measures is evident from the fact that the registers of all the ancient parishes have now been deposited either in the National Library or in one of the Welsh county record offices, and it is the staff of these institutions who have been responsible for this survey.

Diocesan boundaries
The Welsh church was, until its disestablishment in 1920, an integral part of the Church of England. The diocesan boundaries disregarded (and indeed pre-dated) those of England and Wales. The four ancient Welsh dioceses covered the following areas:

Bangor	Anglesey, most of Caernarfonshire, parts of Merioneth and Montgomeryshire, and the deanery of Dyffryn Clwyd in central Denbighshire
Llandaff	most of Glamorgan and Monmouthshire
St Asaph	most of Flintshire and Denbighshire, with parts of Caernarfonshire, Merioneth, Montgomeryshire and Shropshire
St David's	Carmarthenshire, Cardiganshire, Pembrokeshire, Brecknockshire, most of Radnorshire, and parts of Montgomeryshire, Glamorgan, Monmouthshire and Herefordshire

There was only one peculiar exempt from episcopal jurisdiction — Hawarden in Flintshire.

English dioceses also included parts of Wales:

Chester   parts of Flintshire and Denbighshire

Lichfield   parish of Penley in Flintshire, and Welsh part of parish of Llany-
                   mynech, Shropshire

Hereford   parts of Montgomeryshire, Radnorshire and Monmouthshire

Some of these parishes in English dioceses were transferred to Welsh ones in 1849. A substantial exchange of parishes was effected in 1859 between the dioceses of Bangor and St Asaph, the deanery of Dyffryn Clwyd being transferred to St Asaph in exchange for the deanery of Cyfeiliog and Mawddwy. A further transfer of border parishes followed the Welsh Church Act of 1914, which took effect in 1920. Parishes belonging to Welsh dioceses, but lying wholly in England, were transferred to English dioceses, and vice versa. Of nineteen parishes situated partly in Wales and partly in England, seventeen were, 'with reference to the general wishes of the parishioners', treated as being in England, while in the remaining two parishes the choice was put to the vote, and one, Llansilin, opted for inclusion in Wales. (The registers of Welsh parishes remaining in the Church of England have been deposited in the appropriate county record office over the border — Cheshire, Shropshire, or Herefordshire.) Two new Welsh dioceses were created — Monmouth out of Llandaff in 1921, and Swansea and Brecon out of St David's in 1923.

County boundaries
The text of this volume is arranged by the historic counties of Wales as they were at the time of their disappearance under the reorganization of local government in 1974, when the thirteen ancient counties were divided or amalgamated into eight new ones. In 1996 local government in Wales was again reorganized, and certain of the ancient counties of Wales have reappeared, although some of these do not have the same boundaries as they had before 1974. As a result the names of some record offices have changed from those in the first edition of this book, but no parish registers have been transferred from one repository to another. In south Wales, joint archive services — Glamorgan, Gwent, and West Glamorgan — provide record offices in the old counties of Glamorgan and Monmouth. Some new authorities — Conwy, Neath Port Talbot (under West Glamorgan Archive Service), and Wrexham — have established archive service points which hold microfilms of parish registers for the areas that they serve.

Parish registers
Registers in Wales, even in counties where their survival has been better than average, do not match those of English border counties. The keeping of registers was ordered by Thomas Cromwell in 1538, but in only one parish (Gwaenysgor, co Flint) is there a 1538 register in existence. Even this is not an original paper volume, but a parchment

copy made at some time after the confirmation in 1598 of a constitution of the previous year which ordered a more careful keeping of parish registers. By contrast, Shropshire has five registers dating from 1538, and Herefordshire seven.[16] Of just over a thousand ancient parishes and chapelries in Wales, only seventy have registers which begin before 1600; far more than half have registers which start only in the eighteenth century. Indeed, many parishes, particularly in south Wales, have no registers earlier than 1754, when separate marriage registers begin, or even 1813, when printed volumes for baptisms and burials were introduced. In such parishes the earlier registers (usually of parchment), including baptisms, marriages and burials in one volume, have entirely disappeared.

The registers have survived better in some dioceses than others. St Asaph has the highest proportion of early registers, and St David's (where over half of the parishes have no registers earlier than 1754) the lowest. Generally, north Wales has earlier registers than the south. On a county basis, the registers of Flintshire come first. It has the only 1538 register; eighteen out of the twenty-nine ancient parishes (62%) have registers starting before 1660; and every parish has registers which begin before 1754. In a hierarchy based on the percentage of parishes with pre-1660 registers, the north Wales counties of Montgomery (49%), Denbigh (33%) and Merioneth (29%) follow. In south Wales only Monmouthshire (20%) comes near to the survival rate in the north. At the bottom end of the scale, Cardiganshire (4%) has no registers earlier than 1653; nearly two thirds of the parishes have no registers dating before 1754; and as many as thirteen have no registers before 1813.

Two earlier detailed surveys of parish registers in Wales, compiled when the records remained in the churches, reveal what volumes have been lost in the last hundred and seventy years. The first was based on enquiries made of clergymen at the time of the 1831 census.[17] The returns gave details, usually volume by volume, of registers prior to 1813, and sometimes gave reasons for recent losses. (For some dioceses, visitation returns of the late eighteenth and early nineteenth centuries also give dates of registers.) The 1831 survey has been much used as a source for later writers,[18] although the returns are often inaccurate — sometimes wildly so. More recent surveys were carried out, diocese by diocese, by the National Library of Wales between 1933 and 1940.[19] Again, the survey was based on a questionnaire rather than examination of the registers, but the results are usually sufficiently detailed to allow further comparisons. Some subsequent surveys, based on inspection, were made by county record offices. Details of registers lost since these surveys were carried out have been incorporated into the text.

136 parishes have lost one or more registers since 1831, and in 51 other cases registers noted in the 1930s have disappeared. (In a few parishes, registers earlier than those noted in either survey have come to light, however, and in several parishes registers have been rediscovered since the first edition of this book was published in 1986. On the other hand, in one north Wales parish, registers have been stolen from the church in recent

years and not recovered.) The losses have been heavier in south Wales; about a third of the ancient parishes in the counties of Brecknock, Cardigan, Glamorgan and Radnor, and about a quarter of those in Carmarthen and Pembroke, have lost registers since 1831.

Registers have been accidentally lost in fires (Llanddeusant, Llangynog, and Pendine, co Carmarthen; Llansanffraid Glan Conwy, co Denbigh; Hanmer and Llanfynydd, co Flint; Diserth and Pilleth, co Radnor; Rhodogeidio in Anglesey; Christchurch and St Arvans, co Monmouth; Angle and Castlemartin, co Pembroke); and floods (Llechryd, co Cardigan). At Cilymaenllwyd, co Carmarthen, and Cadoxton-juxta-Neath, co Glamorgan, they were deliberately used to stoke the parsonage fire. They have been taken by parish officials (Nantglyn, co Denbigh), incumbents (Caerau with Ely, co Glamorgan), and thieves (Bishton, co Monmouth). In Carmarthenshire, a curate of Llangain is alleged to have sold a register for £40; in Cardiganshire, an early register of Llanfihangel Genau'r-glyn is supposed to have been taken away to be produced in a court of law and never returned; and in Pembrokeshire the early registers of Llanwnda and Letterston were reputedly destroyed at the time of the French invasion of 1797. The register of one unidentified Anglesey parish is said to have been eaten by a cow.[20]

Little need be said of the content of the registers, for their history is the same as those of England, which have received extensive treatment.[21] Most entries were made in Latin until about 1732. The use of Welsh is very rare and is restricted to a few parishes for short periods in the seventeenth and eighteenth centuries. It occasionally happened that in very poor, rural parishes no separate registers were kept before 1813, but entries were made in the registers of an adjoining parish. For example, in the parish of Llanfaelrhys, co Caernarfon, there are no registers before 1811, but entries for the earlier period are to be found in the registers of Aberdaron. Cross-references are provided in the text of this volume where necessary. The illustrations in this volume have been selected with the aim of illustrating as wide a range of registers as possible, including examples of the separate registers of marriages introduced, from 1754, and of baptisms and burials, from 1813.

Bishop's transcripts
The annual return to the bishop of a copy of the register entries for the year — known as a bishop's transcript, or BT — was effectively established in the Church of England by a constitution of 1597, the procedure being codified by a canon of 1603.[22] Whereas many parishes in England have transcripts going back to the 1597 injunction and beyond, those of Wales have virtually no transcripts dated earlier than 1660. This conforms with the general pattern of Welsh diocesan records. Indeed the only Welsh parishes which do have pre-1660 transcripts are the dozen or so along the border which belonged to the dioceses of Chester and Hereford.[23] Even after 1660, the transcripts have not always been well kept. For instance, some bundles of wills now in the National Library of Wales were found to have parchment labels made from eighteenth-century transcripts belonging to the diocese of St David's.

The dates of the Welsh transcripts may be summarised by diocese as follows:

Bangor	1662–1917	(mostly 1675–1880)
Llandaff	1696–1916	(mostly 1725–1870)
St Asaph	1661–1898	(mostly 1661–1850)
St David's	1671–1911	
archdeaconry of:		
Brecon	1685–1874	(mostly 1700–1850)
Cardigan & St David's	1673–1911	(mostly 1799–1880)
Carmarthen	1671–1902	(mostly 1671–1870)
Gower	1671–1910	(mostly 1671–1880)

As can be seen, the dates of the main body of transcripts for most Welsh dioceses are somewhat shorter than the outside dates given. The terminal dates vary considerably. Some ninety parishes continued to send in returns after 1900; the 1917 transcript for Llangoed in Anglesey seems to be the latest of all. It may be added that there is no parish with a full set of transcripts corresponding to the outside dates shown above.

Nearly all the existing transcripts for Wales are housed at the National Library, to which they were transferred with the other diocesan archives in 1944.[24] Originally they were kept in annual bundles at the diocesan registries. Between about 1870 and the time of their deposit at the library, the transcripts of the archdeaconry of Brecon were rearranged and bound in volumes by parish. The other transcripts have been rearranged in a similar way since their transfer to Aberystwyth. Those of St Asaph and the archdeaconries of the diocese of St David's other than Brecon have in recent years been filed between hinged boards. For the time being the transcripts of Bangor and Llandaff are kept loose in boxes. All the transcripts were listed as integral parts of their respective diocesan records, and the lists may be consulted in the typescript schedules of the Church in Wales records available at NLW and the various county record offices, viz: Bangor, vol 2, pp 1–58; Llandaff, vol 3, pp 1–29; St Asaph, vol 1, pp 312–35; and St David's, vol 2, pp 162–252. These lists form the basis of the BT entries in the present volume.

The dates covered annually by the transcripts before 1812 vary from parish to parish, and from time to time within each parish. Before the adoption of the Gregorian calendar in 1752, Ladyday (25 March), Easter, or the date of the bishop's (or archdeacon's) visitation were the customary dividing lines between one return and the next; and they remained in common, if gradually declining, use in many Welsh parishes until the provisions of Rose's Act became effective on 1 January 1813. From then on, virtually all the transcripts run from 1 January to 31 December. For the purposes of this survey, and in order that the gaps in the sequence of returns may be shown more clearly, each transcript has been given a single-year value, irrespective of its inclusion of entries for the first few months of the following year. For example, the Abergele transcript for the period from 7 April 1670 to 21 May 1671 is listed simply as 1670.

Most of the transcripts are on parchment, some of which may have been used previously for other purposes. For example, the Llanddoget, co Denbigh, transcripts for 1702–3 were entered on leaves cut out of the earliest register of the parish, on which entries dated 1638 or thereabouts are still faintly discernible. The transcripts often supplement the entries given in the original registers.[25] Marriages are not as a rule included in the bishop's transcripts after the commencement of civil registration in July 1837, for incumbents were then required to supply copies of marriage entries to the local registrar of births, marriages and deaths.

Bishop's transcripts to be found at repositories other than the National Library of Wales include a) odd strays which occasionally turn up among parish records deposited at local record offices (all apparently post-1820); b) those belonging to churches in the peculiar of Hawarden, which are among the records of the parish in the Flintshire Record Office; and c) those from parishes which used to or still do belong to English dioceses, in which cases the transcripts remain with the diocesan records at the appropriate county record office at Chester, Hereford, or Lichfield. Similarly, a few English parishes which were at one time in Welsh dioceses have some of their transcripts located at the National Library.[26]

Microfilm copies of bishop's transcripts
The transcripts for all the Welsh dioceses were microfilmed in the early 1950s by the Church of Jesus Christ of Latter-Day Saints. However, many of the early returns went unfilmed, because the records had not been fully sorted at that stage. Copies of these microfilms for the diocese of St Asaph are held by the Flintshire Record Office at Hawarden and the Denbighshire Record Office at Ruthin. Microfilms of the BTs for some individual parishes have been acquired by record offices, generally when the transcripts are much earlier than the surviving registers.

Microfilms and facsimiles of parish registers
Each repository prepares bound facsimiles of the registers placed in its care. These facsimiles are handed over to the incumbents to be kept in their respective parishes. In some instances where the register may still be in current use at the parish church, the repository may have made a facsimile copy for its own use and returned the original to the parish. Such was also the procedure in the 1930s when a number of parishes sent their earliest registers to be repaired and rebound at the National Library. During their stay at the library, most of them were copied on microfilm or photostat. The wisdom of that course is shown by the fact that some of the originals which were returned to their parishes have subsequently disappeared: Llandanwg, Llandeilo Fawr, and Llandysul (co Cardigan).

The exchange of microfilms and facsimiles between repositories is a growing trend. Much has been done already, and work was continuing as the volume went to press. As stated above, the reorganization of local government in 1996 has not resulted in the movement of original registers from one repository to another, but the new archive services at Colwyn Bay, Llandudno, and Wrexham have obtained microfilms of registers for some of the parishes included in their areas. To save wear and tear, some repositories ask readers to use facsimiles or microfilms in place of the original registers, a practice which is likely to be adopted by others in the not-too-distant future.

Copies

The term 'copies' rather than 'transcripts' has been adopted to avoid confusion with the BTs. Every effort has been made to distinguish between full copies and extracts, but some early copies may in fact be extracts, for example those held by the Society of Genealogists. An attempt has been made to include details of every known copy of an extensive nature, including the few which have been published, and the many which have been transcribed by enthusiasts and family history societies during the last hundred years or so in manuscript and typescript. In recent years a great deal of work on the copying of registers has been done by the family history societies. These copies will generally be held by the appropriate record office, the National Library, and the Society of Genealogists.

Notes

14 J Conway Davies, 'The Records of the Church in Wales', *National Library of Wales Journal*, IV (1945–6), 1.

15 A G Veysey, 'Ecclesiastical Parish Records in Wales', *Journal of the Society of Archivists*, VI (1978–81), 31–3. Powys was the only Welsh county which, in 1976, had no county record office. An archivist was appointed in 1984. The Parochial Registers and Records Measure 1978, which regulates the care of parish records in England, does not apply to the disestablished Church in Wales.

16 D J Steel, *National Index of Parish Registers*, V: *South Midlands and Welsh Border Counties*, 3rd ed (London, 1976), 75–92 *passim*, 146.

17 *Abstract of the Answers and Returns made pursuant to an Act. . . for taking an Account of the Population of Great Britain. . .: Parish Register Abstract* (London, 1833), 198–203, 416–85.

18 For example, A M Burke, *Key to the Ancient Parish Registers of England and Wales* (London, 1908).

19 The replies are preserved as bound volumes, arranged by diocese, among the records of the Church in Wales in the NLW. Bound facsimiles are available in the Manuscript Reading Room of the library.

20 R M & G A Benwell, 'Interpreting the Parish Registers and Bishop's Transcripts for Anglesey and Llŷn', *Anglesey Antiquarian Society and Field Club Transactions* (1975), 77.

21 Most comprehensive is D J Steel, *National Index of Parish Registers*, I (London, 1968). R W McDonald, 'The Parish Registers of Wales', *National Library of Wales Journal*, XIX (1975–6), is a detailed account, providing extracts from registers from all parts of Wales. W E Tate, *The Parish Chest*, 3rd ed (Cambridge, 1969) covers parish records in general as well as registers. J C Cox, *The Parish Registers of England* (London, 1910), gives many examples, although for England alone.

22 Dorothy M Owen, *The Records of the Established Church in England* (British Records Association, 1970), 26–7.

23 A stray transcript for Nevern, co Pembroke, for the year 1634, now at the National Library, came to light earlier this century among a bundle of papers at the Carmarthen probate registry (Francis Green MSS, vol 8, p 175).

24 *NLW Annual Report 1944*, 32–4; *1945*, 34.

25 Benwell, *op cit*, 87–9.

26 Steel, *op cit*, V, 65–92 *passim*, 143–83 *passim*.

FORM OF ENTRY

Parish or church

Entries are arranged under the old counties, and then alphabetically by name of parish or church. The arrangement is by the Welsh form of the name, using the spelling given in Elwyn Davies, *Gazetteer of Welsh Place-Names* (Cardiff, 1967). The Welsh form is followed, after an oblique stroke, by the English name, or an Anglicized version of the Welsh name, and obsolete forms are given in round brackets. Where the English name is greatly different from the Welsh, a second entry is provided under that name, preceded by an asterisk.

The name of the church is followed by an abbreviation indicating the *modern* diocese in which it is found. For the four ancient dioceses, this provides a guide to the diocese under which the bishop's transcripts for the church are filed. In the case of the new dioceses, the transcripts for Monmouth will be found among the records of the ancient diocese of Llandaff, and for Swansea and Brecon among those of St David's.

For modern parishes and chapelries, the next line of the entry gives the names of the older parish or parishes from which it was formed, the symbol < being used to denote 'formed out of'. Where known, the date that follows is either the date of construction of the church or the creation of the new parish, whichever seems more appropriate. The aim is to indicate to the reader where to look for registers for the earlier period.

Registers

Each entry has been checked against the returns made in the census of 1831, the surveys carried out by the National Library in the 1930s, and later surveys by record offices, and any registers which have disappeared are noted.

The dates of the registers of christenings (C), marriages (M) and burials (B) are based on the outside dates of each volume, given in the list compiled by the repository where it is held. The entry will therefore note gaps between volumes, but not gaps within a volume unless they were of sufficient length to have been noted in the list. Where appropriate, dates of registers retained by incumbents are given.

Bishop's transcripts

Since all repositories holding bishop's transcripts for Welsh parishes have now listed them in detail, the entry notes any break in the series. It should be remembered that, as explained above, the early transcripts do not normally cover a calendar year.

Facsimiles, microfilms and copies

Facsimiles (Fac), whether photostats, photocopies, or printouts from microfilm, and microfilms (Mf) of registers and bishop's transcripts are noted at the end of each entry. Details of copies — printed, typescript (ts) or manuscript (ms) — are given in the final paragraph.

ABBREVIATIONS

B	burials	Mf	microfilm
BT	bishop's transcript	Mfc	microfiche
C	christenings	ms	manuscript
Cop	copy	nd	no date
Fac	facsimile	PR	parish register
M	marriages	ts	typescript

DIOCESES

B	Bangor	*M*	Monmouth
C	Chester	*SA*	St Asaph
H	Hereford	*SB*	Swansea and Brecon
L	Lichfield	*SD*	St David's
LL	Llandaff		

REPOSITORIES

ACRO Anglesey County Record Office, Shire Hall, Glanhwfa Road, Llangefni, Anglesey, LL77 7TW. Tel: 01248 752080 Fax: 01248 750365

CACB Conwy Archive, Colwyn Bay Library Archive Access Point, Woodland Road West, Colwyn Bay, LL29 7DH. Tel: 01492 532358 Fax: 01492 534474 Email: cblib@dircon.co.uk

CALL Conwy Archive, Llandudno Library Archive Access Point, Mostyn Street, Llandudno, LL30 2RP. Tel: 01492 574020/574010 Fax: 01492 876826 Email: tudnolib@dircon.co.uk

Carm RO Carmarthenshire Archives Service, County Hall, Carmarthen, Carmarthenshire, SA31 1JP. Tel: 01267 224184 Fax: 01267 224104 Email: archives@carmarthenshire.gov.uk

Cer RO Ceredigion Archives, County Offices, Marine Terrace, Aberystwyth, Ceredigion, SY23 2DE. Tel: 01970 633697/633698 Email: archives@ceredigion.gov.uk

Ches RO Cheshire Record Office, Duke Street, Chester, CH1 1RL. Tel: 01244 602574 Fax: 01244 603812 Email: recordoffice@cheshire.gov.uk

DRO   Denbighshire Record Office, 46 Clwyd Street, Ruthin, Denbighshire, LL15 1HP. Tel: 01824 708250 Fax: 01824 708258 Email: dcc_archives@denbighshire.gov.uk

FRO   Flintshire Record Office, The Old Rectory, Hawarden, Flintshire, CH5 3NR. Tel: 01244 532364 Fax: 01244 538344 Email: archives@flintshire.gov.uk

GASC   Gwynedd Archives Service Caernarfon Record Office, Victoria Dock, Caernarfon (Correspondence address: County Offices, Shirehall Street, Caernarfon, Gwynedd, LL55 1SH). Tel: 01286 679088 Fax: 01286 679637 Email: archives@gwynedd.gov.uk

GASD   Archifdy Meirion, Cae Penarlâg, Dolgellau, Gwynedd LL40 2YB. Tel: 01341 424444 Fax: 01341 424505 Email: archives.dolgellau@gwynedd.gov.uk

Glam RO   Glamorgan Record Office, Glamorgan Building, King Edward VII Avenue, Cathays Park, Cardiff, CF10 3NE. Tel: 029 2078 0282 Fax: 029 2078 0284 Email: glamro@cardiff.ac.uk

Gwent RO   Gwent Record Office, County Hall, Cwmbrân, NP44 2XH. Tel: 01633 644886 or 01633 644888 Fax: 01633 648382 Email: 113057.2173@compuserve.com

HRO   Herefordshire Record Office, The Old Barracks, Harold Street, Hereford, HR1 2QX. Tel: 01432 260750 Fax: 01432 260066 Email: shubbard@herefordshire.gov.uk

Lichfield RO   Lichfield Record Office, Lichfield Library, The Friary, Lichfield, Staffordshire, WS13 6QG. Tel: 01543 510720 Fax: 01543 510715 Email: lichfield.record.office@staffordshire.gov.uk

NLW   Department of Manuscripts and Records, National Library of Wales, Aberystwyth, Ceredigion, SY23 3BU. Tel: 01970 632880 Fax: 01970 632883 Email: ymh.lc@llgc.org.uk

PCAO   Powys County Archives Office, County Hall, Llandrindod Wells, Powys, LD1 5LG. Tel: 01597 826088 Fax: 01597 827162 Email: archives@powys.gov.uk

Pemb RO   Pembrokeshire Record Office, The Castle, Haverfordwest, Pembrokeshire, SA61 2EF. Tel: 01437 763707

Soc Gen   Society of Genealogists, 14 Charterhouse Buildings, Goswell Road,
London, EC1M 7BA. Tel: 0171 251 8799
Email: genealogy@sog.org.uk

SRR   Shropshire Records and Research Centre, Castle Gates, Shrewsbury,
SY1 2AQ. Tel: 01743 255350 Fax: 01743 255355
Email: research@shropshire-cc.gov.uk

WAS   Wrexham Archive Service, Wrexham Library, Rhosddu Road,
Wrexham, LL11 1AU. Tel: 01978 292622 Fax: 01978 292611

WGAS   West Glamorgan Archive Service, County Hall, Oystermouth Road,
Swansea, SA1 3SN. Tel: 01792 636589 Fax: 01792 637130
Email: archives@swansea.gov.uk

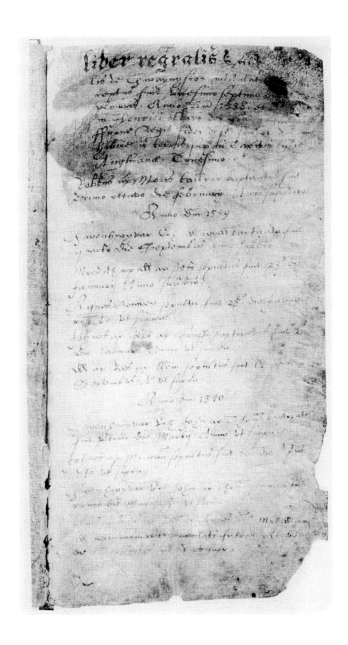

1   Tudalen cyntaf cofrestr plwyf Gwaunysgor, sir y Fflint — yr unig gofrestr sydd ar gael yng Nghymru yn dyddio yn ôl i 1538

The first page of the parish register of Gwaenysgor, co Flint — the only 1538 register surviving in Wales

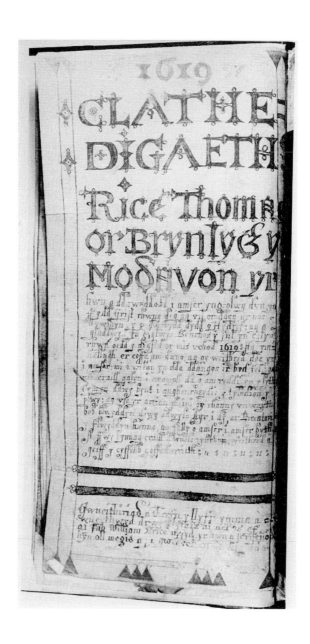

2   Cofrestr Penrhosllugwy, sir Fôn — enghraifft brin o gofrestr gyda chofnodion Cymraeg o'r ail ganrif ar bymtheg

Register of Penrhosllugwy, co Anglesey — a rare example of a register kept in Welsh in the seventeenth century

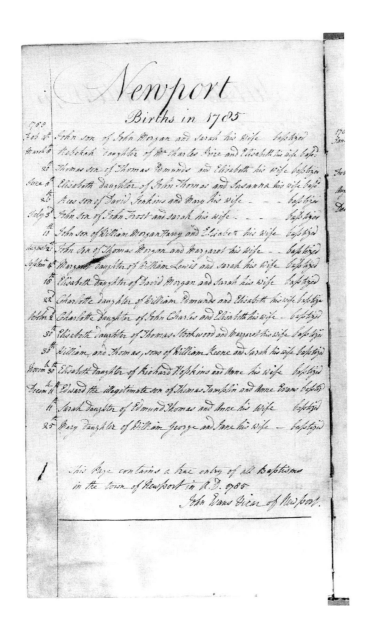

Newport
Births in 1785

1785	
Feb 4	John son of John Morgan and Sarah his wife baptized
March 6	Rebekah daughter of Mr Charles Price and Elizabeth his wife bap:
25	Thomas son of Thomas Edmunds and Elizabeth his wife baptized
June 6	Elisabeth daughter of John Thomas and Susanna his wife bap:
26	Rees son of David Jenkins and Mary his wife — — baptized
July 3	John son of John Frost and Sarah his wife — — baptized
10	John son of William Morgan Harry and Elizabeth his wife baptized
August 21	John son of Thomas Morgan and Margaret his wife — baptized
Septem 4	Margaret daughter of William Lewis and Sarah his wife baptized
18	Elizabeth daughter of David Morgan and Sarah his wife baptized
22	Charlotte daughter of William Edmunds and Elizabeth his wife baptized
October 2	Charlotte daughter of John Charles and Elizabeth his wife — baptized
30	Elisabeth daughter of Thomas Stockwood and Margaret his wife baptized
30	William and Thomas, sons of William Keene and Sarah his wife baptized
Novem 30	Elizabeth daughter of Richard Hopkins and Anne his wife baptized
Decem 11	Edward the illegitimate son of Thomas Tamplin and Anne Evans baptized
11	Sarah daughter of Edmund Thomas and Anne his wife baptized
25	Mary daughter of William George and Jane his wife — baptized

This Page contains a true entry of all Baptisms
in the town of Newport in A.D. 1785

John Evans Vicar of Newport

3 Cofrestr S Woolos, Casnewydd, sir Fynwy, yn cofnodi bedydd John Frost, arweinydd y Siartwyr, ar 3 Gorffennaf 1785
Register of St Woolos, Newport, co Monmouth, recording the baptism on 3 July 1785 of the Chartist leader, John Frost

[8]

B A P T I S M S.

Date.	Aged.		Name of the Child.	Names of the Father and Mother.
	—	Days.		
178_ May the 4th			John Smith, Son of	John Smith, Labourer, and Mary his Wife, formerly Mary Evans.
1783 August 25	29 years		Elizabeth Davis, Daughter of	John Davis, Baker, and Martha his Wife, formerly Martha Thorn
July 24		10 Days	William Pratt, Son of	Thomas Gregorie, Surveyor, and Hannah his Wife, formerly Hannah Pratt
August 24	2 Weeks		Robert Phillips, Son of	William Phillips, Farmer, and Mary his Wife, formerly Mary Martin
September 20	2 Weeks		Charles Thomas, Son of	David Thomas, Taylour, and Margaret his Wife, formerly Margaret Morgan
October 12		1 Week	Mary Jones, Daughter of	Michael James, Farmer, and Mary his Wife, formerly Mary Gorge

The above is the first christening since Duty commenced on Baptisms, Marriages, and Burials, the 29 Day of September 1783.

---

4 Enghraifft brin o'r gofrestr argraffedig, *Proposed Form of Register for Baptims*, a gyhoeddwyd yn 1781. Plwyf Hubberston, sir Benfro, biau hon. Mae ail hanner y gyfrol wedi ei dudalennu â fformat cyfatebol ar gyfer claddedigaethau
A rare example of the printed register, Proposed Form of Register for Baptisms, published in 1781. This one belongs to the parish of Hubberston, co Pembroke. The other half of the volume has a similar format for burial entries

BAPTISMS solemnized in the Parish of *Clyro* in the County of *Radnor* in the Year 18 66 *and* 1867

When Baptised.	Child's Christian Name.	Parent's Name.		Abode.	Quality, Trade, or Profession.	By whom the Ceremony was performed.
		Christian.	Surname.			
1866 October 7th No. 585	Eliza daughter of	Samuel & Jane	Collett	Lower Cabalva	Land Steward	R. F. Kilvert
1866 November 29th No. 586	Kate daughter of	James and Catherine	Handley	Grafton Villa Nr Hereford	Gentleman's Servant	R. F. Kilvert Curate
1866 December 16th No. 587	George son of	John and Elizabeth	Harris	Village	Carpenter	R. F. Kilvert Curate
1866 December 23rd No. 588	Alfred son of	Henry and Anne	Perkins	Village	Mason	R. F. Kilvert Curate
1867 January 19th No. 589	William son of	William and Mary	Phillips	Pentllan	Farmer	R. F. Kilvert Curate
1867 February 3rd No. 590	Herbert son of	Henry & Ann	Batts	Village	Coal Agent late Pentllan	R. F. Kilvert
1867 February 3rd No. 591	Sarah daughter of	Frederick & Sarah	Dance	Cwm. Clyro	Game keeper	R. F. Kilvert
1867 March 12th No. 592	Arthur Frederick son of	Charles James & Elizabeth	Partridge	Clyro Court Farm	Farmer	R. F. Kilvert Curate

5   Cofrestr bedyddiadau Cleirwy, sir Faesyfed, yn cynnwys cofnodion gan y curad, Francis Kilvert y dyddiadurwr, 1866–7. Defnyddiwyd y patrwm printiedig hwn am y tro cyntaf yn 1813
      Baptismal register of Clyro, co Radnor, with entries by the curate, the diarist Francis Kilvert, 1866–7. This printed format was used from 1813

THE
Register-Book
OF
MARRIAGES
IN ALL
Parish Churches & Chapels,

Conformable to an Act of the Twenty Sixth of King
GEORGE II. Intitled,

AN ACT FOR THE BETTER PREVENTING ALL

CLANDESTINE MARRIAGES.

PUBLISHED ACCORDING TO ACT OF PARLIAMENT.

MERTHYR TYDFIL:
PRINTED BY WILLIAM WILLIAMS.

1811.

6   Cofrestr priodasau Aberdâr, sir Forgannwg, 1811 — enghraifft o gofrestr a argraffwyd yn lleol cyn
dyfodiad cyfrolau safonol 1813
*Marriage register of Aberdare, co Glamorgan, 1811 — an example of a locally-printed register which predates
the standard volumes of 1813*

7   Cofrestr priodasau Clynnog Fawr, sir Gaernarfon, 1830 gyda chofnod priodas Mary Williams ac Ebenezer Thomas *(Eben Fardd)*. Defnyddiwyd cofrestri safonol ar wahân i gofnodi priodasau am y tro cyntaf yn 1754. Dyma'r patrwm (yn cynnwys mân newidiadau 1812) a barhaodd hyd 1837

Marriage register of Clynnog Fawr, co Caernarfon, 1830. The first entry records the marriage of Mary Williams and Ebenezer Thomas (the poet Eben Fardd). Separate standard registers for marriages were kept from 1754 and these continued in use (with minor changes in 1812) until 1837

Page 27.

18 39. Marriage solemnized ... in the ... Parish of Hawarden ... in the County of Flint

No.	When Married.	Name and Surname.	Age.	Condition.	Rank or Profession.	Residence at the Time of Marriage.	Father's Name and Surname.	Rank or Profession of Father.
53	June 25	Peter Hughes & Elizabeth Edward Whittle Spinster	Full Age	Bachelor Spinster	Perpetual Curate	Gloucester	Thomas Hughes John Edwards	Labourer Labourer

Married in the *Mother* church ... according to the Rites and Ceremonies of the *Esta blished* church ... by me, James R. S. Maurice

This Marriage was solemnized between us, { Peter Hughes, The mark X of Elizabeth Edward }

in the Presence of us, { Eliza Pattat Geo. S. Pattat }   Curate

18 39. Marriage solemnized Mother church in the Parish of Hawarden in the County of Flint

No.	When Married.	Name and Surname.	Age.	Condition.	Rank or Profession.	Residence at the Time of Marriage.	Father's Name and Surname.	Rank or Profession of Father.
54	July 25	William Ewart Gladstone & Catherine Glynne	full age	Bachelor Spinster	Member of Parliament	Hawarden Castle	John Gladstone Stephen Richard Glynne	Esqre late Member of Parliament Barnet

Married in the Mother church ... according to the Rites and Ceremonies of the Established church ... by me,

This Marriage was solemnized between us, { William Ewart Gladstone, Catharine Glynne }

in the Presence of us, { ... }

8   Cofrestr priodasau Penarlâg, sir y Fflint, lle y cofnodir priodas W E Gladstone a Catherine Glynne, 1839. Sefydlwyd patrwm y math hwn o gofrestr pan ddaeth cofrestru sifil i fodolaeth yn 1837, ac fe'i defnyddiwyd gyda dim ond ambell fân amrywiad hyd ei ddisodli gan y patrwm dwyieithog yn 1971

Marriage register of Hawarden, co. Flint.   The lower entry records the marriage of W E Gladstone and Catherine Glynne of Hawarden Castle, 1839. Registers in this format, introduced when civil registration began in 1837, were used with only minor alterations until bilingual volumes were substituted for them in 1971

xlii

9   Cofrestr gostegion Pen-bre, sir Gaerfyrddin, 1829. Nodir ar waelod y ddalen sut na bu modd i David Davies (y cofnod uchaf) briodi oherwydd y cafwyd ef yn euog o ffeloniaeth a'i drawsgludo am saith mlynedd

Banns register of Pembrey, co Carmarthen, 1829. A note at the foot records that the marriage of David Davies (first entry) was prevented by his being transported for seven years for felony

10 Patrwm cofrestr brintiedig a luniwyd i gydymffurfio â Deddf Stamp 1783. Dangosir yma'r tudalen yng nghofrestr Llanfihangel-yng-Ngwynfa, sir Drefaldwyn, sy'n cofnodi claddu Ann Griffiths yr emynyddes ar 12 Awst 1805

A sample of the printed register designed to comply with the provisions of the Stamp Act 1783. The page shown here from the register of Llanfihangel-yng-Ngwynfa, co Montgomery, records the burial of Ann Griffiths, the hymn-writer, on 12 August 1805

BURIALS in the Parish of _Aberavon_
in the County of _Glamorgan_ in the Year 18.30/1

Name.	Abode.	When buried.	Age.	By whom the Ceremony was performed.
Elizabeth Bradley No. 185 (Illegitimate)	Aberavon	22nd Decr	2 Whs.	E. Thomas Curate of Aberavon with Baglan & Chaplain Curate of Britton
Samuel Hopkin No. 186.	Aberavon	14th Feby	1 Yr 3 Mts	E. Thomas Curate
Edward David No. 187. (Illegitimate)	Corlanna Aberavon	22nd Feb.y	1½ Yrs	E. Thomas Curate
Leina Lawrence No. 188.	Aberavon	15th March	6 Yrs	E. Thomas Curate
Mary Thomas No. 189.	Cwm-Avon	5th April	28 Yrs	E. Thomas Curate
John Rowland No. 190.	Cwcu Cribbur Tythegstone	11th April	65 Yrs	E. Thomas Curate
Richard Jeffreys No. 191.	Aberavon	26th May	39 Yrs	E. Thomas Curate
*Richard Lewis No. 192.	Merthyr Tydfil	14th Augst	23 Yrs	E. Thomas Curate

1831

* The above unfortunate man was Executed at Cardiff on the 13th August 1831, for Stabbing Donald Black, one of the 93rd Highlanders who were stationed on duty at Merthyr, during the Riots on the 3rd of June last. He was indicted under 9 Geo IV cap 31. s.12.

11 Cofrestr claddedigaethau Aberafan, sir Forgannwg, 1830–1 — y math o gofrestr argraffedig sydd
mewn bodolaeth er 1813. Ar 4 Awst 1831 cofnodir claddu Dic Penderyn (Richard Lewis) a
ddienyddiwyd am anafu milwr ar ddyletswydd ym Merthyr yn ystod terfysgoedd Mehefin 1831
*Burial register of Aberavon, co Glamorgan, 1830–1 — a printed register of the type used from 1813. The
entry for 14 August 1831 records the burial of Dic Penderyn (Richard Lewis) who was executed for wounding a
soldier stationed in Merthyr during the riots of June 1831*

ABERTEIFI
CARDIGANSHIRE

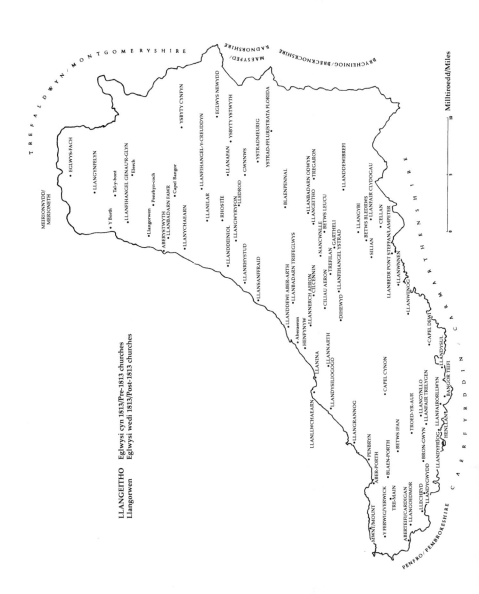

LLANGEITHO   Eglwysi cyn 1813/Pre-1813 churches
Llangorwen   Eglwysi wedi 1813/Post-1813 churches

ABERAERON *SD*
<Henfynyw
M 1877–1995 **NLW** Mf **Cer RO**

ABER-PORTH *SD*
C 1662–1971 M 1662–1971 (Banns 1824–1956) B 1662–1929 **NLW** Mf **Cer RO**
BT 1674–6, 1678–81, 1683–6, 1689, 1799–1804, 1806–71, 1874 **NLW**
Cop ts PR M 1813–37 with index **NLW Cer RO & Soc Gen**

ABERTEIFI/CARDIGAN *SD*
C 1654–1959 M 1653–1971 (Banns 1823–75) B 1654–1911 **NLW** Mf **Cer RO**
BT 1675–6, 1678–83, 1685–6, 1688, 1701, 1799–1801, 1803, 1806–10, 1812–75 **NLW**
Cop ts PR CMB 1669–97, 1700 **NLW** ts PR M 1813–37 with index **NLW Cer RO &
Soc Gen**

ABERYSTWYTH St Michael *SD*
<Llanbadarn Fawr 1787
C 1788–1961 St Mary 1908–91 M 1804–6, 1861–1971 (Banns 1861–1942) St Anne
1971–92 B 1791–1906, 1911–20 **NLW** Mf C 1788–1933 M 1804–6, 1861–1953 B
1791–1920 **Cer RO**
BT 1811, 1813–14, 1816–19, 1822–74, 1876, 1878–80, 1882, 1885–7 **NLW**
Cop ts index PR M 1861–75 B 1813–79 **NLW & Cer RO**

ABERYSTWYTH Holy Trinity *SD*
<Llanbadarn Fawr 1886
C 1886–1976 M 1887–1974 B 1886–1928 **NLW** Mf **Cer RO**

BANGOR TEIFI *SD*
Diocesan records suggest that *c*1790 this parish had registers going back 'about 60 years'
C 1802–11, 1813–1991 M 1804–1970 B 1813–1991 **NLW** Mf **Cer RO**
BT 1676, 1683–6, 1688–9, 1706, 1711, 1799–1811, 1813–80, 1882 **NLW**
Cop ts PR M 1813–37 with index **NLW Cer RO & Soc Gen**

BETWS BLEDRWS *SD*
PR CMB 1775–1812 recorded in 1831 apparently lost
CB 1813–1984 M 1813–1970 **NLW** Mf **Cer RO**
BT 1801–2, 1804–8, 1810–14, 1816–17, 1819–20, 1822–9, 1831–8, 1840–2, 1844–5,
1847–55, 1857–80 **NLW**
Cop ts PR M 1814–35 with index **NLW Cer RO & Soc Gen**

BETWS IFAN *SD*
C 1726–1992 M 1726–1813, 1816–1967 B 1726–1992 **NLW** Mf **Cer RO**
BT 1678, 1680–1, 1688, 1703, 1799, 1801–3, 1806, 1808–63, 1865–6, 1873–8, 1882–3,
1885–8, 1890–3, 1896–7 **NLW**
Cop ms PR (extracts) CMB 1792–1832 **NLW** ts PR M 1816–37 with index **NLW Cer
RO & Soc Gen**

BETWS LEUCU   *SD*
Entries for CMB before 1812 in PR Llanddewibrefi. PR M 1813–38 recorded in 1933
  apparently lost. No burials here
C 1813–1986 M 1837–1971 **NLW** Mf **Cer RO**
BT 1813–15, 1825–9, 1832–4, 1840–1, 1846–8, 1853–8, 1860–1, 1863–72, 1876–9, 1882,
  1885–8, 1890–9, 1902, 1905–9, 1911 **NLW**
Cop ts BT M 1813–34 with index **NLW Cer RO & Soc Gen**

BLAENPENNAL   *SD*
Entries for CMB before 1812 in PR Llanddewibrefi. PR CM 1797–1812 recorded in 1831
  apparently lost
C 1813–1977 M 1837–1971 B 1830–1986 **NLW** Mf **Cer RO**
BT 1813–19, 1823–35, 1850–77, 1879, 1882, 1885–7 **NLW**
Cop ts BT M 1814–35 with index **NLW Cer RO & Soc Gen**

BLAEN-PORTH   *SD*
C 1716–1992 M 1716–53, 1767–1837 B 1716–1991 **NLW** Mf **Cer RO**
BT 1674–6, 1678, 1680–9, 1700, 1702, 1704–5?, 1802–60, 1862, 1865–6 **NLW**
Cop ts PR CB 1716–1812 M 1716–53 **NLW & Soc Gen** ts BT M 1813–37 with index
  NLW Cer RO & Soc Gen

BORTH, Y   *SD*
<Llanfihangel Genau'r-glyn
C 1913–93 M 1887–1989 B 1892–1992 **NLW** Mf **Cer RO**

BRON-GWYN   *SD*
C 1726–1992 M 1726–99, 1803–1970 (Banns 1824–35, 1863, 1912–79) B 1726–1990
  NLW Mf **Cer RO**
BT 1678, 1680–1, 1688, 1703, 1803–52, 1858–9, 1876, 1886, 1891–3 **NLW**
Cop ms PR (extracts) CMB 1788–1809 **NLW** ts PR M 1813–37 with index **NLW Cer
  RO & Soc Gen**

CAPEL BANGOR (MELINDWR)   *SD*
<Llanbadarn Fawr 1839
C 1839–1993 M 1846–1968, 1974–90 Goginan 1872–1952 B 1839–1993 **NLW** Mf **Cer
  RO**
BT 1847–63, 1865–80, 1888 **NLW**

CAPEL CYNON   *SD*
<Llandysiliogogo. Not in use *c*1790 'for want of endowment'. Rebuilt chapel consecrated
  1822
C 1822–1978 M 1824–1971 (Banns 1826–1931) Talgarreg 1930–71 B 1824–1971 **NLW**
  Mf **Cer RO**
BT 1824–45, 1847–50, 1852–5, 1857–9, 1861–72 **NLW**
Cop ts PR M 1824–37 with index **NLW Cer RO & Soc Gen**

CAPEL DEWI   *SD*
<Llandysul
C 1843–1932 M 1843–1971 B 1843–1932 **NLW** Mf **Cer RO**

CAPEL TYGWYDD gweler/see LLANDYGWYDD

★ CARDIGAN/ABERTEIFI   *SD*
C 1654–1959 M 1653–1971 (Banns 1823–75) B 1654–1911 **NLW** Mf **Cer RO**
BT 1675–6, 1678–83, 1685–6, 1688, 1701, 1799–1801, 1803, 1806–10, 1812–75 **NLW**
Cop ts PR CMB 1669–97, 1700 **NLW** ts PR M 1813–37 with index **NLW Cer RO & Soc Gen**

CELLAN   *SD*
C 1779–1992 M 1780–1969 B 1780–1993 **NLW**
BT 1674, 1676, 1678–82, 1684, 1687, 1689, 1705, 1711, 1799, 1803–38, 1840, 1842, 1844–5, 1847, 1849, 1852–4, 1857, 1863–73, 1875–82 **NLW**
Cop ms PR C 1779–1812 MB 1780–1812 **NLW** ts BT M 1813–37 with index **NLW Cer RO & Soc Gen**

CILCENNIN   *SD*
Entries of CMB 1724–33 included in PR Llanbadarn Trefeglwys
C 1734–1993 M 1734–1971 B 1734–1992 **NLW** Mf **Cer RO & Soc Gen**
BT 1678, 1681–3, 1685, 1811–39, 1841–57, 1863–73 **NLW**
Cop ms PR CB 1734–51 M 1734–51, 1754–83 **NLW** ts PR M 1724–1837 with index **NLW Cer RO & Soc Gen**

CILIAU AERON   *SD*
PR CB 1715–[74] M 1715–73 recorded in 1831 apparently lost
C 1775–1960 M 1806–1969 (Banns 1823–34) B 1775–1991 **NLW** Mf **Cer RO**
BT 1678–83, 1685–6, 1705, 1711, 1799–1839, 1841, 1843–65, 1867–75 **NLW**
Cop ts PR M 1813–37 with index **NLW Cer RO & Soc Gen**

DIHEWYD   *SD*
PR CMB 1718–1807 recorded in 1831 apparently lost. A description of it, with extracts, appears in G Eyre Evans, *Cardiganshire and Its Antiquities* (1903), 217
C 1807–1953 M 1807–1970 (Banns 1828–71) B 1807–1993 **NLW** Mf C 1807–1953 M 1807–1970 (Banns 1828–71) B 1807–80 **Cer RO**
BT 1676, 1678–81, 1683, 1685–6, 1705, 1800–3, 1806–15, 1818–78 **NLW**
Cop ts PR M 1813–37 with index **NLW Cer RO & Soc Gen**

EGLWYS-FACH (YSGUBOR-Y-COED)   *SD*
<Llanfihangel Genau'r-glyn 1855. Alias Llanfihangel Edwyn (NLW, SD/SB/3, Owen Owen, 29 July 1769). In 1814 the minister wrote, 'This chapel was built in the year 1623 and they say they baptized, married, and buried here since the said date. Therefore, the old registers have been lost here as in all other churches in the neighbourhood' (NLW, SD/Misc/873)

C 1774–1992 M 1754–1837 (Banns 1824–1990) B 1784–1993 **NLW** Mf **Cer RO**
BT 1813–69, 1877–8 **NLW**
Cop ts PR M 1754–1837 with index **NLW Cer RO & Soc Gen**

EGLWYS NEWYDD (HAFOD)   *SD*
C 1773–1991 M 1774–89, 1803–1970 (Banns 1823–61) B 1773–1992 **NLW** Mf **Cer RO**
BT 1811–61, 1863–79, 1882, 1885, 1887–8 **NLW**
Cop ts PR M 1774–1837 with index **NLW Cer RO & Soc Gen**

ELERCH   *SD*
<Llanbadarn Fawr & Llanfihangel Genau'r-glyn 1868
C 1865–1993 M 1868–1970 B 1868–1993 **NLW** Mf **Cer RO**
BT 1869–79, 1882, 1885 **NLW**

FERWIG, Y/VERWICK   *SD*
Diocesan records suggest that *c*1790 this parish had PR going back 30 years
C 1813–1992 M 1769–1970 B 1813–1955 **NLW** Mf **Cer RO**
BT 1674–5, 1679–84, 1686–7, 1699–1700, 1799, 1801, 1803–7, 1810–55, 1865–6 **NLW**
Cop ts PR M 1813–37 with index **NLW Cer RO & Soc Gen**

GARTHELI   *SD*
Entries for CMB before 1812 in PR Llanddewibrefi. PR M 1813–38 recorded in 1933
  apparently lost
C 1813–1986 M 1839–1971 B 1871–1986 **NLW** Mf **Cer RO**
BT 1813–15, 1821–3, 1827–37, 1850–79, 1885–8, 1890–2, 1894–9, 1901–2, 1905–6,
  1908–11 **NLW**
Cop ts BT M 1813–37 with index **NLW Cer RO & Soc Gen**

GOGINAN gweler/see CAPEL BANGOR

GWENLLI gweler/see LLANDYSILIOGOGO St Mark

GWNNWS (LLANWNNWS)   *SD*
C 1760–2, 1770–2, 1789–1991 M 1765–6, 1775–84, 1789–96, 1803–1969 (Banns 1823–81)
  B 1789–98, 1812–1968 **NLW** Mf C 1811–64 M 1805–37 (Banns 1823–81) B 1812–1968
  Cer RO
BT 1811, 1813–62, 1864–78 **NLW**
Cop ts PR M 1765–1837 with index **NLW Cer RO & Soc Gen**

HAFOD gweler/see EGLWYS NEWYDD

HENFYNYW   *SD*
PR CB 1718–1812 M 1718–72 recorded in 1831 apparently lost
C 1813–1993 M 1772–1991 (Banns 1824–42, 1900–2) B 1813–1982 **NLW** Mf **Cer RO**
BT 1674, 1679–80, 1682, 1684, 1799, 1802, 1804, 1806–68 **NLW**
Cop ts PR M 1773–1837 with index **NLW Cer RO & Soc Gen**

HENLLAN   *SD*
C 1798–1991 M 1780–1970 B 1814–1990 **NLW** Mf C 1798–1812 M 1780–1970 **Cer RO**
BT 1676, 1683–6, 1688–9, 1706, 1711, 1799–1811, 1813–80, 1882 **NLW**
Cop ts PR M 1813–36 with index **NLW Cer RO & Soc Gen**

* LAMPETER/LLANBEDR PONT STEFFAN   *SD*
C 1695–1805, 1813–1937 Maestir 1869–85 M 1739–44, 1746–92, 1795–1970 (Banns 1824–57) B 1695–1805, 1813–1968 **NLW** Mf **Cer RO**
BT 1799–1808, 1811–17, 1823–37, 1839–80 **NLW**
Cop ms PR CB 1695–1745 M 1739–44 **NLW** CB 1695–1734 *Welsh Gazette* (1903–5) ts PR M 1813–37 with index **NLW Cer RO & Soc Gen**

LLANAFAN   *SD*
C 1751, 1772, 1774, 1780–1988 M 1767–72, 1774–9, 1781, 1784–5, 1790, 1792–4, 1796–1800, 1815–1988 (Banns 1823–5, 1838) B 1772–3, 1775, 1782–1993 **NLW** Mf C 1813–80 M 1815–37 B 1813–1947 **Cer RO**
BT 1811, 1813, 1815, 1818, 1820–78 **NLW**
Cop ts PR M 1767–1800, 1815–37 with index **NLW Cer RO & Soc Gen**

LLANBADARN FAWR   *SD*
C 1678–1736, 1752, 1766–1953 M 1695–1736, 1754–1987 (Banns 1849–52) B 1678–1736, 1752, 1766–1981 **NLW** Mf C 1678–1736, 1752, 1766–1837 M 1695–1736, 1754–1837 (Banns 1849–52) B 1678–1736, 1752, 1766–1841 **Cer RO**
BT 1678, 1680–1, 1703, 1773, 1811–79, 1882, 1885–92 **NLW**
Cop ts PR (extracts) CMB 1678–1736 **NLW** ts index PR CB 1830–79 M 1804–82 **NLW & Cer RO** ts PR M 1695–1837 with index **NLW Cer RO & Soc Gen**

LLANBADARN ODWYN   *SD*
Entries for CMB before 1812 in PR Llanddewibrefi. PR CMB 1777–1812 recorded in 1831 apparently lost. C 1956– in PR Llanddewibrefi
C 1815–1956 M 1808–1942 (Banns 1823–36, 1913) B 1813–1930 **NLW** Mf C 1815–1956 M 1813–37 (Banns 1823–36, 1913) **Cer RO**
BT 1683–5, 1811, 1813–35, 1841–56, 1866, 1871, 1873, 1875, 1877 **NLW**
Cop ts PR M 1813–37 with index **NLW Cer RO & Soc Gen**

LLANBADARN TREFEGLWYS   *SD*
PR CB 1789–1813 M 1798–9, 1805–12 recorded in 1933 apparently lost
C 1724–88, 1813–1978 M 1724–88, 1813–37 B 1724–88, 1813–1993 **NLW** Mf C 1724–1978 M 1724–88, 1813–57 B 1724–1960 **Cer RO**
BT see Cilcennin
Cop ms PR CMB 1724–85 **NLW** ts PR M 1724–1837 with index **NLW Cer RO & Soc Gen**

LLANBEDR PONT STEFFAN/LAMPETER   *SD*
C 1695–1805, 1813–1937 Maestir 1869–85 M 1739–44, 1746–92, 1795–1970 (Banns
   1824–57) B 1695–1805, 1813–1968 **NLW** Mf **Cer RO**
BT 1799–1808, 1811–17, 1823–37, 1839–80 **NLW**
Cop ms PR CB 1695–1745 M 1739–44 **NLW** CB 1695–1734 *Welsh Gazette* (1903–5) ts
   PR M 1813–37 with index **NLW Cer RO & Soc Gen**

LLANDYFRÏOG   *SD*
C 1725–1812 with gaps, 1813–1973 M 1725–1971 (Banns 1835–66, 1893–5, 1918–83) B
   1725–1869 with gaps, 1869–1955 **NLW** Mf **Cer RO**
BT 1676, 1680, 1682, 1686, 1703, 1799–1803, 1805–12, 1819–20, 1823–58, 1861–74
   NLW
Cop ts PR CB 1725–1812 M 1725–1837 **NLW & Soc Gen** ts PR M 1813–37 with index
   NLW Cer RO & Soc Gen

LLANDYGWYDD   *SD*
C 1677–1740, 1745–1958 M 1677–1740, 1745–1988 (Banns 1839–44, 1868, 1872–1994)
   Capel Tygwydd 1886–1970 B 1677–1740, 1745–1909 **NLW** Mf C 1745–1812 M
   1745–1837 (Banns 1839–44, 1868) B 1745–1909 **Cer RO**
BT 1674–6, 1678–85, 1687, 1699–1702, 1704–5, 1711, 1799–1865, 1867, 1874–5 **NLW**
Cop ts PR CMB 1677–1802 **NLW & Soc Gen** ts index PR C 1813–1958 M 1837–1970
   Capel Tygwydd 1886–1970 **NLW & Cer RO** ts PR M 1813–37 with index **NLW Cer
   RO & Soc Gen**

LLANDYSILIOGOGO   *SD*
C 1727–52, 1765–1993 M 1727–52, 1766–1970 (Banns 1823–64) St Mark 1942–70 B
   1727–1752, 1765–1992 **NLW** Mf **Cer RO**
BT 1679–81, 1683–9, 1702–3, 1706, 1799–1880 **NLW**
Cop ms PR (extracts) CMB 1738–45 **NLW** ts PR M 1813–37 with index **NLW Cer RO
   & Soc Gen**

LLANDYSUL   *SD*
PR CMB 1722–65 recorded in 1933 apparently lost. Diocesan records suggest that *c*1790
   this parish had registers going back to 1680
C 1798–1914 M 1755–1885 B 1799–1925 Fac CMB 1722–65 **NLW** Mf **Cer RO**
BT 1675, 1681–6, 1688–9, 1693, 1705, 1799, 1801–11, 1813–51, 1853–4, 1856–7,
   1868–70, 1872–3, 1876–9 **NLW**
Cop ts PR (extracts) CMB 1727–85 **NLW** ts PR M 1813–29 with index **NLW Cer RO &
   Soc Gen**

LLANDDEINIOL   *SD*
Alias Carrog (NLW, SD/SB/3, David Jones, 5 Dec 1771)
C 1776–7, 1780–1978 M 1754–1811, 1814–1971 (Banns 1825–1965) B 1776–7,
   1780–1977 **NLW** Mf **Cer RO**
BT 1811, 1813–16, 1820, 1822–5, 1827–79, 1882, 1885–91 **NLW**
Cop ts PR M 1754–1837 with index **NLW Cer RO & Soc Gen**

LLANDDEWI ABER-ARTH *SD*
C 1737–1992 M 1737–1809, 1813–1970 (Banns 1823–1977) B 1737–1993 **NLW** Mf C
1737–1854 M 1737–1809, 1813–1970 B 1737–1868 **Cer RO**
BT 1811–18, 1821–57, 1859–63, 1865–72 **NLW**
Cop ms PR CB 1737–1812 M 1737–1801 **NLW** ts PR M 1737–1837 with index **NLW**
Cer RO & Soc Gen

LLANDDEWIBREFI *SD*
C 1775–1992 M 1776–1807, 1813–1943 (Banns 1826–8, 1830–43, 1851–7, 1860–1928) B
1775–1886 **NLW** Mf C 1775–1859 M 1776–1807, 1813–37 (Banns 1826–8) B
1775–1886 **Cer RO**
BT 1683–5, 1702–3, 1811–59, 1861–7, 1871, 1873, 1875–9, 1882, 1885–6 **NLW**
Cop ms PR C 1776–1812 M 1776–1807 B 1776–1835 **NLW** ts PR M 1775–1837 with
index **NLW Cer RO & Soc Gen**

LLANFAIR CLYDOGAU *SD*
C 1813–1910 M 1813–1970 B 1813–1965 **NLW** Mf **Cer RO**
BT 1676, 1678–9, 1684, 1686, 1799, 1806, 1808–9, 1811–16, 1818–34, 1836, 1838–40,
1853–4, 1859–80, 1882 **NLW**
Cop ms PR C 1748–1813 M 1748–53, 1755–1810 B 1748–1811 **NLW** Mf **Cer RO** Cop
ts BT M 1813–36 with index **NLW Cer RO & Soc Gen**

LLANFAIRORLLWYN *SD*
PR CMB 1768–1812 recorded in 1831 as being bound up 'in great confusion' apparently
lost. For a description of it see G Eyre Evans, *Cardiganshire and Its Antiquities* (1903), 139
C 1813–1991 M 1813–1970 B 1813–1963 **NLW** Mf **Cer RO**
BT 1676, 1679–87, 1700–1, 1703, 1799–1814, 1816, 1818–28, 1830–67, 1874–5, 1878–9
NLW
Cop ts PR M 1813–37 with index **NLW Cer RO & Soc Gen**

LLANFAIR TRELYGEN *SD*
Church disused since the beginning of the nineteenth century. PR & BT included in those
of Llandyfríog. A marginal note in PR Llandyfríog M 1813–37, p 28, relating to a wedding
on 16 June 1823 reads 'NB There was no marriage solemnized in the old ruins of Llanfair
trefhelygen before today for twenty five years back'.

LLANFIHANGEL GENAU'R-GLYN *SD*
'Earlier registers are known to have once been in existence, but, it is said, were taken away
to Shrewsbury to be produced at some trial, and were never returned to the parish' (G Eyre
Evans, *Cardiganshire and Its Antiquities,* 207)
C 1736–73, 1779–1979 M 1736–1982 (Banns 1823–1976) B 1736–73, 1783–1927 **NLW**
Mf **Cer RO**
BT 1675, 1680–3, 1686, 1688–9, 1692, 1699, 1702–3, 1811, 1813–15, 1823–74, 1876–80,
1882 **NLW**
Cop ts PR M 1735–1837 with index **NLW Cer RO & Soc Gen**

LLANFIHANGEL-Y-CREUDDYN   *SD*
C 1791–1990 Llantrisant 1895–1991 M 1786–1970 (Banns 1786–1812, 1823–1900) B
   1781–1993 **NLW** Mf C 1791–1890 M 1786–1970 (Banns 1786–1812, 1823–1900) B
   1781–1909 **Cer RO**
BT 1674–5, 1680–2, 1686, 1701, 1811, 1813–16, 1820, 1822–37, 1839–66, 1869–72,
   1874–6 **NLW**
Cop ts PR M 1786–1837 with index **NLW Cer RO & Soc Gen**

LLANFIHANGEL YSTRAD   *SD*
PR CMB 1748–1812 recorded in 1933 apparently lost
C 1712–46, 1813–1993 M 1712–46, 1812–1970 (Banns 1823–93) B 1712–46, 1813–1992
   NLW Mf C 1813–69 M 1813–1970 (Banns 1823–93) B 1813–1915 **Cer RO**
BT 1676, 1678–9, 1681–3, 1689, 1799–1867, 1869–82, 1885–8, 1890 **NLW**
Cop ts PR M 1813–37 with index **NLW Cer RO & Soc Gen**

LLANGEITHO   *SD*
C 1769–1950 M 1761, 1770–1971 B 1769–1986 **NLW** Mf **Cer RO**
BT 1811, 1813–35, 1840–1, 1846–8, 1852–8, 1860–79, 1882, 1885–8 **NLW**
Cop ms PR C 1769–1832 M 1761–1812 B 1769–1812 **NLW** ts PR M 1761–1837 with
   index **NLW Cer RO & Soc Gen**

LLANGOEDMOR   *SD*
PR CMB 1725–63 recorded in 1831 apparently lost. Diocesan records suggest that *c*1790
   this parish had registers going back to 1684
C 1764–1980 M 1754–1985 (Banns 1754–1804, 1823–44, 1856–1996) B 1764–1938 **NLW**
   Mf C 1764–1812 M 1754–1837 (Banns 1754–1804, 1823–44) B 1764–1938 **Cer RO**
BT 1674–5, 1678, 1680–1, 1683–6, 1689, 1705, 1710, 1799–1861, 1863–80 **NLW**
Cop ts PR M 1813–37 with index **NLW Cer RO & Soc Gen**

LLANGORWEN   *SD*
<Llanbadarn Fawr 1842
C 1841–1991 M 1843–1971 (Banns 1842–1990) B 1842–1992 **NLW** Mf **Cer RO**
BT 1841–67, 1869–72, 1874, 1878–82, 1885–7 **NLW**

LLANGRANNOG   *SD*
PR CB 1763–1812 recorded in 1831 apparently lost
C 1813–1993 M 1762–1969, 1972–88 (Banns 1824–82, 1923) B 1813–1992 **NLW** Mf C
   1813–1922 M 1762–1836 (Banns 1824–82, 1923) B 1813–1914 **Cer RO**
BT 1679–81, 1683–9, 1702–3, 1706, 1799–1880 **NLW**
Cop ts PR M 1813–36 with index **NLW Cer RO & Soc Gen**

LLANGWYRYFON   *SD*
C 1729–1991 M 1729–1970 (Banns with gaps 1823–1992) B 1729–1992 **NLW** Mf C
   1729–1883 M 1729–1837 B 1729–1929 **Cer RO**
BT 1674–5, 1678, 1680–1, 1683–5, 1687, 1699, 1811–66, 1868–79, 1887–90 **NLW**
Cop ts PR M 1725–1837 with index **NLW Cer RO & Soc Gen**

LLANGYBI   *SD*
Entries of CMB 1748–1812 included in PR Llanfair Clydogau
C 1813–1993 M 1813–1970 B 1813–1992 **NLW** Mf M 1813–1970 **Cer RO**
BT 1678, 1683–4, 1799–1806, 1808–16, 1818–40, 1859–80, 1882 **NLW**
Cop ts PR M 1813–37 with index **NLW Cer RO & Soc Gen**

LLANGYNFELYN   *SD*
C 1770–1861 M 1754–1970 (Banns 1824–1968) B 1770–1949 **NLW** Mf **Cer RO**
BT 1675, 1678–9, 1681–3, 1687–9, 1691, 1699, 1701–3, 1705, 1803, 1811–53, 1855–63,
   1865–71, 1873–80, 1882, 1885–6 **NLW**
Cop ts PR M 1754–1837 with index **NLW Cer RO & Soc Gen**

LLANGYNLLO   *SD*
PR CB 1784–1812 recorded in 1831 apparently lost. Diocesan records suggest that *c*1790
   this parish had registers going back to 1724
C 1756–83, 1813–1957 M 1755–1970 B 1756–83, 1813–1958 **NLW** Mf **Cer RO**
BT 1675–6, 1679, 1681, 1683–8, 1690, 1702–3, 1705, 1799–1804, 1806–11, 1813–14,
   1816, 1818–72, 1875, 1885–6 **NLW**
Cop ts PR M 1813–37 with index **NLW Cer RO & Soc Gen**

LLANILAR   *SD*
C 1685–1984 M 1685–1970 (Banns 1823–1992) B 1685–1992 **NLW** Mf C 1685–1844 M
   1685–1970 (Banns 1823–51) B 1685–1869 **Cer RO**
BT 1675–6, 1678–9, 1682–3, 1688, 1699, 1702–3, 1705, 1811–72, 1874–6 **NLW**
Cop ts PR M 1687–1837 with index **NLW Cer RO & Soc Gen**

LLANINA   *SD*
PR earliest entries in Llannarth PR. Entirely separate PR begins 1781
C 1688–1992 M 1688–1754, 1781–1970 B 1688–1992 **NLW** Mf **Cer RO**
BT see Llannarth
Cop ts PR M 1813–37 with index **NLW Cer RO & Soc Gen**

LLANLLWCHAEARN   *SD*
C 1720–1913 M 1720–1837 (Banns 1823–70) B 1720–1898 **NLW** Mf **Cer RO**
BT 1674, 1678, 1680–1, 1684–8, 1699–1700, 1702, 1799–1800, 1802–4, 1806–74 **NLW**
Cop ts PR M 1814–37 with index **NLW Cer RO & Soc Gen**

LLANNARTH   *SD*
C 1688–1855 M 1688–1969 (Banns 1824–57) Mydroilyn 1928–64 B 1688–1864 **NLW**
   Mf **Cer RO**
BT 1674, 1679, 1681, 1683–5, 1688–9, 1799–1800, 1802–6, 1808–80, 1882, 1885–8,
   1890–2 **NLW**
Cop ts PR M 1813–37 with index **NLW Cer RO & Soc Gen**

LLANNERCH AERON   *SD*
PR CB 1730–1812 [M 1730–54?] recorded in 1831 apparently lost
C 1813–1992 M 1754–1970 (Banns 1827–1939) B 1813–1993 **NLW** Mf **Cer RO**
BT 1705, 1799–1802, 1804–5, 1807–9, 1811–78 **NLW**
Cop ts PR M 1813–37 with index **NLW Cer RO & Soc Gen**

LLAN-NON gweler/see LLANSANFFRAID

LLANRHYSTUD   *SD*
C 1738–97, 1800–1977 M 1738–1971 (Banns 1823–37) B 1738–97, 1800–1978 **NLW** Mf
  Cer RO
BT 1676, 1678, 1699, 1703, 1811, 1813–74, 1876–8 **NLW**
Cop ms PR C 1738–59, 1800–1900 M 1738–54, 1801–1950 B 1738–59, 1800–1953
  NLW ts PR M 1739–1837 with index **NLW Cer RO & Soc Gen**

LLANSANFFRAID   *SD*
Diocesan records suggest that *c*1790 this parish had registers going back to 1696. No
  mention of PR M 1813–37 in 1933 survey
C 1796–1993 M 1754–1812, 1837–1988 B 1796–1966 **NLW** Mf **Cer RO**
BT 1678, 1681, 1811–65, 1870–80, 1882 **NLW**
Cop ts PR/BT M 1754–1837 with index **NLW Cer RO & Soc Gen**

LLANTRISANT gweler/see LLANFIHANGEL-Y-CREUDDYN

LLANWENOG   *SD*
C 1722–1993 M 1722–54, 1796–1802, 1813–1986 B 1722–1850, 1855–1993 Fac M
  (Banns 1855–1942) **NLW** Mf C 1813–54 M 1813–37 B 1813–50 **Cer RO**
BT 1676, 1681, 1799–1845, 1847–9, 1855–6, 1865–6, 1892 **NLW**
Cop ms PR (extracts) CMB 1722–1812 **NLW** ts PR M 1813–37 with index **NLW Cer
  RO & Soc Gen**

LLANWNNEN   *SD*
PR C 1799–1812 B 1796–1812 recorded in 1831 apparently lost. CB 1776–95 in PR
  Llanwenog
C 1776–95, 1813–1993 M 1765–1801, 1813–36, 1839–1970 B 1776–95, 1813–1993 **NLW**
  Mf M 1765–1801 **Cer RO**
BT 1684–6, 1689, 1702, 1705, 1799–1803, 1807, 1811, 1813–36, 1840–7, 1849–80, 1882,
  1885–8 **NLW**
Cop ts Fac PR M 1813–36 **NLW Cer RO & Soc Gen**

LLANWNNWS gweler/see GWNNWS

LLANYCHAEARN   *SD*
Diocesan records suggest that *c*1790 this parish had PR going back 'about 40 years'
C 1803–1993 M 1754–1971 (Banns 1825–86) B 1805–1992 **NLW** Mf **Cer RO**
BT 1689, 1702–3, 1811–19, 1823–5, 1827–48, 1850–80, 1882, 1893 **NLW**
Cop ts PR M 1754–1837 with index **NLW Cer RO & Soc Gen**

LLECHRYD   *SD*
PR CB 1787–1812 M 1787–1804 recorded in 1831 apparently lost in the floods of 1861 (G
 Eyre Evans, *Cardiganshire and Its Antiquities,* 251)
C 1813–1996 M 1805–1970 (Banns 1824–1996 with gaps) B 1813–1969 **NLW** Mf **Cer
 RO**
BT 1799–1855, 1862–3, 1876–7 **NLW**
Cop ts PR M 1813–37 with index **NLW Cer RO & Soc Gen**   ts index PR M 1837–1970
 NLW & Cer RO

LLEDROD   *SD*
PR M 1804–12 recorded as missing in 1831
C 1770–2, 1778–1850, 1853–1991 M 1766–1804, 1813–1970 B 1770–2, 1778–1992 **NLW**
 Mf C 1770–2, 1778–1850 M 1766–1804, 1813–37 (Banns 1823–4) B 1770–2, 1778–1945
 Cer RO
BT 1674–5, 1678–80, 1682, 1684, 1687, 1699–1700, 1703, 1811–17, 1819–29, 1831–75,
 1880 **NLW**
Cop ts PR M 1765–1837 with index **NLW Cer RO & Soc Gen**

MAESTIR gweler/see LLANBEDR PONT STEFFAN/LAMPETER

MELINDWR gweler/see CAPEL BANGOR

MWNT/MOUNT   *SD*
PR CMB 1778–1810 recorded as being on loose and imperfect leaves in 1831 apparently lost
C 1813–1993 M 1813–1971 B 1813–1993 **NLW** Mf **Cer RO**
BT 1674, 1676, 1679–85, 1799–1800, 1802–3, 1805, 1808–13, 1815–29, 1831–7, 1839–40,
 1842–54, 1865, 1867, 1871–5 **NLW**
Cop ts PR M 1813–37 with index **NLW Cer RO & Soc Gen**

MYDROILYN gweler/see LLANNARTH

NANCWNLLE   *SD*
PR C 1768–1811 M 1763–1809 B 1771–1811 microfilmed in 1960 apparently lost
C 1813–1968 M 1813–1971 (Banns 1957–67) B 1813–1987 **NLW** Mf C 1768–1809,
 1813–1968 M 1768–1809, 1813–1971 (Banns 1957–67) B 1768–1809, 1813–57 **Cer RO**
BT 1675, 1799, 1811, 1813, 1815–17, 1820, 1822–43, 1845–72, 1874–80, 1882, 1885–8
 NLW
Cop ts PR M 1764–1837 with index **NLW Cer RO & Soc Gen**

PENBRYN *SD*
C 1726–1993 M 1726–1987 (Banns 1824–82) Sarnau, St John 1947–70, 1972–9 B
 1726–1992 **NLW** Mf **Cer RO**
BT 1678, 1680–3, 1685, 1687–8, 1703, 1799, 1801–3, 1805–11, 1813–18, 1820–63,
 1865–6, 1870–4, 1876–7 **NLW**
Cop ms PR (extracts) CMB 1796–1812 **NLW** ts PR M 1813–37 with index **NLW & Cer
 RO** ts PR C 1726–1838 M 1736–1837 B 1736–94 **Soc Gen**

PENRHYN-COCH *SD*
<Llanbadarn fawr
C 1883–1993 M 1881–1970 (Banns 1937–55) B 1893–1993 **NLW** Mf **Cer RO**

RHOSTÏE *SD*
The church was a ruin at visitation in 1755. Rebuilt *c*1815. United with Llanilar 1875. Try
 Llanilar or Llangwyryfon for records before 1815
C 1815–1920 M 1822–1925 B 1824–54 **NLW** Mf **Cer RO**
BT 1816, 1821–4, 1828–49, 1851–63, 1865–71, 1873–5 **NLW**
Cop ts PR/BT M 1821–37 with index **NLW Cer RO & Soc Gen**

SILIAN *SD*
CM 1792–1812 in churchwardens' account book 1792–1852 recorded in 1933 apparently
 lost. Some entries CB 1776–91 in PR Llanwenog
C 1776–91, 1813–1964 M 1813–1970 (Banns 1830–4, 1838–48) B 1776–91, 1813–1984
 Fac CB 1776–91 **NLW** Mf C 1813–1964 M 1813–1970 (Banns 1830–4, 1838–48) B
 1813–1984 **Cer RO**
BT 1683–6, 1689, 1702, 1705, 1802, 1811, 1813–16, 1820, 1823–37, 1840–72, 1874–80,
 1882, 1885–8 **NLW**
Cop ts PR M 1813–35 with index **NLW Cer RO & Soc Gen**

★ STRATA FLORIDA/YSTRAD-FFLUR *SD*
 C 1750–1873 M 1750–1971 B 1750–65, 1783–1940 **NLW** Mf **Cer RO**
 BT 1811–13, 1823, 1825–35, 1837–51, 1853–60, 1864–5, 1867–72, 1874–5, 1877–8,
  1885–99, 1901–2 **NLW**
 Cop ts PR M 1750–1837 with index ts PR CMB 1750–1812 **NLW Cer RO & Soc Gen**

TALGARREG gweler/see CAPEL CYNON

TAL-Y-BONT *SD*
<Llanfihangel Genau'r-glyn
C 1922–92 M 1911–70 **NLW**

TREFILAN *SD*
C 1705–1800, 1813–1993 M 1705–53, 1757–1811, 1813–1971 (Banns 1878–1973) B
 1705–1800, 1813–1983 **NLW** Mf **Cer RO**
BT 1678, 1684, 1811–38, 1840–71, 1873–83 **NLW**
Cop ts PR M 1708–1837 with index **NLW Cer RO & Soc Gen**

TREGARON   *SD*
C 1653–1931 M 1662–1979 (Banns 1830–1915) B 1665–1937 **NLW** Mf **Cer RO**
BT 1678, 1680, 1700, 1811–17, 1828–9, 1831–9, 1841–66, 1869–79, 1882 **NLW**
Cop ts PR M 1653–1837 with index **NLW Cer RO & Soc Gen**

TRE-MAIN   *SD*
C 1763–1988 M 1763–1971 B 1763–1990 **NLW** Mf CB 1763–1812 M 1763–1971 **Cer RO**
BT 1676, 1678–84, 1686–9, 1700–1, 1705, 1799, 1801–3, 1806–66 **NLW**
Cop ts PR M 1813–37 with index **NLW Cer RO & Soc Gen**

TROED-YR-AUR   *SD*
C 1655–1990 M 1655–1966 (Banns 1823–1967) B 1655–1875 **NLW** Mf **Cer RO**
BT 1674, 1678–81, 1683–9, 1702–3, 1705, 1799, 1801–53, 1855–83 **NLW**
Cop ms PR (extracts) C 1814–75 **NLW** ts PR M 1813–37 with index **NLW & Cer RO**
  ts PR CB 1655–1803 M 1655–1753 **Soc Gen**

★ VERWICK/Y FERWIG   *SD*
Diocesan records suggest that *c*1790 this parish had PR going back 30 years
C 1813–1992 M 1769–1970 B 1813–1955 **NLW** Mf **Cer RO**
BT 1674–5, 1679–84, 1686–7, 1699–1700, 1799, 1801, 1803–7, 1810–55, 1865–6 **NLW**
Cop ts PR M 1813–37 with index **NLW Cer RO & Soc Gen**

YSBYTY CYNFYN   *SD*
Diocesan records suggest that *c*1790 this chapel of ease to Llanbadarn Fawr had 'a register
  which goes back 20 years'
C 1789–1991 M 1762–1970 B 1787–1863, 1865–1991 **NLW** Mf **Cer RO**
BT 1813, 1815, 1819–20, 1822–67, 1870–6, 1878–81 **NLW**
Cop ts PR M 1762–1837 with index **NLW Cer RO & Soc Gen**

YSBYTY YSTWYTH   *SD*
C 1781–1915 M 1782–1956 B 1781–1886, 1897–1916, 1928–92 **NLW** Mf **Cer RO**
BT 1682, 1811, 1813–53, 1858–79, 1884–93 **NLW**
Cop ts PR M 1782–1837 with index **NLW Cer RO & Soc Gen**

YSTRAD gweler/see LLANFIHANGEL YSTRAD

YSTRAD-FFLUR/STRATA FLORIDA   *SD*
C 1750–1873 M 1750–1971 B 1750–65, 1783–1940 **NLW** Mf **Cer RO**
BT 1811–13, 1823, 1825–35, 1837–51, 1853–60, 1864–5, 1867–72, 1874–5, 1877–8,
  1885–99, 1901–2 **NLW**
Cop ts PR M 1750–1837 with index ts PR CMB 1750–1812 **NLW Cer RO & Soc Gen**

YSTRADMEURIG   *SD*
C 1798–1916 M 1798–1836, 1838–1970 B 1798–1916, 1949–76 Mf C 1949–86 **NLW**
  Mf **Cer RO**

BT 1682, 1813, 1823, 1825–80, 1885–90 **NLW**
Cop ts PR M 1798–1837 with index **NLW Cer RO & Soc Gen**

BRYCHEINIOG
BRECKNOCKSHIRE

YSTRADGYNLAIS Eglwysi cyn 1813/Pre-1813 churches
Cefncoedycymer Eglwysi wedi 1813/Post-1813 churches

ABER-CRAF/ABERCRAVE   *SB*
<Ystradgynlais 1925
M 1912–89 **WGAS**   Fac M 1912–30 **Glam RO**

ABERHONDDU/BRECON St David (LLAN-FAES)   *SB*
C 1730–63, 1768–1944 M 1730–1971 (Banns 1823–51, 1904–65) B 1730–63, 1768–1969
  NLW Mf C 1730–63, 1768–1944 M 1730–1921 (Banns 1823–51, 1904–65) B 1730–63,
  1768–1969 **PCAO**
BT 1715–31, 1733–97, 1799–1809, 1813–14, 1817, 1823–44 **NLW**
Cop PR CB 1730–63, 1768–1810 M 1730–53 in Edwin Davies, *Parochial Registers and
  Records,* 1 (Brecon, 1906), 20–72

ABERHONDDU/BRECON St John Evangelist   *SB*
C 1727–1939 M 1727–1982 (Banns 1787–1823, 1870–1956, 1983–8) B 1727–1963 **NLW**
  Mf C 1727–1939 M 1727–1971 (Banns 1787–1823, 1870–1956, 1983–8) B 1727–1963
  PCAO
BT 1716, 1720–2, 1724–46, 1748–53, 1755–1809, 1813–37, 1840, 1864–5 **NLW**

ABERHONDDU/BRECON St Mary   *SB*
C 1684–1958 M 1684–1976 (Banns 1883–1971) B 1684–6, 1693 (see St John for later B)
  NLW Mf **PCAO** Mf C 1684–1900 M 1684–1920 (Banns 1883–1913) B 1684–6, 1693
  Soc Gen
BT 1701, 1713, 1716–21, 1724–30, 1735–41, 1743–55, 1757–65, 1767–71, 1774–82, 1786,
  1789, 1791–5, 1797–1809, 1813–40, 1864–6 **NLW**

ABERYSGIR/ABERYSKIR   *SB*
Diocesan records suggest that *c*1790 this parish had PR beginning in 1720
C 1802–1990 M 1755–1833, 1838–1971 B 1802–1991 **NLW** Mf **PCAO**
BT 1715–17, 1721, 1723–6, 1729–43, 1745–53, 1755–61, 1763–9, 1771–82, 1784,
  1786–95, 1797–1809, 1813–19, 1821–48, 1865–6, 1869–71 **NLW**

ALLT-MAWR   *SB*
Pre-1813 entries included in PR Llanafan Fawr (1831 survey); the only nineteenth-century
  records extant in 1935, but now apparently lost, were eight entries of M 1813–37 on 'three
  sheets mounted on gauze' and four entries of M 1842–93 in 'a portion of a register'
M 1912–71 **NLW** Mf **PCAO** C 1915– B 1914– incumbent
BT 1713, 1720, 1729–30, 1738, 1741, 1751, 1756–60, 1762–9, 1771, 1773–5, 1777–83,
  1785–9, 1793–1809, 1813–16, 1819–37, 1839–40, 1843 **NLW**

BATEL, Y/BATTLE   *SB*
PR M 1813–35 recorded in 1935 apparently lost
C 1720–1991 M 1720–50, 1754–1812, 1838–1971 B 1778–1992 **NLW** Mf **PCAO**
BT 1714–15, 1717–18, 1720–1, 1724–50, 1753–4, 1756–75, 1777–8, 1780–1809, 1813–19,
  1821–5, 1827, 1829–33, 1835–41 **NLW**

BETWS PEN-PONT gweler/see PEN-PONT

* BRECON/ABERHONDDU St David (LLAN-FAES)   *SB*
  C 1730–63, 1768–1944 M 1730–1971 (Banns 1823–51, 1904–65) B 1730–63, 1768–1969
  NLW Mf C 1730–63, 1768–1944 M 1730–1921 (Banns 1823–51, 1904–65) B 1730–63,
  1768–1969 **PCAO**
  BT 1715–31, 1733–97, 1799–1809, 1813–14, 1817, 1823–44 **NLW**
  Cop PR CB 1730–63, 1768–1810 M 1730–53 in Edwin Davies, *Parochial Registers and
  Records,* 1 (Brecon, 1906), 20–72

* BRECON/ABERHONDDU St John Evangelist   *SB*
  C 1727–1939 M 1727–1982 (Banns 1787–1823, 1870–1956, 1983–8) B 1727–1963 **NLW**
  Mf C 1727–1939 M 1727–1971 (Banns 1787–1823, 1870–1956, 1983–8) B 1727–1963
  PCAO
  BT 1716, 1720–2, 1724–46, 1748–53, 1755–1809, 1813–37, 1840, 1864–5 **NLW**

* BRECON/ABERHONDDU St Mary   *SB*
  C 1684–1958 M 1684–1976 (Banns 1883–1971) B 1684–6, 1693 (see St John for later B)
  NLW Mf **PCAO** Mf C 1684–1900 M 1684–1920 (Banns 1883–1913) B 1684–6, 1693
  Soc Gen
  BT 1701, 1713, 1716–21, 1724–30, 1735–41, 1743–55, 1757–65, 1767–71, 1774–82, 1786,
  1789, 1791–5, 1797–1809, 1813–40, 1864–6 **NLW**

BRONLLYS   *SB*
Diocesan records suggest that *c*1790 this parish had registers going back to 1759
C 1813–1992 M 1755–1971 B 1813–1939 **NLW** Mf **PCAO**
BT 1713, 1715–16, 1719–25, 1727, 1729–30, 1733–5, 1737–52, 1754–1809, 1813,
  1818–41, 1845–8, 1865, 1871–2 **NLW**

BRYN-MAWR   *SB*
<Llangatwg/Llangattock and Llanelli/Llanelly 1875
C 1850–1954 M 1873–1977 (Banns 1943–53) B 1888–1943 **Gwent RO**

* BUILTH/LLANFAIR-YM-MUALLT   *SB*
  C 1681–1730, 1750–65, 1767–1976 M 1681–1730, 1750–65, 1770–1987 (Banns
  1877–1979) B 1681–1730, 1750–65, 1769–1867, 1869, 1873–4, 1879–1981 **NLW** Mf C
  1681–1730, 1750–65, 1767–1943 M 1681–1730, 1750–65, 1770–1910 (Banns 1877–1952)
  B 1681–1730, 1750–65, 1769–1867, 1869, 1873–4 **PCAO**
  BT 1687, 1713–16, 1719–21, 1723–5, 1728–42, 1744–95, 1797–1804, 1806–9, 1813–22,
  1824–31, 1836–41 **NLW**

CALLWEN (GLYNTAWE)   *SB*
<Defynnog 1868. PR M 1813–[37] recorded in 1935 apparently lost
C 1685–94, 1760–1958 M 1685–94, 1760–1808, 1840–1922, 1924–71 (Banns 1833–1977)
  B 1685–94, 1778–1958 **WGAS** Fac C 1685–94, 1760–1958 M 1685–94, 1760–1808,
  1840–1922, 1924–39 B 1685–94, 1778–1958 **Glam RO** Fac 1685–94, 1760–1808 **NLW**
BT 1775, 1777, 1783–95, 1797–8, 1800, 1802–9, 1813–38, 1840 **NLW**

CANTREF   *SB*
C 1779–1991 M 1754–1811, 1815–37, 1839–1971 B 1784–1811, 1813–1992 **NLW** Mf
  PCAO
BT 1714–15, 1719–20, 1723–5, 1729–42, 1745, 1747–78, 1780–8, 1790, 1792–4,
  1797–1809, 1813–41, 1864–5, 1871 **NLW**

CAPEL COELBREN gweler/see COELBREN, Y

CAPEL GLYN COLLWYN gweler/see GLYNCOLLEN/GLYNCOLLWNG

CAPEL ILLTUD gweler/see LLANILLTUD/LLANILLTYD

CAPEL NANT-DDU   *SB*
C 1779–1808, 1813–1967 M 1813–14, 1858–1971 B 1779–1930 **NLW** Mf **PCAO**
BT see Cantref

CAPEL TAF FECHAN   *SB*
<Llanddeti/Llanthetty. PR CMB 1772–1812 recorded in 1831 apparently lost. PR M
disused 1926 with closure and demolition of church
C 1813–1981 M 1891–1925 **NLW** Mf **PCAO**

CAPEL-Y-FFIN   *SB*
<Llanigon. PR M disused 1907 after it was realised that the chapel had never been licensed
  for the solemnization of marriages
C 1821–1992 M 1845–1907 B 1821–1992 **NLW** Mf **PCAO**
BT see Llanigon

CATHEDIN/CATHEDINE   *SB*
C 1732–1991 M 1732–1812, 1814–35, 1838–1971 B 1732–1991 **NLW** Mf **PCAO**
BT 1687, 1713–16, 1718, 1720–6, 1728–65, 1767–8, 1770–6, 1778–83, 1785–90, 1794–7,
  1799–1809, 1813–15, 1821–41, 1865, 1867 **NLW**

CEFNCOEDYCYMER   *SB*
<Y Faenor/Vaynor. C 1910–24 entered in PR Y Faenor/Vaynor
C 1877–1910, 1924–50 M 1883–1973 (Banns 1926–51) **NLW** Mf **PCAO**

CLAS-AR-WY, Y/GLASBURY St Peter   *SB*
The Radnorshire portion of this parish has been served since 1882 by the church of All
  Saints (see under Maesyfed/Radnorshire)
C 1660–1955 M 1660–1976 (Banns 1823–1940) B 1660–1929 **NLW** Mf **PCAO**
BT 1715–16, 1719–69, 1771–4, 1776–1808, 1810, 1813–38, 1873–4 **NLW**
Cop printed PR CMB 1660–1837 with index (ed T Wood, 1904)

COELBREN, Y   *SB*
An ancient chapelry of Ystradgynlais. Earlier CMB in PR of the mother church
C 1902–25 M 1863–1990 B 1902–25 **WGAS** Fac CB 1902–25 M 1863–1923 **Glam RO**

CRAI/CRAY   *SB*
An ancient chapelry in the parish of Defynnog possibly without its own PR before 1813.
 Consent was given to rebuild the 'ruinated chapel called Lanthew chapel otherwise Cray
 chapel' in 1752 (NLW, SD/MISC/1339)
C 1820–1986 M (Banns 1884–1992) B 1885–1992 **NLW** Mf **PCAO** M 1884–
incumbent

CRICKADARN gweler/see CRUCADARN

CRICKHOWELL gweler/see CRUCYWEL

CROSS OAK gweler/see LLANFEUGAN

CRUCADARN/CRICKADARN   *SB*
Diocesan records suggest that *c*1790 this parish had registers going back to 1705
C 1734–56, 1775–82, 1813–1992 M 1734–1971 B 1734–56, 1775–82, 1813–1983 **NLW**
 Mf **PCAO** Mf C 1734–56, 1775–82 M 1734–1971 B 1734–56, 1775–82, 1813–1983
 Soc Gen Fac (Banns 1823–1985) **NLW**
BT 1705–8, 1710, 1713, 1720–60, 1762–75, 1777–1809, 1813–38, 1841, 1844–7, 1865–73
 NLW

CRUCYWEL/CRICKHOWELL   *SB*
C 1633–84 with gaps, 1700–20, 1726–1936 M 1633–84 with gaps, 1700–20, 1754–1944
 (Banns 1824–1971) B 1633–84 with gaps, 1700–20, 1725–1941 **NLW** Mf **PCAO &**
 Gwent RO
BT 1714–21, 1723–5, 1728–95, 1797–1809, 1813, 1815, 1821–9, 1835–6 **NLW** Mf
 1797–1809 **Gwent RO**

DEFYNNOG   *SB*
C 1695–1763, 1771–1939 M 1695–1763, 1771–1997 B 1695–1763, 1771–1984 **NLW** Mf
 C 1695–1763, 1771–1939 M 1695–1763, 1771–1983 B 1695–1763, 1771–1984 **PCAO**
BT 1713–14, 1717–21, 1723–68, 1771–88, 1790, 1792, 1795, 1797–1809, 1813–36,
 1839–48, 1864–73 **NLW**

DYFFRYN HONDDU (UPPER CHAPEL)   *SB*
<Merthyr Cynog. Diocesan records suggest that *c*1790 this chapel had registers beginning in
 1716
C 1825–44 M 1826–32, 1855–1971 **NLW** Mf **PCAO**

EGLWYS OEN DUW   *SB*
Built 1865. Ecclesiastical parish <Llanafan Fawr, Llanfihangel Abergwesyn, Llangamarch &
 Llanllywenfel/Llanlleonfel 1874
C 1866–1987 M 1867–1971 B 1875–1987 **NLW** Mf **PCAO**

FAENOR, Y/VAYNOR   *SB*
PR 1759–1812 recorded in 1935 apparently lost. M 1868–92 recorded in 1900 parish

inventory (NLW, SD/Misc.B/102) was missing in 1935 and has not been recovered
C 1813–1923 M 1755–1868, 1892–1975 (Banns 1823–1903) B 1813–1905, 1923–50 **NLW**
  Mf **PCAO** Mf C 1813–1923 M 1755–1847 B 1813–1905, 1923–50 **Soc Gen**
BT 1714–15, 1717–47, 1749–62, 1764–95, 1797–1809, 1813–23, 1825–37, 1840–2 **NLW**

GARTHBRENGI   *SB*
Diocesan records suggest that *c*1790 this parish had registers going back to 1653
C 1733–52, 1758–63, 1766–86, 1804, 1813–1978 M 1733–52, 1758–63, 1767, 1776–9,
  1789–99, 1803–4, 1813–1971 B 1733–52, 1758–63, 1766–86, 1804, 1813–1982 **NLW**
  Mf **PCAO**
BT 1687, 1707–8, 1712–41, 1744–95, 1797–1809, 1813–31, 1833–52, 1854 **NLW**

GELLI, Y/HAY   *SB*
C 1688–1895 M 1688–1971 (Banns 1841–1949) B 1688–1991 **NLW** Mf **PCAO** Mfc M
  1751–2 with index **Soc Gen**
BT 1687, 1713–14, 1720, 1723–52, 1756–95, 1797–1809, 1813, 1815–55, 1867 **NLW**

★ GLASBURY/Y CLAS-AR-WY St Peter   *SB*
The Radnorshire portion of this parish has been served since 1882 by the church of All
  Saints (see under Maesyfed/Radnorshire)
C 1660–1955 M 1660–1976 (Banns 1823–1940) B 1660–1929 **NLW** Mf **PCAO**
BT 1715–16, 1719–69, 1771–4, 1776–1808, 1810, 1813–38, 1873–4 **NLW**
Cop printed PR CMB 1660–1837 with index (ed T Wood, 1904)

GLYN gweler/see LLANILLTUD

GLYNCOLLEN/GLYNCOLLWNG   *SB*
An ancient chapelry in the parish of Llanfeugan
C 1914–25 **NLW** Mf **PCAO**

GLYNTAWE gweler/see CALLWEN

GWENDDWR   *SB*
C 1752–3, 1798–1990 M 1766–1801, 1812–1971 B 1752–3, 1798–1992 **NLW** Mf
  PCAO
BT 1713–18, 1721–34, 1736–56, 1758–67, 1769–95, 1797–1809, 1813–17, 1819–20,
  1822–35, 1837–8, 1841, 1844–58, 1865–73 **NLW**

★ HAY/Y GELLI   *SB*
C 1688–1895 M 1688–1971 (Banns 1841–1949) B 1688–1991 **NLW** Mf **PCAO** Mfc M
  1751–2 with index **Soc Gen**
BT 1687, 1713–14, 1720, 1723–52, 1756–95, 1797–1809, 1813, 1815–55, 1867 **NLW**

LLANAFAN FAWR   *SB*
PR M 1771–1812 recorded in 1935 apparently lost
C 1720–59, 1762–1991 M 1720–70, 1813–1971 (Banns 1790–1840, 1888–90, 1948–55) B

1720–59, 1762–1992 **NLW** Mf C 1720–59, 1762–1991 M 1720–70, 1813–1971 (Banns 1790–1840) B 1720–59, 1762–1992 **PCAO**
BT 1708, 1710, 1714–23, 1730, 1736–63, 1765–95, 1797–1809, 1813–42, 1844 **NLW**

LLANAFAN FECHAN (LLANFECHAN)　　*SB*
A few entries CB 1753–5 in PR Llanafan Fawr
C 1799–1994　M 1755–97, 1801–11, 1813–1971　B 1799–1998 **NLW**　Mf M 1755–97, 1801–11, 1813–1970 **PCAO**
BT 1701, 1713–16, 1719–31, 1733–8, 1740–51, 1753–4, 1756–64, 1766–95, 1797–1809, 1813–30, 1832–6, 1839–40, 1842 **NLW**

LLANBEDR YSTRAD YW　　*SB*
C 1675–1708, 1712–1964　M 1675–1971　B 1675–1708, 1712–1894 **NLW** Mf **PCAO**
BT 1713–19, 1721–7, 1730, 1732–47, 1749–59, 1761–92, 1794–5, 1798, 1800–9, 1813–15, 1817, 1819–36 **NLW**

LLANDEFAELOG gweler/see LLANDYFAELOG

LLANDEFALLE gweler/see LLANDYFALLE

LLANDEILO'R-FÂN　　*SB*
PR CMB 1770– recorded in 1831 apparently lost
C 1809–1949　M 1813–1971　B 1809–1918 **NLW**　Mf **PCAO**
BT 1714–16, 1719–95, 1797–1809, 1813–38, 1840, 1843–4 **NLW**

LLANDYFAELOG FACH　　*SB*
C 1715–54, 1762–79, 1783–1981　M 1715–54, 1783–1971 (Banns 1787–1812, 1865, 1910, 1938–79)　B 1715–54, 1762–79, 1783–1980 **NLW** Mf **PCAO**
BT 1712–25, 1727–56, 1759–95, 1797–1809, 1813–15, 1817–29, 1831–2, 1834–8, 1866, 1872–3 **NLW** Mf 1712–1837 **Soc Gen**

LLANDYFAELOG TRE'R-GRAIG　　*SB*
Some entries of CMB in PR Llanfilo
C 1786–98　M 1755–1827, 1845–1971　B 1782–99 **NLW**　Mf M 1755–1827, 1845–1937 **PCAO**
BT 1710–17, 1729–30, 1732, 1740, 1743, 1746, 1749, 1752, 1754, 1765, 1774, 1786–9, 1791, 1795, 1797–1809, 1820–1, 1823–30, 1832–9, 1842 **NLW** Mf 1710–1839 **Soc Gen**

LLANDYFALLE　　*SB*
PR CMB 1720–1812 recorded in 1935 apparently lost
C 1813–1930　M 1813–1971　B 1813–1981 **NLW** Mf **PCAO & Soc Gen**
BT 1705–8, 1710, 1713, 1715, 1719–38, 1740–65, 1767–8, 1771–84, 1786–95, 1797–1809, 1813–47 **NLW**

LLANDDETI/LLANTHETTY   *SB*
PR 1693–1812 recorded in 1831 apparently lost, except for the cover of one volume with entries of CB 1740–1
C 1740–1, 1813–1975 M 1813–1971 (Banns 1824–1970) B 1740–1, 1813–1974 **NLW** Mf **PCAO**
BT 1708, 1714–95, 1797–1809, 1813–34, 1836, 1839–44 **NLW**

LLAN-DDEW   *SB*
PR 1709–1805 recorded in 1831 apparently lost
C 1813–1991 M 1813–1971 B 1813–1991 **NLW** Mf **PCAO**
BT 1687, 1698, 1707–8, 1712–58, 1761–95, 1797–1809, 1813–31, 1833–8 **NLW**

LLANDDEWI ABERGWESYN   *SB*
PR 1738–1812 recorded in 1831 and M 1754–79 recorded in 1935 apparently lost. Parish united with Llanfihangel Abergwesyn 1885 (NLW, SD/Misc.B/99(p)). No separate marriage register thereafter
C 1813–1984 M 1813–73 (Banns 1826–62, 1957–9) B 1813–1986 **NLW** Mf **PCAO**
BT 1714–51, 1753–60, 1762–95, 1797–1809, 1813–44 **NLW**
Cop ms PR CB 1738–1812 M 1738–56, 1765–1812 **Cardiff Central Library** (MS 2.238) Mf **NLW**

LLANDDEWI'R-CWM   *SB*
C 1765–1810, 1813–1992 M 1754–1837, 1839–1971 B 1765–1810, 1813–1992 **NLW** Mf **PCAO**
BT 1716–17, 1719–25, 1727, 1729–32, 1734–71, 1773–85, 1787–95, 1797–1809, 1813–23, 1825–31, 1836–41 **NLW**

LLANDDULAS gweler/see TIRABAD

LLANELEU/LLANELIEU   *SB*
PR CB 1746–1812 M 1746–53 recorded in 1831 apparently lost
C 1813–1964 M 1754–1811, 1814–36, 1838–1971 B 1813–1943 **NLW** Mf **PCAO**
BT 1713–16, 1718–21, 1724–5, 1727–33, 1735–6, 1739–50, 1752–5, 1757–1809, 1813, 1817–32, 1834–6, 1838–9, 1848–50 **NLW**

LLANELLI/LLANELLY   *SB*
C 1701–1924 M 1701–52, 1754–1933 (Banns 1842–1921) B 1708–1811, 1813–1925 **Gwent RO** Fac C 1701–1811 M 1701–1809, 1847–74 B 1701–1847 **NLW**
BT 1712–13, 1715–18, 1720, 1722–35, 1737–95, 1797–1809, 1812–37 **NLW**
Cop ts index PR B 1738–1925 **Gwent RO**

LLAN-FAES gweler/see ABERHONDDU/BRECON St David

LLANFAIR-YM-MUALLT/BUILTH   *SB*
C 1681–1730, 1750–65, 1767–1976 M 1681–1730, 1750–65, 1770–1987 (Banns 1877–1979) B 1681–1730, 1750–65, 1769–1867, 1869, 1873–4, 1879–1981 **NLW** Mf C

1681–1730, 1750–65, 1767–1943 M 1681–1730, 1750–65, 1770–1910 (Banns 1877–1952)
B 1681–1730, 1750–65, 1769–1867, 1869, 1873–4 **PCAO**
BT 1687, 1713–16, 1719–21, 1723–5, 1728–42, 1744–95, 1797–1804, 1806–9, 1813–22, 1824–31, 1836–41 **NLW**

LLANFECHAN gweler/see LLANAFAN FECHAN

LLANFEUGAN   *SB*
C 1747–1976 M 1747–1971 (Banns 1754–1818, 1892–4, 1898–1987) Cross Oak 1890–1953 B 1747–1988 **NLW** Mf **PCAO**
BT 1687, 1714, 1717–21, 1723–37, 1739–64, 1766, 1768–95, 1797–1809, 1813–36, 1865–7 **NLW**

LLANFIHANGEL ABERGWESYN   *SB*
PR M disused 1957 with closure of church
C 1730–1970 M 1730–1923 (Banns 1825–63, 1897) B 1730–1987 **NLW** Mf C 1730–1970
M 1730–1837 (Banns 1825–63, 1897) B 1730–1987 **PCAO**
BT 1713–25, 1727–42, 1744, 1747–74, 1776–95, 1797–1809, 1813–38, 1840, 1842–4 **NLW**

LLANFIHANGEL BRYNPABUAN   *SB*
PR CB 1722–1812 M 1723–54 recorded in 1935 apparently lost
C 1762–1804, 1813–1991 M 1755–93, 1813–1971 B 1762–1804, 1813–1985 **NLW** Mf **PCAO**
BT 1698, 1708, 1710, 1713–20, 1723, 1726, 1728–39, 1741–50, 1752–7, 1760–95, 1797–1809, 1813–36, 1839–42, 1844 **NLW**

LLANFIHANGEL CWM DU (ST MICHAEL CWMDU)   *SB*
C 1734–1922 M 1734–1971 (Banns 1802–1968) B 1734–1992 **NLW** Mf **PCAO & Gwent RO**
BT 1688, 1714–15, 1719–21, 1725, 1729–95, 1797–1809, 1813–38, 1840 **NLW** Mf 1797–1809 **Gwent RO** Mf C 1688–1799 **Soc Gen**

LLANFIHANGEL FECHAN   *SB*
<Llandyfaelog Fach. Diocesan records suggest that *c*1790 this chapel had no PR of its own
C 1819–1979 M 1872–1971 B 1819–1981 **NLW** Mf **PCAO**
BT 1765, 1819–27, 1830–1, 1833–52, 1854 **NLW**

LLANFIHANGEL NANT BRÂN   *SB*
PR CMB 1758–1812 recorded in 1831 apparently lost
C 1813–1991 M 1813–19, 1835–1971 B 1813–1991 **NLW** Mf **PCAO**
BT 1714–15, 1719–1809, 1813–38, 1840–4 **NLW**

LLANFIHANGEL TAL-Y-LLYN   *SB*
PR CB 1700–13 M 1750 recorded in 1831 apparently lost
C 1785–1991 M 1767–1810, 1813–1971 B 1785–1992 **NLW** Mf **PCAO**
BT 1714–17, 1720–1, 1723–33, 1735–88, 1790–1809, 1813–16, 1818–19, 1821–34,

1837–8, 1843, 1845–8, 1865, 1871, 1873 **NLW**
Cop ms PR CB 1785–1812 M 1767–1810 **NLW**

LLANFILO (LLANFILLO) *SB*
C 1680–1739, 1786–1990 M 1680–1739, 1755–1971 B 1680–1739, 1782–1967 **NLW** Mf
PCAO
BT 1687, 1713, 1717, 1719–21, 1723, 1725–7, 1729–35, 1737–95, 1797–1809, 1813–45,
1864–73 **NLW**

LLANFRYNACH *SB*
PR CB 1695–1776 M 1695–1754 recorded in 1831 apparently lost
C 1776–1935 M 1754–1971 (Banns 1823–1961) B 1776–1912 **NLW** Mf **PCAO**
BT 1707, 1713–16, 1718–22, 1725–7, 1729–32, 1734–57, 1759–64, 1767–1809, 1813–14,
1820–40 **NLW**

LLANGAMARCH *SB*
C 1763–1918 M 1767–1971 (Banns 1782–1980) B 1763–1955 **NLW** Mf C 1763–1918 M
1767–1971 (Banns 1782–1854) B 1763–1955 **PCAO**
BT 1713, 1715–30, 1732–4, 1736–1809, 1813–44, 1864–8 **NLW**
Cop ts PR M 1837–1941 **PCAO**

LLANGANTEN *SB*
PR CMB 1738–50 recorded in 1831 and CB 1769–1812 M 1813–36 recorded in 1935
apparently lost
C 1792–5, 1813–1998 M 1754–1812, 1837–1971 B 1792–5, 1813–1984 **NLW** Mf C
1792–5 M 1754–1812, 1837–1971 B 1792–5, 1813–1984 **PCAO**
BT 1714, 1720, 1723–38, 1740–54, 1756–95, 1797–1809, 1813–33, 1835–53 **NLW**

LLANGASTY TAL-Y-LLYN *SB*
C 1718–68, 1770–1990 M 1718–1971 B 1718–68, 1770–1991 **NLW** Mf **PCAO**
BT 1685, 1714–17, 1719, 1721–45, 1747, 1749–66, 1772–6, 1778–84, 1786–9, 1791–5,
1797–1809, 1813–15, 1821–40, 1842–52, 1865–6 **NLW**

LLANGATWG/LLANGATTOCK *SB*
C 1703–1961 M 1703–1986 (Banns 1823–48) B 1703–1992 **NLW** Mf **PCAO & Gwent
RO**
BT 1714–32, 1734–94, 1797–1809, 1812–37 **NLW** Mf 1797–1809 **Gwent RO**

LLANGENNI/LLANGENNY *SB*
C 1695–1891 M 1695–1971 B 1695–1911 **NLW** Mf **PCAO**
BT 1687, 1714, 1716–97, 1799–1809, 1813–32, 1834–5, 1838–9 **NLW**

LLAN-GORS/LLANGORSE *SB*
C 1693–1789, 1794–1965 M 1693–1753, 1756–1971 B 1693–1789, 1794–1927 **NLW** Mf
PCAO
BT 1714–17, 1720, 1723–34, 1736–8, 1740–58, 1760–83, 1785–91, 1793–5, 1797–1809,

1813–30, 1832–43, 1865–8 **NLW**
Cop ms PR CB 1695–1790 M 1695–1753 **NLW**

LLANGYNIDR   *SB*
PR CB 1736–81 M 1736–54 recorded in 1831 apparently lost
C 1783–1992 M 1754–1989 (Banns 1852–1939) B 1783–1992 **NLW** Mf **PCAO**
BT 1707–8, 1713–27, 1729–95, 1797–1808, 1813–36, 1838–41 **NLW**

LLANGYNOG   *SB*
PR M disused 1957 with closure of church
C 1745–1934 M 1746–71, 1801–37, 1844–1929 B 1745–1932 **NLW** Mf **PCAO**
BT 1717, 1722, 1730, 1732, 1736–41, 1743–9, 1751, 1753–4, 1757–89, 1791–3, 1795–9,
 1801–9, 1813–33, 1835–40, 1843–6 **NLW**

LLANHAMLACH   *SB*
C 1717–46, 1755–1991 M 1717–46, 1754–1971 B 1717–46, 1755–1930 **NLW** Mf
 PCAO
BT 1716–38, 1741, 1744–6, 1749–51, 1753–8, 1760, 1762–5, 1769–72, 1774–95,
 1797–1809, 1813–29, 1831, 1834 **NLW**

LLANIGON   *SB*
C 1712–85, 1788–1906 M 1712–1971 (Banns 1824–1976) B 1712–53, 1783–1953 **NLW**
 Mf C 1712–85, 1788–1906 M 1712–1837 (Banns 1824–1976) B 1712–53, 1783–1953
 PCAO
BT 1720–1, 1723–82, 1784–95, 1797–1809, 1813–52 **NLW**

LLANILID/LLANULID gweler/see CRAI/CRAY

LLANILLTUD/LLANILLTYD (CAPEL ILLTUD)   *SB*
A chapel of ease to Defynnog without its own PR before 1776. Separate parish 1887
C 1776–1983 M 1776–1817, 1862–1971 St John, Glyn 1925–71 B 1776–1945 **NLW** Mf
 PCAO
BT 1776, 1783–4, 1787–92, 1795, 1797–1800, 1802–9, 1813–39, 1842–5, 1847, 1864, 1871
 NLW

LLANLLYWENFEL/LLANLLEONFEL   *SB*
PR CB 1764–1812 M 1755–94 recorded in 1831 apparently lost
C 1813– 1998 M 1794–1971 B 1813–1998 **NLW** Mf M 1794–1971 **PCAO**
BT 1714, 1716, 1718–24, 1726–33, 1735–67, 1769–83, 1785–95, 1797–1809, 1813–29,
 1831–5, 1837–47 **NLW**

LLANSANFFRAID (-AR-WYSG)   *SB*
C 1718–47, 1749–1986 M 1718–47, 1749–1971 (Banns 1823–1986) B 1718–47,
 1749–1988 **NLW** Mf **PCAO**
BT 1716–19, 1721–4, 1726–95, 1797–1809, 1814–30, 1832–6, 1838–68 **NLW**

LLANSBYDDYD/LLANSPYDDID   *SB*
C 1699–1811, 1813–1983 M 1699–1971 B 1699–1811, 1813–1909 **NLW** Mf **PCAO**
BT 1687, 1713–14, 1717, 1719–35, 1737–1809, 1813–42, 1845–6, 1864, 1871 **NLW**

★ LLANTHETTY/LLANDDETI   *SB*
PR 1693–1812 recorded in 1831 apparently lost, except for the cover of one volume with
  entries of CB 1740–1
C 1740–1, 1813–1975 M 1813–1971 (Banns 1824–1970) B 1740–1, 1813–1974 **NLW** Mf
  PCAO
BT 1708, 1714–95, 1797–1809, 1813–34, 1836, 1839–44 **NLW**

LLANWRTYD   *SB*
C 1748–1986 M 1748–57, 1770–1971 St James 1896–1971 B 1748–1991 **NLW** Mf C
  1748–1986 M 1748–57, 1770–1950 B 1748–1991 **PCAO**
BT 1713, 1715–26, 1728–31, 1733–5, 1737–71, 1773–4, 1776–95, 1797–1809, 1813–44,
  1864–8 **NLW**

LLANWRTHWL   *SB*
PR CMB 1713–1812 recorded in 1935 apparently lost
C 1813–1922 M 1813–1971 **NLW** Mf **PCAO** B 1813– incumbent
BT 1696, 1713, 1715–95, 1797–1809, 1813–41, 1865 **NLW**
Cop ts PR C 1837–96 **PCAO**

LLANYNYS   *SB*
C 1731–4, 1736–60, 1767–1971 M 1733–5, 1737–1971 (Banns 1805–50) B 1731–40,
  1742–8, 1767–1988 **NLW** Mf **PCAO**
BT 1713–17, 1719–95, 1797–1809, 1813–17, 1819–42, 1844–5, 1847–8 **NLW**

LLAN-Y-WERN   *SB*
C 1653–9, 1664, 1666, 1674, 1688–9, 1695–1708, 1711–15, 1717–1800, 1813–1990 M
  1653–9, 1664, 1666, 1674, 1688–9, 1695–1708, 1711–15, 1717–1836, 1847–1971 B
  1653–9, 1664, 1666, 1674, 1688–9, 1695–1708, 1711–15, 1717–1800, 1813–1962 **NLW**
  Mf **PCAO**
BT 1713–14, 1718–19, 1724–7, 1729–33, 1735–47, 1749–58, 1760–83, 1785–95,
  1797–1809, 1813–40, 1842–5, 1847–50, 1871 **NLW**
Cop ms PR CB 1653–1800 M 1656–1812 **NLW**

LLYS-WEN   *SB*
C 1718–1981 M 1718–55, 1758–60, 1773–94, 1813–36, 1839–1971 B 1718–1812,
  1814–1980 **NLW** Mf **PCAO**
BT 1716, 1718–21, 1723–70, 1772–95, 1797–1809, 1813–30, 1833–5, 1837–8, 1842–6,
  1853 **NLW**

LLYWEL   *SB*
C 1694–1730, 1733–1938 M 1694–1730, 1733–53, 1782–1971 (Banns 1809–1983) B
  1694–1730, 1733–1900 **NLW** Mf C 1694–1730, 1733–1938 M 1694–1730, 1733–53,

1782–1809, 1813–1837 B 1694–1730, 1733–1900 **PCAO**
BT 1708, 1713–19, 1721–31, 1733–49, 1751–1809, 1813–54, 1856–8 **NLW**

MAESMYNYS   *SB*
C 1684–1713, 1743–80, 1813–1991 M 1684–1836, 1838–1971 (Banns 1805–50) B
1684–1992 **NLW** Mf **PCAO**
BT 1687, 1690, 1705, 1707, 1714–16, 1718–95, 1797–1804, 1806–9, 1813–42, 1844–5,
1847–8 **NLW**

MERTHYR CYNOG   *SB*
PR CB 1681–1768, 1782–1804 M 1681–1755 recorded in 1831 apparently lost
C 1813–1981 M 1756–66, 1777–1800, 1803–1971 (Banns 1803–1979) B 1813–1951 **NLW**
  Mf C 1813–87   M 1756–66, 1777–1800, 1803–1971 (Banns 1803–1979) B 1813–1951
  PCAO
BT 1713–95, 1797–1809, 1813–50, 1864, 1866–7, 1871 **NLW**

NANT-DDU gweler/see CAPEL NANT-DDU

NEWBRIDGE-ON-WYE gweler/see MAESYFED/RADNORSHIRE

PATRISIO/PARTRISHOW   *SB*
PR CB 1793–1812 M 1750–1812 recorded in 1831 apparently lost
C 1728–92, 1813–1991 M 1728–49, 1813–1971 B 1728–92, 1813–1992 **NLW** Mf
  PCAO
BT 1713–17, 1719, 1721–30, 1732–64, 1766–95, 1797–1809, 1813–15, 1817–19, 1821–36
  NLW

PENDERYN   *SB*
C 1762–1805, 1807–1990 M 1754–1971 (Banns 1823–95) B 1762–84, 1807–1979 **NLW**
  Mf **PCAO**
BT 1713–14, 1717–21, 1723–5, 1727–95, 1797–1809, 1813–17, 1819–32, 1835–6 **NLW**

PEN-PONT (BETWS PEN-PONT)   *SB*
<Llansbyddyd/Llanspyddid
C 1813–1992 M 1835–6, 1840, 1843–1933 (Banns 1884–1998) B 1814–1991 **NLW** Mf
  PCAO
BT 1803–4, 1814, 1817, 1821, 1824–5, 1827–9, 1831–6, 1842–4, 1866–9, 1871–2 **NLW**

PONTNEWYDD-AR-WY gweler/see MAESYFED/RADNORSHIRE

RHYD-Y-BRYW   *SB*
<Llywel 1861. Diocesan records suggest that *c*1790 this chapel had no PR of its own
C 1813–1985 M 1852–1971 B 1813–1983 **NLW** Mf C 1813–1985 M 1852–1954 B
  1813–1983 **PCAO**
BT 1803, 1813–32, 1834–54, 1857–8, 1864 **NLW**

TAF FECHAN gweler/see CAPEL TAF FECHAN

TALACH-DDU   *SB*
PR CMB 1640–79 transcribed by John Lloyd *c*1904 apparently lost
C 1601–40, 1725–1992 M 1601–40, 1725–1971 B 1601–40, 1725–1992 **NLW** Mf
  PCAO
BT 1708, 1713–56, 1758–62, 1764–8, 1770–4, 1776–95, 1797–1801, 1803–9, 1813,
  1815–33, 1835, 1837–8 **NLW**
Cop ms PR CMB 1600–44, 1653–79 **PCAO**   printed PR CMB 1600–79 in J Lloyd,
Historical Memoranda of Breconshire 2 (1904), 84–118

TALGARTH   *SB*
C 1695–1957 M 1695–1971 (Banns 1823–40, 1850–1914) B 1695–1971 **NLW** Mf
  PCAO
BT 1686, 1708, 1714–23, 1725, 1731, 1734, 1736–95, 1797–1809, 1813–14, 1817–32,
  1834–8, 1840 **NLW**

TIRABAD (LLANDDULAS)   *SB*
This chapel in the parish of Llangamarch was built at the expense of Sackville Gwynne, and
  consecrated in 1726 (NLW, SD/Misc.B/41 and SD/MISC/1273). PR CMB 1729–1812
  recorded in 1831 apparently lost
C 1813–1986 M 1814–36, 1956–71 (Banns 1807–62, 1956–64) B 1813–1982 **NLW** Mf C
  1813–1986 M 1814–36 (Banns 1807–62, 1956–64) B 1813–1982 **PCAO**
BT 1807–9, 1813–38, 1840, 1842–8 **NLW**
Cop ms PR M 1845–1939 in PR M Llanddewi Abergwesyn **NLW**

TRAEAN-GLAS   *SB*
<Llywel 1890
M 1891–1971 **NLW** Mf **PCAO**

TRALLWNG/TRALLONG   *SB*
PR M 1752–1812 recorded in 1831 apparently lost. Diocesan records suggest that *c*1790 this
  parish had 'imperfect' PR back to 1700
C 1752–6, 1771–1804, 1813–1992 M 1813–1971 (Banns 1824–30, 1865–70, 1923–98) B
  1771–1804, 1813–1991 **NLW** Mf **PCAO**
BT 1687, 1712–14, 1737–8, 1740–2, 1744–5, 1747, 1749–51, 1772–95, 1797–1809, 1813,
  1815–36, 1870 **NLW**

TRETŴR/TRETOWER   *SB*
<Llanfihangel Cwm Du. PR include CB at Glanusk's private chapel, Penmeiarth
C 1813–1992 B 1813–1992 **NLW** Mf **PCAO** M 1877– incumbent
BT see Llanfihangel Cwm Du

UPPER CHAPEL gweler/see DYFFRYN HONDDU

★ VAYNOR/Y FAENOR *SB*

PR 1759–1812 recorded in 1935 apparently lost. M 1868–92 recorded in 1900 parish inventory (NLW, SD/Misc.B/102) was missing in 1935 and has not been recovered

C 1813–1923 M 1755–1868, 1892–1975 (Banns 1823–1903) B 1813–1905, 1923–50 **NLW** Mf **PCAO** Mf C 1813–1923 M 1755–1847 B 1813–1905, 1923–50 **Soc Gen**

BT 1714–15, 1717–47, 1749–62, 1764–95, 1797–1809, 1813–23, 1825–37, 1840–2 **NLW**

YSTRADFELLTE *SB*

PR CB 1737–58 M 1737–53 recorded in 1831 apparently lost. A volume (now NLW MS 23155D) containing CMB 1727–30 was used in 1827 to compile a catalogue of the library of Ystradmeurig School

C 1759–1959 M 1754–1971 (Banns 1754–1823) B 1759–1811, 1815–82 **WGAS** CMB 1727–30 **NLW** Fac C 1759–1959 M 1754–1970 B 1759–1811, 1815–82 **Glam RO**

BT 1713, 1715–62, 1764–95, 1797–1809, 1813–36, 1871–3 **NLW**

Cop ms PR CB 1759–1809 **Cardiff Central Library** (MS 4.650) Mf **NLW**

YSTRADGYNLAIS *SB*

C 1721–1969 M 1721–1856, 1893–1971 (Banns 1823–1913, 1940–78) B 1721–1990 **WGAS** Fac C 1721–1916 M 1721–1856 (Banns 1823–1913) B 1721–1902 **PCAO** C 1721–1916 M 1721–1856 B 1721–1902 **Glam RO**

BT 1713–1804, 1806, 1813–16, 1819, 1822–34, 1836 **NLW**

CAERFYRDDIN
CARMARTHENSHIRE

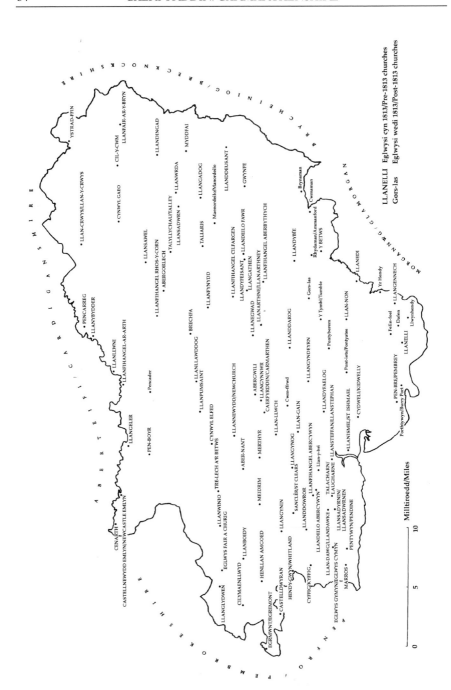

LLANELLI Eglwysi cyn 1813/Pre-1813 churches
Gors-las Eglwysi wedi 1813/Post-1813 churches

Milltiroedd/Miles

0   5   10

ABERGORLECH   *SD*
An ancient chapelry. CMB prior to 1813 included in PR Llanybydder
C 1813–1993 M 1901–69 B 1813–71 **Carm RO**
BT see Llanybydder & Talyllychau/Talley
Cop ts PR index CMB 1876–1985 **Carm RO** ts PR index C 1883–1988 M 1901–69 B
  1813–75 **NLW Carm RO & Soc Gen**

ABERGWILI   *SD*
C 1661–1902 M 1661–1934 B 1661–1902 **NLW** Mf **Carm RO & Soc Gen**
BT 1672, 1674–6, 1680, 1684, 1694, 1698, 1703–5, 1717–18, 1721, 1724–5, 1727–41,
  1743–59, 1763, 1765–1800, 1802–35, 1837–52, 1856–82, 1884–91, 1893–4 **NLW**
Cop ts PR M 1813–37 with index ts PR index CB 1813–75 M 1661–1875 **NLW Carm
  RO & Soc Gen**

ABER-NANT   *SD*
CMB 1763–1812 **NLW** C 1764–1993 M 1754–1965 B 1813–1993 **Carm RO**
BT 1672, 1675–7, 1679, 1681–4, 1686–7, 1690–1, 1693–5, 1697–9, 1701, 1703–4,
  1707–11, 1717, 1721, 1724–40, 1742–6, 1748–68, 1770, 1773, 1775, 1778–9, 1781–5,
  1800, 1802, 1804–64 **NLW**
Cop ts PR M 1813–37 with index ts PR index CB 1813–75 M 1754–1875 **NLW Carm
  RO & Soc Gen**

ALLTYFERIN gweler/see LLANEGWAD

★ AMMANFORD/RHYDAMAN All Saints   *SD*
C 1915–40 M 1915–23, 1935–43, 1953–71 (Banns 1915–73) **Carm RO**

★ AMMANFORD/RHYDAMAN St Michael   *SD*
<Llandybïe & Y Betws 1903
M 1893–1971 (Banns 1892–1964) B 1885–1956 **Carm RO**

BETWS, Y   *SD*
CM 1706–1973 (Banns 1823–1964) B 1706–1909 **Carm RO**
BT 1702, 1707–8, 1716–22, 1728–84, 1786–7, 1789–90, 1793–6, 1798, 1800, 1802–3,
  1805–65 **NLW**
Cop ts PR M 1813–37 with index **NLW Carm RO & Soc Gen**

BRECHFA   *SD*
C 1780–1881 M 1806–1970 (Banns 1831–1976) B 1780–1915 **Carm RO**
BT 1800, 1808–35, 1880–3 **NLW**
Cop ts PR M 1813–37 with index ts PR index C 1813–1986 M 1806–1970 B 1813–1915
  NLW Carm RO & Soc Gen

BRYNAMAN   *SD*
<Llangadog 1889
C 1881–1928 M 1889–1980 (Banns 1924–61) B 1882–1950 **Carm RO**

* BURRY PORT/PORTHTYWYN   *SD*
<Pen-bre/Pembrey
C 1903–79 Pwll 1904–76 M 1902–76 **Carm RO**

CAERFYRDDIN/CARMARTHEN St Peter   *SD*
C 1671–1923 M 1671–1916 (Banns 1823–1915) B 1671–1885 **Carm RO**
BT 1675–6, 1678, 1682–3, 1686, 1691–4, 1701, 1704, 1707, 1712–13, 1719–22, 1728–36,
  1739–40, 1742–3, 1749–63, 1767–93, 1796–1800, 1802–58, 1860, 1862–1901 **NLW**
Cop printed PR/BT C 1671–94, 1699–1746, 1748–99 M 1671–94, 1699–1745, 1748–99
  B 1671–94, 1699–1745, 1748–99 *West Wales Historical Records,* 7–14 (1918–29)
Cop ts CMB 1671–1799 (from *WWHR)* and ts PR M index 1671–1800 **Carm RO** ms PR
  CB 1671–90, 1699–1812 M 1671–90, 1699–1754 **NLW** ts PR M 1813–37 with index
  NLW Carm RO & Soc Gen ts PR index C 1841–51 M 1813–37, 1841–51 **NLW**

CAERFYRDDIN/CARMARTHEN St David   *SD*
<St Peter 1844
C 1841–1965 M 1842–1976 Christ Church 1873–1971 B 1841–1952 **Carm RO**
BT 1841–5 **NLW**
Cop ts PR index CMB 1841–51 **NLW & Carm RO**

CAPEL IFAN gweler/see PONTYBEREM

CARMARTHEN gweler/see CAERFYRDDIN

CASTELLDWYRAN   *SD*
M 1754–82, 1837–1926 **NLW** Mf **Carm RO**
BT see Cilymaenllwyd
Cop ts PR M 1754–82 **NLW**

CASTELLNEWYDD EMLYN/NEWCASTLE EMLYN   *SD*
The chapel of ease to Cenarth built here *c*1780 seems to have been without separate PRs
  until the late 1830s. District assigned to new church 1843
C 1839–1915 M 1971–90 B 1842–1957 **NLW** Mf C 1839–1915 B 1842–1957 **Carm
  RO** M 1838–1970 incumbent
BT 1874, 1885–8, 1890, 1898 **NLW**

CENARTH   *SD*
C 1701–68, 1775–1909 M 1701–1970 (Banns 1824–60, 1934–5) B 1701–68, 1775–1975
  NLW Mf C 1701–1909 M 1701–1935 B 1701–68 **Carm RO** Mf C 1701–68,
  1775–1909 M 1701–1837 (Banns 1824–60, 1934–5) B 1701–68, 1775–1844 **Soc Gen**
BT 1676, 1678, 1680, 1682, 1684–9, 1699, 1704, 1799–1806, 1808–58, 1860–1 **NLW**
Cop ts PR M 1813–37 with index **NLW Carm RO & Soc Gen** ts PR index C 1813–75
  M 1701–1875 (Banns 1823–60, 1934–5) **NLW & Carm RO** ts PR index M 1755–1837
  Soc Gen

CILRHEDYN gweler/see PENFRO/PEMBROKESHIRE

CIL-Y-CWM   *SD*
C 1701–1882 M 1701–1970 (Banns 1755–1885) B 1701–1876 **Carm RO**
BT 1673, 1677–9, 1684, 1690–1, 1693–5, 1703, 1707–8, 1711, 1713, 1716–18, 1720–7,
  1729–68, 1780–2, 1784–94, 1796–1800, 1802–4, 1806–48, 1850–80, 1882, 1887–1900,
  1902 **NLW**
Cop ts PR M 1813–37 with index **NLW Carm RO & Soc Gen**

CILYMAENLLWYD   *SD*
PR earliest reputedly used to stoke parsonage fire *c*1765 (NLW Facs 75, p 7)
C 1742–1956 M 1742–1836 B 1742–1812 **NLW** M 1837–1947 B 1813–1977 Fac C
  1742–1956 M 1742–1947 B 1742–1972 **Carm RO**
BT 1671–2, 1675, 1677–9, 1681–7, 1690–1, 1693–9, 1711, 1713, 1715–18, 1720–2,
  1724–92, 1794–1800, 1802–3, 1805–41 **NLW**
Cop ts PR CMB 1742–1812 **NLW & Carm RO** ts PR/BT M 1813–36 with index **NLW
  Carm RO & Soc Gen**

CONWIL CAIO gweler/see CYNWYL GAEO

CROSS HANDS gweler/see GORS-LAS

CWMAMAN   *SD*
<Y Betws, Llandybïe, Llandeilo Fawr, & Llan-giwg/Llanguicke 1843
C 1840–1930 M 1842–1948 (Banns 1842–67, 1887–1949) B 1842–1959 **Carm RO**
BT 1840–52, 1854–67, 1869–74 **NLW**

CWM-FFRWD gweler/see LLANDYFAELOG

CWMLLYNFELL gweler/see MORGANNWG/GLAMORGAN

CYDWELI/KIDWELLY   *SD*
C 1626–1809, 1813–1962 M 1626–1971 (Banns 1754–1809, 1823–71) B 1626–1809,
  1813–1947 **Carm RO**
BT 1672, 1677–8, 1681–4, 1686–7, 1690–1, 1693–6, 1699, 1705, 1715, 1717–21, 1724–5,
  1727–33, 1735, 1737–59, 1761–80, 1782–1800, 1802–82, 1884–5 **NLW**
Cop ts PR M 1813–37 with index ts PR index C 1813–1923 M 1628–1971 B 1813–1947
  NLW Carm RO & Soc Gen ts PR CB (extracts) 1765–1809 M 1627–1753 with index
  Soc Gen

CYFFIG/KIFFIG   *SD*
PR CMB 1725–1812 recorded in 1831 apparently lost
CB 1813–1979 M 1813–1931 **Carm RO**
BT 1675, 1677–9, 1682–7, 1690, 1693–1702, 1707–8, 1711, 1715–21, 1724–31, 1733–59,
  1761–75, 1777–81, 1784–9, 1791–8, 1802–40, 1842–81 **NLW**
Cop ts PR M 1813–37 with index **NLW Carm RO & Soc Gen**

CYNWYL ELFED   *SD*
C 1743–1968 M 1743–1896 (Banns 1842–94) B 1743–1982 **NLW** Mf **Carm RO**
BT 1672–3, 1676, 1681–2, 1684, 1686, 1689–91, 1693–8, 1700–3, 1707–8, 1711, 1713,
   1716–18, 1720–1, 1724–6, 1728–34, 1736–40, 1742–6, 1748–68, 1770, 1772–4, 1779,
   1783–4, 1799–1800, 1802, 1805–64 **NLW**
Cop ts PR M 1813–37 with index **NLW Carm RO & Soc Gen** ts PR index M
   1743–1875 B 1813–75 **NLW & Carm RO** ts PR CB 1813–75 M 1743–1837 **Soc Gen**

CYNWYL GAEO   *SD*
PR M 1754–83 recorded as being 'supposed lost' in 1831
C 1698–1979 M 1698–1754, 1783–1970 (Banns 1783–1806, 1850–73) B 1698–1979 **NLW**
   Mf **Carm RO & Soc Gen**
BT 1672, 1677–9, 1681–3, 1693, 1695, 1702–3, 1705, 1707–9, 1713, 1718–27, 1729–45,
   1747–90, 1792–4, 1796–1800, 1802, 1804–36, 1838–40, 1855–6 **NLW**
Cop ts PR M 1813–37 with index ts PR index CB 1813–75 M 1698–1875 **NLW Carm
RO & Soc Gen**

DAFEN   *SD*
<Llanelli 1879
C 1874–1947 M 1874–1959 (Banns 1874–1963) **Carm RO** B 1878– incumbent

EGLWYS FAIR A CHURIG   *SD*
PR CMB 1761–1812, recorded in 1831 as being 'much decayed and very imperfect until
   1805', apparently lost
M 1813–1941 **Carm RO** CB 1813– incumbent
BT see Henllan Amgoed
Cop ts PR/BT M 1813–37 with index ts PR index M 1813–75 **NLW Carm RO & Soc
Gen**

EGLWYS FAIR GLYN TAF gweler/see HENDY-GWYN/WHITLAND

EGLWYS GYMYN/EGLWYS CYMYN   *SD*
PR M 1754–1812 recorded in 1831 apparently lost
C 1731–1982 M 1731–51, 1838–1970 B 1731–1984 **Carm RO**
BT 1690, 1693–6, 1698–9, 1701–3, 1705, 1707–8, 1716, 1720–2, 1725–7, 1729–30, 1733,
   1739–41, 1744–51, 1753–1800, 1802–16, 1818–67, 1869 **NLW** Mf **Soc Gen**
Cop PR C 1732–1812 M 1732–51 B 1731–1812 *Transactions of the Carmarthenshire
   Antiquarian Society,* 5 & 8 (1909–10)
Cop ts BT M 1813–37 with index **NLW Carm RO & Soc Gen**

EGRMWNT/EGREMONT   *SD*
PR all prior to 1813 recorded as lost in 1831. Diocesan records suggest that *c*1790 they went back only to 1778
C 1813–1968 M 1813–65 B 1819–1901 **Carm RO**
BT 1671, 1677–9, 1683–4, 1686, 1699, 1703, 1794, 1796–1800, 1802–3, 1805–7, 1809–10, 1812–37, 1851–2, 1863–5, 1870, 1875–6 **NLW**
Cop ts PR M 1813–36 with index **NLW Carm RO & Soc Gen**

FELINDRE gweler/see PEN-BOYR St Barnabas

FELIN-FOEL   *SD*
<Llanelli 1879
C 1858–1948 M 1858–1976 (Banns 1858–1963) B 1858–1956 **Carm RO**

GORS-LAS   *SD*
<Llanarthne/Llanarthney, Llandybïe, Llanfihangel Aberbythych 1879
C 1880–1951 M 1880–1982 Cross Hands 1959–79 B 1881–1945 **Carm RO**

GWYNFE   *SD*
An ancient chapelry, with CMB prior to 1812 entered in PR Llangadog
M 1837–1970 **Carm RO** CB 1862– incumbent
BT see Llangadog

HENDY, YR   *SD*
<Llanedi
C 1911–77 M 1892–1977 (Banns 1925–74) **Carm RO**

HENDY-GWYN/WHITLAND (EGLWYS FAIR GLYN TAF)   *SD*
Formerly a chapelry to Llanboidy. Ecclesiastical parish <Cyffig/Kiffig, Llanboidy, Llan-gan, and Llanbedr Felffre/Lampeter Velfrey 1910. PR CB 1783–1807 M 1765–1812 recorded in 1831 apparently lost
C 1813–1932 M 1813–1952 B 1813–1913 **Carm RO**
BT see Llanboidy
Cop ts PR M 1813–37 with index **NLW Carm RO & Soc Gen**

HENLLAN AMGOED   *SD*
PR CMB prior to 1812 were reported in 1831 to be 'completely decayed' by dampness, whereas the imprecise return of 1933 suggests there were then extant records beginning in 1787 now apparently lost. Diocesan records suggest that *c*1790 the registers went back to 1754
M 1826–1969 **Carm RO**
BT 1671–2, 1675, 1678–84, 1686–7, 1693, 1695, 1697–9, 1702–3, 1707–8, 1713, 1716–18, 1720–2, 1724–30, 1732–59, 1762–3, 1768–70, 1772–7, 1780–1800, 1802–16, 1818–21, 1824–5, 1827–33, 1835–9, 1846–7, 1849, 1855, 1864, 1866–7 **NLW**
Cop ts PR/BT M 1813–36 with index **NLW Carm RO & Soc Gen**

* KIDWELLY/CYDWELI   *SD*
C 1626–1809, 1813–1962   M 1626–1971 (Banns 1754–1809, 1823–71)   B 1626–1809,
1813–1947 **Carm RO**
BT 1672, 1677–8, 1681–4, 1686–7, 1690–1, 1693–6, 1699, 1705, 1715, 1717–21, 1724–5,
1727–33, 1735, 1737–59, 1761–80, 1782–1800, 1802–82, 1884–5 **NLW**
Cop ts PR M 1813–37 with index ts PR index C 1813–1923 M 1628–1971 B 1813–1947
NLW Carm RO & Soc Gen ts PR CB (extracts) 1765–1809 M 1627–1753 with index
Soc Gen

* KIFFIG/CYFFIG   *SD*
PR CMB 1725–1812 recorded in 1831 apparently lost
CB 1813–1979 M 1813–1931 **Carm RO**
BT 1675, 1677–9, 1682–7, 1690, 1693–1702, 1707–8, 1711, 1715–21, 1724–31, 1733–59,
1761–75, 1777–81, 1784–9, 1791–8, 1802–40, 1842–81 **NLW**
Cop ts PR M 1813–37 with index **NLW Carm RO & Soc Gen**

* LAUGHARNE/TALACHARN   *SD*
C 1651–1974 M 1639–1971 (Banns 1801–47, 1857–1907) B 1645–1972 **Carm RO** Fac C
1651–1812 M 1639–1800 B 1645–1812 **NLW & Soc Gen**
BT 1672, 1677–9, 1681–2, 1686, 1704–5, 1711, 1715, 1717, 1721, 1725–1800, 1802–39,
1841, 1854–5, 1857, 1859–61, 1864, 1868–82, 1884–5, 1887–9 **NLW**
Cop ts PR M 1813–37 with index **NLW Carm RO & Soc Gen** ts PR index CB
1813–75 M 1639–1875 **NLW & Carm RO** ts PR CB (extracts) 1646–1749 M
1639–1747 with index **Soc Gen**

LLANARTHNE/LLANARTHNEY   *SD*
C 1720–1891 M 1720–1909 (Banns 1754–96, 1829–47) B 1720–1953 **Carm RO** Fac CB
1720–1812 M 1720–1811 **NLW**
BT 1672–3, 1678, 1681, 1707, 1717, 1720, 1725, 1727, 1730–46, 1748–53, 1755–89,
1791–1800, 1802–67, 1871–81 **NLW**
Cop ts PR M 1813–37 with index ts PR index CB 1813–75 M 1720–1875 **NLW Carm
RO & Soc Gen**

LLANBOIDY   *SD*
Diocesan records suggest that *c*1790 the PR began in 1694
C 1748/9–1992 M 1748–1970 B 1748–1991 **Carm RO**
BT 1672, 1679, 1681–4, 1687, 1690–1, 1694–9, ?1703, 1707–8, 1711, 1714–20, 1722,
1724–56, 1758–74, 1776–8, 1780–91, 1794–5, 1798, 1802, 1804, 1806–9, 1811–13, 1815,
1817–41, 1843–4, 1849, 1852, 1864–6 **NLW**
Cop ts PR index 1748–1875 **Carm RO** ts PR M 1813–37 with index **NLW Carm RO &
Soc Gen** ts PR index C 1813–75 **NLW & Soc Gen**

LLAN-CRWYS/LLAN-Y-CRWYS   *SD*
PR CB 1720–1812 M 1746–1812 recorded in 1831 apparently lost
C 1813–1992 M 1813–85, 1890–1970 B 1813–1992 **NLW** Mf M 1813–85 **Carm RO**
BT 1677–9, 1681, 1684, 1686–7, 1690, 1693–4, 1696–9, 1703, 1708–9, 1716, 1718,
    1720–2, 1724–8, 1730–46, 1750–1, 1754–70, 1772–9, 1781–6, 1788–9, 1791, 1794,
    1809–11, 1813–39, 1841–2, 1852–5, 1874–6 **NLW**
Cop ts PR index C 1813–1992 M 1813–1994 B 1813–1992 **NLW** ts PR M 1813–37 with
    index **NLW Carm RO & Soc Gen**

LLAN-DAWG/LLANDAWKE   *SD*
Diocesan records suggest that *c*1790 the PR went back to 1754
C 1771–1812, 1832–1963 M 1771–1812, 1815–29, 1846–1958 B 1771–1812, 1822–1962
    Carm RO
BT see Pentywyn/Pendine
Cop ts PR M 1815–29 with index **NLW Carm RO & Soc Gen** ts PR index 1771–1875
    Carm RO

LLANDEBIE gweler/see LLANDYBÏE

LLANDEFAELOG gweler/see LLANDYFAELOG

LLANDEILO ABERCYWYN   *SD*
PR CMB 1807–12 recorded in 1831 apparently lost
CB 1707–1806 M 1707–84 **NLW** C 1813–88 M 1819–64, 1928–47 B 1813–95 Fac CB
    1707–1806 M 1707–84 Mf C 1707–18, 1813–88 M 1707–84, 1819–1947 B 1707–1806,
    1813–95 **Carm RO**
BT 1672, 1675, 1677–9, 1681, 1691, 1695–7, 1699, 1702, 1715–18, 1720–2, 1724–6,
    1728–30, 1732, 1734, 1736–8, 1740–5, 1748–54, 1757–8, 1761–2, 1764, 1766–71,
    1773–9, 1781–1800, 1803–6, 1808–9, 1811, 1813–19, 1821–6, 1836, 1844–7, 1865–6,
    1871, 1881 **NLW**
Cop ts PR M 1813–37 with index **NLW Carm RO & Soc Gen** ts PR index 1715–1875
    Carm RO

LLANDEILO FAWR   *SD*
PR 1679–1724 transcribed in 1955 apparently lost
C 1732–1937 M 1732–95, 1822–1961 (Banns 1754–69, 1823–1956) B 1732–1966 **Carm
    RO** Fac C 1720–4 M 1683–1722, 1754–69 B 1679–1723 **NLW**
BT 1679, 1681–2, 1684, 1686–7, 1730, 1732–7, 1739–71, 1773–1800, 1802–11, 1813–38,
    1840, 1842–68, 1873–6 **NLW**
Cop ts PR/BT C 1679–1776 M 1683–1769 B 1679–1779 **Soc Gen** ts PR/BT M index
    1732–1875 **Carm RO** ts PR/BT M index 1732–1837 **NLW & Soc Gen** ts PR/BT M
    1813–37 with index **NLW Carm RO & Soc Gen**

LLANDINGAD (LLANYMDDYFRI/LLANDOVERY)   *SD*
Diocesan records suggest that *c*1790 the earliest PR here went back to 1660
C 1733–1909 M 1733–1904, 1907–65 (Banns 1823–1905) B 1733–1911 **NLW** Fac **Carm RO** Mf **Soc Gen**
BT 1672, 1677–9, 1681–4, 1686–7, 1711, 1715–16, 1718, 1721–2, 1724, 1728–31, 1733–45, 1748–83, 1785–94, 1796–1800, 1802–54, 1856–7, 1859–60, 1865 **NLW**
Cop ts PR index CB 1813–75 M 1733–1875 (Banns 1823–75) **NLW & Soc Gen** ts PR M 1813–37 with index **NLW Carm RO & Soc Gen**

LLANDOVERY gweler/see LLANDINGAD

LLANDYBÏE   *SD*
C 1695–1765, 1778–1919 M 1695–1925 (Banns 1823–63, 1866–1962) B 1695–1765, 1778–1948 **Carm RO**
BT 1672, 1677–8, 1681–2, 1711, 1713, 1717–22, 1724–5, 1730–3, 1735–7, 1739–57, 1761, 1763, 1767–73, 1776–84, 1787–99, 1802–70 **NLW**
Cop ts PR index CB 1813–75 M 1695–1875 ts PR M 1813–37 with index **NLW Carm RO & Soc Gen**

LLANDYFAELOG   *SD*
C 1695–1966 M 1695–1805, 1808–1970 (Banns 1808–12, 1882, 1884, 1900–94) Cwm-ffrwd 1877–1970 B 1695–1911 **NLW** Mf (except Banns) **Carm RO**
BT 1672, 1679, 1683–4, 1686–7, 1690, 1693, 1697–1701, 1703, 1707–8, ?1710, 1711, 1713, 1717–20, 1722, 1724–31, 1733–51, 1753–66, 1768–99, 1802–52, 1854–62 **NLW**
Cop ts PR index CB 1813–75 M 1695–1875 ts PR M 1813–37 with index **NLW Carm RO & Soc Gen**

LLANDYFEISANT   *SD*
PR CMB 1755–82 recorded in 1933 apparently lost
C 1784–1946 M 1784–1953 (Banns 1784–1902) B 1813–1970 **Carm RO**
BT 1813–22, 1824–7, 1832–5, 1838–46, 1850–1, 1853–8, 1860, 1862, 1864, 1869–71 **NLW**
Cop ts PR M 1814–37 with index **NLW Carm RO & Soc Gen**

LLANDYRY gweler/see PEN-BRE/PEMBREY

LLANDDAROG   *SD*
C 1736–1869 M 1736–1919 B 1736–1944 **Carm RO**
BT 1671–2, 1677–9, 1681–7, 1690, 1693–7, 1701–3, 1705, 1707, 1713, 1716–22, 1726–30, 1732–80, 1782–4, 1786–93, 1796–1800, 1802–41, 1843–65, 1867, 1869–70, 1872 **NLW**
Cop ts PR M 1813–37 with index ts PR index CB 1813–75 M 1736–1875 **NLW Carm RO & Soc Gen**

LLANDDEUSANT   *SD*

PR prior to 1813 were reported in 1831 to have been 'partially destroyed by fire', leaving only a few very imperfect loose leaves 1784–1809 then extant and now apparently lost. Diocesan records suggest that *c*1790 there was here a PR going back 40 years

C 1816–1980 M 1813–1924 (Banns 1824–1966) B 1816–81 **Carm RO** Fac C 1816–1980 **NLW**

BT 1677–8, 1681–7, 1690, 1693, 1697–9, 1702–3, 1707, 1716, 1719, 1721, 1724–8, 1730–1, 1735–6, 1738–40, 1742, 1744–51, 1753–80, 1782–3, 1785–1800, 1802–6, 1809–12, 1814–67, 1871 **NLW**

Cop ts PR M 1813–37 with index **NLW Carm RO & Soc Gen**

LLANDDOWROR   *SD*

Diocesan records suggest that *c*1790 the earliest PR went back to 1694. No mention of PR M 1813–37 in 1933 survey

C 1726–1979 M 1726–1812, 1837–1969 B 1726–1979 **Carm RO** Fac CB 1813–1957 **NLW**

BT 1671–2, 1677–9, 1681–4, 1686–7, 1698–9, 1708, 1713, 1717–18, 1720–2, 1724–30, 1732–6, 1738, 1740–51, 1759–1800, 1802–6, 1808, 1810–35, 1837–42, 1844–56 **NLW**

Cop ts BT M 1813–37 with index ts PR index CB 1813–75 M 1728–84, 1837–75 **NLW Carm RO & Soc Gen**

LLANEDI   *SD*

C 1708–1977 M 1708–1973 (Banns 1790–1913, 1932–69) B 1708–1976 **Carm RO** Mf CB 1708–83 M 1708–1812 **NLW**

BT 1679, 1690, 1698–9, 1702, 1707–8, 1717–22, 1724–33, 1735–1800, 1802–56, 1858–62 **NLW**

Cop ts PR/BT index C 1689–1812 M 1699–1820 B 1679–1976 **NLW** ts PR M 1813–37 with index **NLW Carm RO & Soc Gen**

LLANEGWAD   *SD*

C 1701–1901 M 1701–1953 (Banns 1849–1976) Alltyferin 1900–70 St John 1901–70 B 1701–1905 **NLW** Mf (except Banns) **Carm RO**

BT 1679, 1681–2, 1686–7, 1690, 1701–3, 1707, 1716–20, 1725–31, 1733–62, 1764–91, 1793–1800, 1802–81 **NLW**

Cop ts PR index C 1813–1901 M 1701–1913 (Banns 1849–1945) Alltyferin 1900–70 St John 1901–70 B 1813–1905 ts PR M 1813–36 with index **NLW Carm RO & Soc Gen**

LLANELLI All Saints   *SD*
<St Elli
C 1874–1927 M 1874–1974 B 1878–94, 1930–53 **Carm RO**

LLANELLI Christ Church   *SD*
<St Paul 1912
C 1898–1954 M 1887–1973 (Banns 1893–1961) **Carm RO**

LLANELLI St Alban   *SD*
<St Elli
C 1912–65 M 1915–70 **Carm RO**

LLANELLI St David   *SD*
<Christ Church
C 1898–1951 M 1901–70 (Banns 1901–66) **Carm RO**

LLANELLI St Elli   *SD*
C 1684–1923 M 1684–1971 (Banns 1754–1940) B 1684–1930 **Carm RO**
BT 1686, 1703, 1711, ?1718, 1724–8, 1730–2, 1735–1800, 1802–55, 1862–89 **NLW**
Cop M 1685–1837 in A Mee, *Llanelly Parish Church* (1888)
Cop ts PR M index 1687–1837 **Carm RO** ts PR C 1688–1800 M 1687–1837 B
  1693–1886 **Soc Gen** ts PR M 1813–37 with index **NLW Carm RO & Soc Gen**

LLANELLI St John   *SD*
<St Paul
C 1898–1940 M 1889–1968 **Carm RO**

LLANELLI St Paul   *SD*
<St Elli 1846
C 1850–1945 M 1851–1970 B 1851–1901 **Carm RO**

LLANELLI St Peter   *SD*
<St Paul
C 1898–1953 M 1880–1981 **Carm RO**

LLANFAIR-AR-Y-BRYN   *SD*
Diocesan records suggest that *c*1790 the earliest PR here went back to 1660 'but not entire'
C 1735–90, 1796–1865 M 1736–46, 1756–1837 (Banns 1823–1905) B 1735–90,
  1796–1844 **NLW** Mf **Carm RO**
BT 1675, 1677–9, 1681–3, 1685–8, 1690–1, 1693–8, 1701–2, 1708, 1711, 1713, 1716–18,
  1721–2, 1725, 1727–36, 1738–83, 1785–94, 1796–1800, 1802–60, 1865 **NLW**
Cop ts PR M 1813–37 with index **NLW Carm RO & Soc Gen**

LLANFAIR CWM-GORS gweler/see GWAUNCAEGURWEN (Morgannwg/Glamorgan)

LLANFALLTEG gweler/see PENFRO/PEMBROKESHIRE

LLANFIHANGEL ABERBYTHYCH   *SD*
C 1674–83, 1695–1922 M 1674–83, 1695–1970 (Banns 1755–1959) St Mary 1959–69 B
  1674–83, 1695–1904 **Carm RO**
BT 1679, 1681–4, 1686, 1707–8, 1710–11, 1717, 1719–22, 1724–30, 1735, 1739–45,
  1747–59, 1761, 1763–1800, 1802–37, 1839–66 **NLW**
Cop ts PR CMB 1675–1766 **Soc Gen** ts PR index C 1813–1922 M 1698–1875 B
  1813–75 ts PR M 1813–37 with index **NLW Carm RO & Soc Gen**

LLANFIHANGEL ABERCYWYN   *SD*

PR C 1759–1812 recorded in 1831 apparently lost. It would be reasonable to suppose that the said register contained B 1759–1812 although the return reported that no register of burials could be found. Diocesan records suggest that *c*1790 there was here a PR going back to 1665

C 1813–1993 M 1754–1970 B 1813–1993 **Carm RO**

BT 1672, 1676–8, 1681, 1683–4, 1686–7, 1690–1, 1693–7, 1705, 1708, ?1715, 1717–18, 1721–2, 1724, 1726–45, 1747–82, 1784–91, 1793–7, 1803–4, 1806–41, 1844, 1846, 1848–57 **NLW**

Cop ts PR index CB 1813–75 ts PR M 1813–37 with index **NLW Carm RO & Soc Gen**

LLANFIHANGEL-AR-ARTH   *SD*

C 1787–1977 M 1756–1971 (Banns 1878–1959) B 1787–1896 **Carm RO** Fac CB 1787–1812 M 1813–37 **NLW**

BT 1672, 1678, 1694, 1697–1700, 1711, 1713, 1716–17, 1719–22, 1724–9, 1731, 1733–4, 1736–43, 1745–9, 1752–62, 1764–7, 1769–72, 1775–8, 1780, 1782–3, 1785, 1787–1800, 1802–12, 1814–33, 1835–53, 1855, 1871–3, 1875–6 **NLW**

Cop ts PR index CB 1813–75 M 1756–1875 ts PR M 1813–37 with index **NLW Carm RO & Soc Gen**

LLANFIHANGEL CILFARGEN   *SD*

C 1746–1934 M 1746–1838 B 1746–1812, 1814–1985 **Carm RO**

BT 1672, 1677–9, 1683–4, 1693, 1757–62, 1764, 1767–81, 1783–1800, 1802–15, 1817–32, 1834, 1837–43, 1846–62, 1866–72 **NLW**

Cop ts PR index 1746–1875 **Carm RO** ts PR index C 1813–1934 M 1755–1875 (Banns 1785–1875) **NLW & Soc Gen** ts PR M 1813–37 with index **NLW Carm RO & Soc Gen**

LLANFIHANGEL RHOS-Y-CORN   *SD*

C 1768–1932 M 1754–1967 (Banns 1823–1937) B 1768–1812 Fac B 1813–1979 **Carm RO**

BT 1672, 1677–9, 1682–6, 1690–1, 1694–6, 1698–9, 1702–4, 1707, 1711, 1713, 1716–17, 1719–20, 1722, 1724–34, 1737, 1739, 1741–2, 1744–51, 1754–6, 1758–64, 1768, 1770–2, 1774–6, 1778, 1780–1, 1785–1800, 1802–35, 1853–5, 1865–7, 1872 **NLW**

Cop ts PR index 1754–1875 **Carm RO** ts PR index C 1813–1986 M 1754–1966 B 1813–1985 **NLW & Soc Gen** ts PR M 1813–37 with index **NLW Carm RO & Soc Gen**

LLANFYNYDD   *SD*

C 1692–1812 M 1692–1782, 1797–1967 (Banns 1823–78) B 1692–1940 **Carm RO**

BT 1672, 1678–9, 1681, 1683–4, 1686–7, 1693, 1696–8, 1701–3, 1707, 1716–17, 1719–22, 1725–31, 1733–57 1759–73, 1775–82, 1786–1800, 1802–56 **NLW**

Cop ts PR index CB 1813–1989 M 1698–1875 ts PR M 1813–37 with index **NLW Carm RO & Soc Gen**

LLANGADOG   *SD*
C 1708–1878 M 1708–1970 (Banns 1823–50) B 1708–1959 **Carm RO**
BT 1677–9, 1681–7, 1690, 1693–6, 1698, 1702, 1704, 1710–11, 1716–17, 1720–1, 1724–6, 1728–9, 1735–41, 1745–84, 1787–96, 1798–1800, 1802–7, 1809–60, 1862–7, 1871 **NLW**
Cop ts PR M 1813–37 with index **NLW Carm RO & Soc Gen**

LLAN-GAIN   *SD*
PR CB 1772–1812 recorded in 1831 and 1760–1806 in 1933 apparently lost. A former curate of this parish is alleged to have given an earlier PR of unknown extent to a Carmarthen solicitor who had offered him £40 for it (NLW, Cwmgwili Document 638 dated 1753). PR going back 'about 50 years' recorded *c*1790
C 1807–1993 M 1772–1837 (Banns 1825–45) B 1813–1993 **Carm RO**
BT ?1672, 1679, 1681–3, 1694, 1696–9, 1701, 1703, 1707–8, 1711, 1713, 1717–18, 1720–7, 1729–47, 1749–62, 1765–70, 1772–88, 1790–1800, 1802–12, 1814–37, 1842–7, 1849–56, 1858–65 **NLW**
Cop ts PR index C 1813–74 M 1772–1875 B 1813–75 ts PR M 1813–37 with index **NLW Carm RO & Soc Gen**

LLAN-GAN gweler/see PENFRO/PEMBROKESHIRE

LLANGATHEN   *SD*
C 1747–1972 M 1747–1969 B 1747–1965 **Carm RO**
BT 1678–9, 1682, 1684, 1696, 1715, 1717–22, 1725–31, 1738–45, 1753–6, 1758–91, 1794–8, 1800, 1802–38, 1844–60, 1865 **NLW**
Cop ts PR index C 1813–1972 M 1747–1970 B 1813–1965 ts PR M 1813–37 with index **NLW Carm RO & Soc Gen**

LLANGELER   *SD*
PR B 1805–12 recorded in 1831 apparently lost
C 1704–1877, 1900–93 M 1704–1801, 1813–1943, 1945–87 (Banns 1795–1833) St James 1904–69 Capel Mair 1906–59 B 1704–1804, 1813–1900 **NLW** Mf C 1704–1877 M 1704–1921 B 1704–1900 **Carm RO** Mf C 1704–1877 M 1704–1921 (Banns 1795–1833) B 1704–1900 **Soc Gen**
BT 1674, 1678–9, 1681–3, 1685, 1687, 1689, 1705, 1799, 1801–11, 1813–63, 1865, 1874 **NLW**
Cop ts PR index CB 1813–75 M 1704–7, 1764–1875 (Banns 1795–1833) ts PR M 1813–37 with index **NLW Carm RO & Soc Gen**

LLANGENDEIRNE gweler/see LLANGYNDEYRN

LLANGENNECH   *SD*
C 1742–1960 M 1742–1970 B 1742–1875 **Carm RO**
BT 1678, 1703, 1707–8, 1711, 1713, 1717, 1719, 1721, 1724–32, 1736–40, 1742–64, 1766–95, 1797–1800, 1802–37, 1839–40, 1842–4, 1850–3 **NLW**
Cop ts PR M 1813–37 with index **NLW Carm RO & Soc Gen**

LLANGLYDWEN   *SD*
C 1765–84, 1793–1810 M 1755–1811, 1814–36 B 1765–84, 1793–1810 **NLW** C
    1814–1989 M 1837–1968 B 1813–1980 **Carm RO** Mf CB 1765–84, 1793–1810 M
    1755–1811, 1814–36 **Carm RO**
BT 1671–2, 1675, 1678–9, 1681, 1683–4, 1686–7, 1690–1, 1693–9, 1708–11, 1713,
    1715–22, 1724–37, 1739–47, 1749, 1752–7, 1759–90, 1793–5, 1797–1800, 1802–6,
    1808–22, 1824–37, 1859, 1867–70, 1872–7 **NLW**
Cop ts PR CMB 1755–1837 **Carm RO** ts PR M 1814–36 with index **NLW Carm RO**
    & Soc Gen

LLANGUNNOR gweler/see LLANGYNNWR

LLANGYNDEYRN   *SD*
PR 1665–1700 recorded in 1933 apparently lost
C 1735–1858 M 1735–1960 B 1735–1972 Fac M 1963–1971 **Carm RO**
BT 1671, 1677–9, 1681–7, 1690, 1692–6, 1700–4, 1707–8, 1711, 1717–21, 1724–43,
    1746–7, 1749–51, 1753–67, 1769–94, 1796–1800, 1802–52, 1854–7, 1859–66 **NLW**
Cop ts PR C (extracts) 1665–1811 M 1671–1754 B (extracts) 1668–1807 **Soc Gen** ts PR
    C 1665–1971 M 1671–1970 B 1668–1972 **Carm RO** ts PR index CB 1813–75 M
    1671–1875 ts PR M 1813–37 with index **NLW Carm RO & Soc Gen**

LLANGYNIN   *SD*
C 1736–1975 M 1756–1970 B 1736–1977 **Carm RO**
BT 1679, 1681–4, 1697, 1729, 1731–4, 1736, 1738, 1740–5, 1747–53, 1755–81, 1783–93,
    1798–9, 1805–10, 1812–16, 1818–23, 1825–31, 1833, 1835, 1837, 1843, 1854–5 **NLW**
Cop ts PR index CB 1813–75 M 1756–1895 ts PR M 1813–36 with index **NLW Carm**
    RO & Soc Gen

LLANGYNNWR/LLANGUNNOR   *SD*
C 1678–1975 M 1678–1938, 1956–75 (Banns 1854–1949) B 1678–1926 **Carm RO** Fac
    CB 1727–1817 M 1727–54 **NLW**
BT 1675, 1677–8, 1681–4, 1686, 1693–9, 1702–4, 1708, 1712, 1717–22, 1724–36,
    1738–41, 1744–1800, 1802–11, 1813–20, 1822–64, 1866–7 **NLW**
Cop ts PR CB 1678–1726 (& extracts to 1784) M 1675–1754 **Soc Gen** ts PR index CB
    1813–75 M 1678–1875 ts PR M 1813–37 with index **NLW Carm RO & Soc Gen**

LLANGYNOG   *SD*
PR prior to 1775 'destroyed by fire' according to 1831 survey
C 1813–1992 M 1768–75, 1783–1965 B 1813–1992 **NLW** Mf **Carm RO**
BT 1693–1700, 1703, 1707–8, 1711, 1713, 1716–18, 1720, 1722, 1724–30, 1732–51,
    1753–67, 1769–76, 1778–9, 1781–1800, 1802–12, 1814–55, 1857–67, 1870–2, 1876–8,
    1880–1 **NLW**
Cop ts PR index CB 1813–75 M 1813–37 **Carm RO & Soc Gen** ts PR/BT M 1814–37
    with index **NLW Carm RO & Soc Gen**

LLANISMEL/ST ISHMAEL *SD*

C 1560–1946 M 1560–1920 (Banns 1929–71) B 1560–1969 **Carm RO** Fac CMB 1560–1761 **NLW**
BT 1671–2, 1675, 1677–9, 1681–4, 1686–7, 1690, 1693–4, 1696–9, 1701–3, 1707–8, 1710–11, 1713, 1716–58, 1760–1800, 1802–40, 1842–6, 1848–50, 1853–5, 1879 **NLW**
Cop ts PR M 1561–1641, 1678–1753 **Soc Gen** ts PR index C 1813–55 M 1561–1875 B 1813–63 ts PR M 1813–37 with index **NLW Carm RO & Soc Gen**

LLANLLAWDDOG *SD*

C 1698–1941 M 1698–1969 B 1698–1923 **Carm RO**
BT 1671, 1673, 1678, 1682–7, 1691, 1693, 1695, 1697–9, 1702–3, 1707, 1712, 1714, 1716–22, 1724–41, 1750, 1754–5, 1757, 1759–60, 1763–7, 1787–91, 1793–1800, 1802–12, 1814–82, 1887–94 **NLW**
Cop ts PR index CB 1813–75 M 1695–1875 ts PR M 1813–37 with index **NLW Carm RO & Soc Gen**

LLAN-LLWCH *SD*

PR CB 1779–[95] recorded in 1831 apparently lost
C 1800–59 M 1754–1970 (Banns 1824–33) B 1796–1943 **Carm RO**
BT 1802–3, 1815–18, 1826–31, 1833–6, 1838–58 **NLW**
Cop ts PR index CB 1813–75 M 1754–1875 ts PR M 1813–37 with index **NLW Carm RO & Soc Gen**

LLANLLWNI *SD*

PR M 1755–1812 recorded in 1831 as being in poor condition now apparently lost
C 1739–58, 1787–1923 M 1739–58, 1813–1983 B 1739–58, 1787–1910 **NLW** Mf C 1739–58, 1787–1923 M 1739–58, 1813–1971 B 1739–58, 1787–1910 **Carm RO & Soc Gen**
BT 1671, 1677, 1679, 1681, 1684, 1690–1, 1699, 1710–11, 1717, 1719–22, 1724–8, 1730, 1733–4, 1737, 1739–65, 1770–87, 1789–90, 1792–3, 1795–1800, 1802–17, 1819–38, 1840–59, 1864–7, 1871–2 **NLW**
Cop ts PR index CB 1813–75 M 1739–1875 ts PR M 1813–37 with index **NLW Carm RO & Soc Gen**

LLANNEWYDD/NEWCHURCH *SD*

PR 1719–38 recorded in 1933 apparently lost
C 1742–1980 M 1742–1970 B 1742–1975 **Carm RO**
BT 1675–7, 1681–2, 1686–7, 1690, 1693, 1696–8, 1702–3, 1705, 1707–8, 1711, 1713, 1716–18, 1720–1, 1724–40, 1743–59, 1762–70, 1773, 1775–85, 1787–99, 1802–58, 1878 **NLW**
Cop ms PR CB 1719–38, 1742–1812 M 1720–38, 1742–1838 **NLW** ts PR index CB 1813–75 M 1742–1875 ts PR M 1813–37 with index **NLW Carm RO & Soc Gen**

LLAN-NON   *SD*
C 1679–1738, 1741–1913   M 1679–1738, 1741–1978 (Banns 1823–1990)   B 1679–1738,
1741–1971 **NLW**   Mf (except Banns) **Carm RO**
BT 1681–4, 1686–7, 1690, 1693, 1695–9, 1703–4, 1716–18, 1720–5, 1727–70, 1772–1800,
1802–35, 1844–5, 1850–2 **NLW**
Cop ts PR M 1813–37 with index **NLW Carm RO & Soc Gen**

LLANPUMSAINT   *SD*
C 1775–1896   M 1755–1971 (Banns 1823–1953)   B 1775–1866 **Carm RO**
BT 1675, 1677–9, 1681–2, 1685–7, 1690, 1693, 1695–7, 1699, 1702, 1707–8, ?1711–12,
1715–22, 1724–41, 1750–1, 1754–5, 1757, 1759, 1763, 1765–7, 1787–91, 1793–1800,
1802–82, 1884–5, 1887 **NLW**
Cop ts PR index CB 1813–75 M 1695–1875   ts PR M 1813–37 with index **NLW Carm
RO & Soc Gen**

LLANSADWRN   *SD*
C 1739–1847   M 1739–55, 1783–1971 (Banns 1823–74)   B 1739–1960 **NLW**   Mf (except
Banns) **Carm RO**
BT 1673, 1678–9, 1681–4, 1686–7, 1690–1, 1693, 1695–9, 1702–4, 1707, 1709, ?1711,
1713–18, 1720–2, 1724–38, 1740–7, 1749–52, 1755–60, 1762–1800, 1802–57 **NLW**
Cop ts BT M 1813–37 with index **NLW Carm RO & Soc Gen**

LLANSADYRNIN/LLANSADWRNEN   *SD*
C 1663–1993   M 1663–1969   B 1663–1992   Mf CB 1813–1972 **Carm RO**   Fac CMB
1663–1812 **NLW & Soc Gen**
BT 1677–8, 1682, 1684, 1686, 1691, 1716–21, 1727–33, 1735–44, 1746–8, 1750–95,
1797–1800, 1802–12, 1814–39, 1849–51, 1854–5, 1857–64, 1868, 1871–2, 1880, 1884–5,
1888 **NLW**
Cop ts PR index 1666–1875 **Carm RO**   ts PR M 1813–36 with index **NLW Carm RO &
Soc Gen**

LLANSAWEL   *SD*
C 1751–1979   M 1751–1970 (Banns 1823–1919)   B 1751–1980 **NLW**   Mf (except Banns)
Carm RO
BT 1675–9, 1682, 1693–5, 1702, 1705, 1707, 1724, 1726–9, 1731, 1733–7, 1739, 1741–4,
1746–7, 1749–54, 1756–60, 1762–5, 1767–88, 1790, 1792–4, 1796–1800, 1802–12,
1814–35, 1838–40, 1849, 1855–7 **NLW**
Cop ts PR M 1813–37 with index **NLW Carm RO & Soc Gen**

LLANSTEFFAN/LLANSTEPHAN   *SD*
C 1762–1812   M 1756–1812   B 1762–1812 **NLW**   C 1697–1762, 1813–88   M 1697–1762,
1813–1982   B 1697–1762, 1813–1982 **Carm RO**   Fac CMB 1697–1762 **NLW**   Mf CB
1697–1812   M 1697–1812 **Carm RO**
BT 1671, 1677, 1680, 1682, 1684, 1687, 1690, 1693, 1695–8, 1703, 1707–8, 1711,
1713–18, 1720, 1724–62, 1764–1800, 1802–81, 1884 **NLW**
Cop ts PR (extracts) C 1677–1753 M 1697–1739 B 1714–58 with index **Soc Gen**   ts PR

index M 1755–1875 **NLW & Soc Gen** ts PR M 1813–37 with index **NLW Carm RO & Soc Gen**

LLANWINIO   *SD*
PR 1729–[66] recorded in 1831 apparently lost
C 1767–1991 M 1767–1967 (Banns 1824–75) B 1767–1910 **Carm RO**
BT 1672, 1678, 1681–8, 1691, 1694, 1696–9, 1702, 1707–8, 1711, 1715–18, 1720, 1724–48, 1751–72, 1774–81, 1784–90, 1792–8, 1802–8, 1810–58, 1860–77 **NLW**
Cop ts PR index CB 1813–75 M 1754–1875 ts PR M 1813–37 with index **NLW Carm RO & Soc Gen**

LLANWRDA   *SD*
C 1684, 1689–1916 M 1684, 1689–1970 (Banns 1824–70) B 1689–1961 **NLW** Mf (except Banns) **Carm RO**
BT 1673, 1677–9, 1681–7, 1690–1, 1693, 1695–9, 1701, 1703, 1707–8, 1716–22, 1724–43, 1745–7, 1749–52, 1755–1800, 1802–57 **NLW**
Cop ts BT M 1813–37 with index **NLW Carm RO & Soc Gen**

LLAN-Y-BRI   *SD*
<Llansteffan/Llanstephan 1863. The ancient chapel here passed in the seventeenth century into the hands of the Independents. The present church and parish are of mid-nineteenth century origin
CB 1861– incumbent M 1863–1970 **Carm RO**
BT 1861–81 **NLW**

LLANYBYDDER   *SD*
C 1783–1972 M 1754–1994 B 1783–1984 **Carm RO**
BT 1679, 1694, 1696, 1699, 1705, 1711, 1719–21, 1723, 1728–34, 1737, 1739, 1741, 1743–4, 1748–50, 1752–5, 1757, 1761, 1763, 1767, 1770, 1772–3, 1789–90, 1793–1800, 1802–44, 1847–9, 1851, 1854–6, 1880, 1892 **NLW**
Cop ts PR index C 1813–75 M 1754–1875 ts PR M 1813–37 with index **NLW Carm RO & Soc Gen**

* LLAN-Y-CRWYS/LLAN-CRWYS   *SD*
PR CB 1720–1812 M 1746–1812 recorded in 1831 apparently lost
C 1813–1992 M 1813–85, 1890–1970 B 1813–1992 **NLW** Mf M 1813–85 **Carm RO**
BT 1677–9, 1681, 1684, 1686–7, 1690, 1693–4, 1696–9, 1703, 1708–9, 1716, 1718, 1720–2, 1724–8, 1730–46, 1750–1, 1754–70, 1772–9, 1781–6, 1788–9, 1791, 1794, 1809–11, 1813–39, 1841–2, 1852–5, 1874–6 **NLW**
Cop ts PR index C 1813–1992 M 1813–1994 B 1813–1992 **NLW** ts PR M 1813–37 with index **NLW Carm RO & Soc Gen**

LLANYMDDYFRI gweler/see LLANDINGAD

LLWYNHENDY   *SD*
<Dafen
C 1882–1946 M 1939–71 **Carm RO**

MAENORDEILO/MANORDEILO   *SD*
<Llandeilo Fawr 1905
C 1861–1939 M 1861–1970 B 1813–1927 **Carm RO**

MARROS   *SD*
C 1738–1984 M 1738–1962 B 1738–1984 **Carm RO**
BT 1813–80 **NLW**
Cop ts PR M 1813–37 with index **NLW Carm RO & Soc Gen**

MEIDRIM   *SD*
C 1653–1994 M 1653–1979 B 1653–1988 **Carm RO**
BT 1671–2, 1675–8, 1681, 1683–7, 1690–1, 1693–5, 1698–1700, 1703, 1705, 1708–9,
   1715, 1717–19, 1721, 1724–96, 1803–57 **NLW**
Cop ts PR index CB 1813–75 M 1654–1875 ts PR M 1813–37 with index **NLW Carm
   RO & Soc Gen**

MERTHYR   *SD*
C 1681–1980 M 1681–1970 B 1681–1980 **Carm RO**
BT 1672–3, 1677–9, 1682, 1686, 1690–1, 1694–9, 1702–3, 1707–8, 1711, 1713, 1715–18,
   1720–1, 1723–36, 1738–1800, 1802–39, 1841–2 **NLW**
Cop ts PR index CB 1813–75 M 1686–1875 **Carm RO & Soc Gen** ts PR M 1813–37
   with index **NLW Carm RO & Soc Gen**

MYDDFAI   *SD*
C 1653–1992 M 1653–1971 (Banns 1823–1925) B 1653–1992 **NLW** Fac C 1653–1854
   M 1653–1971 (Banns 1823–1925) B 1653–1851 **Carm RO**
BT 1671–3, 1677–9, 1681–4, 1686, 1690, 1693–4, 1696–9, 1703, 1707, 1709, 1718–22,
   1724–88, 1790–4, 1796–1800, 1802–6, 1808–68 **NLW**
Cop ts PR M 1813–37 with index **NLW Carm RO & Soc Gen**

⋆ NEWCASTLE EMLYN/CASTELLNEWYDD EMLYN   *SD*
   The chapel of ease to Cenarth built here *c*1780 seems to have been without separate PRs
   until the late 1830s. District assigned to new church 1843
   C 1839–1915 M 1971–90 B 1842–1957 **NLW** Mf C 1839–1915 B 1842–1957 **Carm
   RO** M 1838–1970 incumbent
   BT 1874, 1885–8, 1890, 1898 **NLW**

⋆ NEWCHURCH/LLANNEWYDD   *SD*
   PR 1719–38 recorded in 1933 apparently lost
   C 1742–1980 M 1742–1970 B 1742–1975 **Carm RO**
   BT 1675–7, 1681–2, 1686–7, 1690, 1693, 1696–8, 1702–3, 1705, 1707–8, 1711, 1713,

1716–18, 1720–1, 1724–40, 1743–59, 1762–70, 1773, 1775–85, 1787–99, 1802–58, 1878 **NLW**
Cop ms PR CB 1719–38, 1742–1812   M 1720–38, 1742–1838 **NLW**   ts PR index CB 1813–75 M 1742–1875 ts PR M 1813–37 with index **NLW Carm RO & Soc Gen**

PEMBREY gweler/see PEN-BRE

PEN-BOYR   *SD*
C 1752–1901 M 1752–1970 St Barnabas 1907–64 B 1752–1947 **NLW** Mf **Soc Gen** Mf (except St Barnabas) **Carm RO**
BT 1674–6, 1678–89, 1701, 1703, 1799–1812, 1819, 1823–6, 1828–80, 1882 **NLW**
Cop ts PR index CB 1813–75   M 1752–1970 St Barnabas M 1876–1970 **NLW & Carm RO** ts PR M 1813–37 with index **NLW Carm RO & Soc Gen**

PEN-BRE/PEMBREY   *SD*
C 1700–1958 Llandyry 1904–57 M 1700–1964 (Banns 1823–1973) B 1700–1965 Llandyry 1904–86 **Carm RO**
BT 1671–2, 1675, 1677–8, 1681–3, 1686–7, 1690–1, 1693, 1695–6, 1698–9, 1702–3, 1707–8, 1711, 1715–23, 1725–64, 1766–1800, 1802–15, 1817–67 **NLW**
Cop ts PR C 1701–71 M 1701–54 B 1701–71 ts PR index C 1772–1833 M 1700–1894 B 1800–1900 **Carm RO** ts PR M 1813–37 with index **NLW Carm RO & Soc Gen**

PENCADER   *SD*
<Llanfihangel-ar-arth
C 1883–1952 M 1886–1969 B 1883–1935 **Carm RO**

PENCARREG   *SD*
C 1789–1934 M 1754–1968 B 1789–1992 **NLW** Mf M 1754–1968 **Carm RO**
BT 1679, 1696–7, 1699, 1702–3, 1720–1, 1728–31, 1737–41, 1743, 1756–7, 1761, 1763, 1767, 1772–3, 1789–90, 1793–1800, 1802–11, 1813–32, 1834–64, 1867–72, 1874–5 **NLW**
Cop ts PR index C 1813–1934 M 1754–1971 B 1813–1992 **NLW** ts PR M 1813–37 with index **NLW Carm RO & Soc Gen**

PENTYWYN/PENDINE   *SD*
PR prior to 1813 were said in 1831 to have been destroyed by fire
C 1783–1803, 1813–1977 M 1794–1978 B 1783–1977 **Carm RO**
BT 1716, 1718, 1721–2, 1724–5, 1727, 1743–74, 1776–1800, 1802–83 **NLW**
Cop ts PR M 1814–35 with index **NLW Carm RO & Soc Gen**

PONT-IETS/PONTYATES   *SD*
<Llangyndeyrn & Llanelli
C 1872–1945 M 1858–1970 **Carm RO**

PONTYBEREM (CAPEL IFAN) *SD*
An ancient chapel in the parish of Llanelli apparently restored by the Methodists for their own use in the eighteenth century, repossessed by the Church in the 1830s. The new church consecrated in 1894
PR C 1839–1922 recorded in 1933 apparently lost
C 1921–48 M 1838–1971 B 1835–1932 **Carm RO**

PORTHTYWYN/BURRY PORT *SD*
<Pen-bre/Pembrey
C 1903–79 Pwll 1904–76 M 1902–76 **Carm RO**

PWLL gweler/see PORTHTYWYN/BURRY PORT

RHYDAMAN/AMMANFORD All Saints *SD*
C 1915–40 M 1915–23, 1935–43, 1953–71 (Banns 1915–73) **Carm RO**

RHYDAMAN/AMMANFORD St Michael *SD*
<Llandybïe & Y Betws 1903
M 1893–1971 (Banns 1892–1964) B 1885–1956 **Carm RO**

ST CLEARS gweler/see SANCLÊR

★ ST ISHMAEL/LLANISMEL *SD*
C 1560–1946 M 1560–1920 (Banns 1929–71) B 1560–1969 **Carm RO** Fac CMB 1560–1761 **NLW**
BT 1671–2, 1675, 1677–9, 1681–4, 1686–7, 1690, 1693–4, 1696–9, 1701–3, 1707–8, 1710–11, 1713, 1716–58, 1760–1800, 1802–40, 1842–6, 1848–50, 1853–5, 1879 **NLW**
Cop ts PR M 1561–1641, 1678–1753 **Soc Gen** ts PR index C 1813–55 M 1561–1875 B 1813–63 ts PR M 1813–37 with index **NLW Carm RO & Soc Gen**

SANCLÊR/ST CLEARS *SD*
C 1681–1928 M 1681–1970 (Banns 1937–76) B 1681–1951 **Carm RO** Fac CB 1681–1813 M 1681–1813, 1837–1959 **NLW**
BT 1672–3, 1681–4, 1686–7, 1702, 1705, 1707–8, 1720, 1722, 1726–35, 1737–8, 1740–62, 1764–5, 1769–71, 1774–81, 1783–9, 1797, 1799–1800, 1802–4, 1806, 1808–33, 1835, 1837–8, 1847, 1851, 1854 **NLW** Mf **Soc Gen**
Cop ts PR index CB 1813–75 M 1682–1875 **NLW & Soc Gen** ts PR M 1813–37 with index **NLW Carm RO & Soc Gen**

TALACHARN/LAUGHARNE *SD*
C 1651–1974 M 1639–1971 (Banns 1801–47, 1857–1907) B 1645–1972 **Carm RO** Fac C 1651–1812 M 1639–1800 B 1645–1812 **NLW & Soc Gen**
BT 1672, 1677–9, 1681–2, 1686, 1704–5, 1711, 1715, 1717, 1721, 1725–1800, 1802–39, 1841, 1854–5, 1857, 1859–61, 1864, 1868–82, 1884–5, 1887–9 **NLW**
Cop ts PR M 1813–37 with index **NLW Carm RO & Soc Gen** ts PR index CB

1813–75 M 1639–1875 **NLW & Carm RO** ts PR CB (extracts) 1646–1749 M 1639–1747 with index **Soc Gen**

TALIARIS   *SD*
PR prior to 1813 see Llandeilo Fawr PR
CM 1813– incumbent B 1813–1927 **Carm RO**
BT 1813–15, 1842–60, 1864 **NLW**
Cop ts CB 1802–12 **NLW**

TALYLLYCHAU/TALLEY   *SD*
C 1685–1979 M 1685–1968 B 1685–1976 **Carm RO**
BT 1671, 1675, 1677–8, 1694, 1719, 1732, 1734–9, 1747–9, 1751–3, 1755–1800, 1802–54, 1873–4 **NLW**
Cop ts C 1685–1846 M 1687–1968 B 1686–1893 **NLW & Carm RO** ts PR index C 1813–75 M 1687–1875 ts PR M 1813–37 with index **NLW Carm RO & Soc Gen**

TRE-LECH A'R BETWS   *SD*
C 1663–1897 M 1663–1970 B 1663–1886 **Carm RO** Fac CMB 1663–1796 **NLW**
BT 1678–86, 1690–1, 1693–1703, 1705, 1707–8, 1710–11, 1713, 1715, 1717–18, 1720–2, 1724–62, 1764–72, 1774–8, 1780–1, 1783–90, 1792–7, 1802–8, 1810–14, 1816–77 **NLW**
Cop ts PR index CB 1813–75 M 1663–1875 ts PR M 1813–37 with index **NLW Carm RO & Soc Gen**

TYMBL, Y/TUMBLE   *SD*
<Llan-non
C 1932–69 M 1927–79 **NLW** Mf **Carm RO**

★ WHITLAND/HENDY-GWYN (EGLWYS FAIR GLYN TAF)   *SD*
Formerly a chapelry to Llanboidy. Ecclesiastical parish <Cyffig/Kiffig, Llanboidy, Llan-gan, and Llanbedr Felffre/Lampeter Velfrey 1910. PR CB 1783–1807 M 1765–1812 recorded in 1831 apparently lost
C 1813–1932 M 1813–1952 B 1813–1913 **Carm RO**
BT see Llanboidy
Cop ts PR M 1813–37 with index **NLW Carm RO & Soc Gen**

YSTRAD-FFIN   *SD*
The ancient chapel, Capel Peulin, in the parish of Llanfair-ar-y-bryn, seems to have had no PR until it became a separate parish <Llanfair-ar-y-bryn & Cil-y-cwm 1875. The new church of St Barnabas was substituted for it in 1878
CMB 1875– incumbent
BT 1875–80 **NLW**

CAERNARFON
CAERNARFONSHIRE

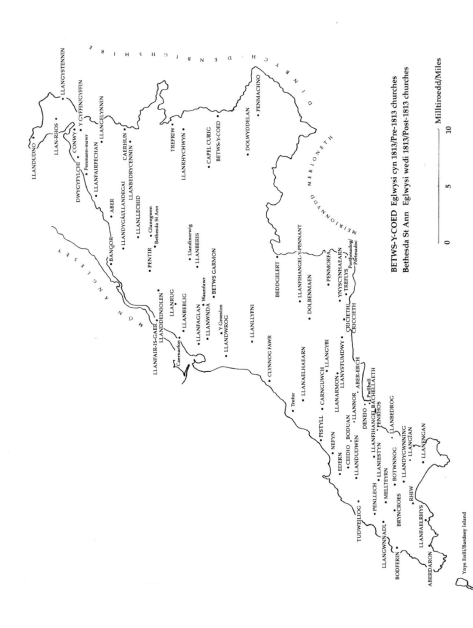

DINBYCH DENBIGHSHIRE

MÔN ANGLESEY

MEIRIONNYDD MERIONETH

LLANDUDNO

LLANGYSTENNIN
LLAN-RHOS
Y CYFFIN/GYFFIN
CONWY
DWYGYFYLCHI
Penmaen-mawr
LLANFAIRFECHAN
LLANGELYNNIN

ABER

LLANDYGAI/LLANDEGAI
LLANBEDRYCENNIN
CAERHUN
LLANLLECHID
Glanogwen
Bethesda St Ann

BANGOR

PENTIR
Llandinorwig
LLANBERIS
LLANWNDA
Waunfawr
BETWS GARMON

Y Groeslon

LLANFAIR-IS-GAER
LLANDDEINIOLEN
LLANRUG
LLANBEBLIG
LLANFAGLAN
LLANDWROG
Caernarfon

LLANLLYFNI

TREFRIW

LLANRHYCHWYN

CAPEL CURIG
BETWS-Y-COED

PENMACHINO

DOLWYDDELAN

BEDDGELERT
LLANFIHANGEL-Y-PENNANT
DOLBENMAEN

PENMORFA
Porthmadog/
Portmadoc
YNYSCYNHAEARN
TREFLYS
CRICIETH/
CRICCIETH

CLYNNOG FAWR

Trefor
LLANAELHAEARN
CARNGUWCH
LLANGYBI
LLANARMON
LLANYSTUMDWY
ABER-ERCH
Pwllheli
LLANNOR
DENEIO
LLANFIHANGEL BACHELLAETH
PENRHOS
LLANIESTYN
LLANBEDROG
LLANDYGWNNING
LLANGIAN
LLANENGAN

PISTYLL
NEFYN
CEIDIO
BODUAN
LLANDUDWEN

EDERN

BOTWNNOG
RHIW

PENLLECH
MELLTEYRN

TUDWEILIOG

BRYNCROES

BODFERIN

LLANFAELRHYS

LLANGWNNADL

ABERDARON

Ynys Enlli/Bardsey Island

BETWS-Y-COED Eglwysi cyn 1813/Pre-1813 churches
Bethesda St Ann Eglwysi wedi 1813/Post-1813 churches

Milltiroedd/Miles

0   5   10

ABER (ABERGWYNGREGYN) *B*
C 1682–1872 M 1682–1837 B 1682–1888 **NLW** M 1837–1971 (Banns 1902–17) **GASC**
Fac C 1682–1872 M 1682–1837 B 1682–1943 **GASC**
BT 1676–82, 1687, 1689–1701, 1703–5, 1707–25, 1727–74, 1777–80, 1782–91, 1793–1854,
1883, 1888–1900 **NLW**
Cop index M 1813–37 GFHS

ABERDARON *B*
PR CMB 1700–29 recorded in 1776 apparently lost
C 1753–1804, 1813–1909 M 1753–1805, 1813–37 B 1753–1804, 1813–93 **NLW** M
1837–1969 B 1894–1941**GASC** Mf C 1753–1909 M 1753–1837 B 1753–1893 **GASC**
BT 1678–80, 1682–3, 1685–6, 1688–90, 1700–1, 1704–6, 1709–11, 1714–16, 1719–40,
1742–6, 1748–66, 1768–80, 1782–1855, 1857–8, 1860, 1862–4, 1890–1 **NLW**
Cop index M 1813–37 GFHS

ABER-ERCH *B*
C 1600–42, 1673–1752, 1783–1812 M 1600–42, 1673–1752, 1783–1837 B 1600–42,
1673–1752, 1783–1868 **GASC** Fac **NLW**
BT 1677, 1679–81, 1683, 1685–6, 1688, 1690–3, 1695–1723, 1726–40, 1742, 1744–6,
1748–1865, 1867–75 **NLW**
Cop PR (extracts) C 1652–1774 M 1684–1762 B 1664–1725 J Jones, *Gleanings from God's
Acre within the Hundred of Lleyn and Commot of Eifionydd* ... (Pwllheli, 1903) Cop index M
1813–37 B 1813–1912 GFHS

ABERGWYNGREGYN gweler/see ABER

BANGOR Cathedral *B*
CMB 1727–99 **GASC** C 1813–1905 M 1754–1932 B 1813–62 **NLW** Fac C 1727–65,
1779–99 Draft 1825–7 M 1727–58 B 1727–67, 1776–99 **NLW** Fac C 1813–1904 M
1754–82, 1785–1851, 1858–1932 B 1813–51, 1854–62 **GASC**
BT 1727–8, 1740–8, 1750–2, 1754, 1756, 1758–9, 1761–2, 1764–6, 1777–91, 1793–1850,
1859–61 **NLW**
Cop ts PR C 1813–1905 M 1754–1932 (Banns 1786–1812) B 1813–62 **Soc Gen** Cop
index M 1813–37 GFHS

BANGOR St James *B*
M 1971–93 **GASC**

BANGOR St Mary *B*
Marriages prior to 1914 were celebrated at the cathedral
C 1864–1918 M 1914–26 **GASC** Mf **CALL**

★ BARDSEY ISLAND/YNYS ENLLI *B*
Formerly an extra-parochial place. Entries relating to the island appear in PR for Aberdaron

BEDDGELERT   *B*
Included township of Nanmor, co Merioneth
C 1734–1847 M 1734–1837 B 1734–1857 **NLW** Mf **GASC** C 1848–1994 M
  1837–1997 B 1857–1989 **GASC** Fac **NLW**
BT 1676–80, 1683–6, 1688–90, 1692, 1695–1700, 1702–5, 1708–13, 1715–17, 1720–5,
  1727–8, 1730–8, 1740, 1742–3, 1745–50, 1752, 1754–1866, 1882–97 **NLW**
Cop index M 1813–37 GFHS

BETWS GARMON   *B*
PR going back 'about forty five years' recorded in 1776 apparently lost. For M 1837–1962
  see Llanbeblig
C 1778–1877 M 1813–1962 B 1778–1862 **GASC** Mf B 1862–1947 **GASC** Fac B
  1862–1947 **NLW**
BT 1676–9, 1681–3, 1686–7, 1689–92, 1704–12, 1714, 1716–18, 1720–4, 1726–7,
  1729–53, 1755–80, 1782–91, 1793–1867, 1872–3, 1880–9, 1896–7 **NLW**
Cop index M 1813–37 GFHS

BETWS-Y-COED   *B*
C 1731–1907 M 1753–1836 St Mary 1924, 1928–57 St Michael 1837–1925, 1968 B
  1731–1942 **GASC** Mf CB 1731–1812 M 1731–53 **NLW** Mf C 1731–1907 M
  1731–1836 B 1731–1885 **CALL**
BT 1679, 1689–1701, 1703, 1705, 1707–38, 1740–80, 1782–91, 1793–1858 **NLW**
Cop index M 1813–37 GFHS

BETHESDA Glanogwen gweler/see GLANOGWEN

BETHESDA St Ann   *B*
<Llandygái/Llandegai 1845
C 1813–1909 B 1848–1917 **GASC**
BT 1813, 1817–19, 1822–8, 1874–83 **NLW**

BODFERIN   *B*
The church for this parish fell into decay after the Reformation. It was returned in 1776 as
  extra-parochial, appurtenant to Llaniestyn. The inhabitants attended Llangwnnadl church,
  but entries relating to Bodferin are also to be found in PR for Aberdaron
C 1901–52 **GASC**
Cop index M 1813–37 GFHS

BODUAN (BODFEAN, BODFUAN)   *B*
C 1678–1992 M 1678–1970, 1972–86, 1988–91 (Banns 1824–53) B 1678–1812,
  1814–1951 **GASC**
BT 1677–83, 1685–6, 1688–92, 1695, 1697–1709, 1711–22, 1724–40, 1742–3, 1745–6,
  1748–64, 1766–1865, 1867–85, 1887 **NLW**
Cop index M 1813–37 GFHS

BOTWNNOG *B*
C 1741–99, 1801–12 M 1741–1811, 1815–37 B 1741–92, 1794–9, 1801–12 **NLW** Mf
  GASC C 1813–1982 M 1837–62 B 1813–1991 **GASC** Fac M 1837–1933 **GASC**
BT 1679–81, 1686–9, 1693, 1695–7, 1699–1702, 1704–12, 1714–19, 1721–6, 1729–46,
  1748–74, 1776–80, 1782–1865, 1867–87, 1890–2, 1895–8 **NLW**
Cop index M 1813–37 GFHS

BRYNCROES *B*
C 1731–6, 1759–64, 1778–1868 M 1731–6, 1753, 1759–71, 1778–1970 B 1731–8,
  1759–64, 1778–1885 **GASC**
BT 1679, 1682, 1684–6, 1689–90, 1695–7, 1699–1701, 1704–5, 1707–35, 1738–9, 1742–6,
  1747 or 1748, 1749–61, 1763, 1765–80, 1782–1868, 1905–6 **NLW**
Cop index M 1813–37 GFHS

BUAN gweler/see BODUAN

CAERHUN *B*
C 1662–1870 M 1662–1970 B 1662–1876 **GASC** Mf C 1662–1870 M 1662–1837 B
  1662–1876 **CALL**
BT 1676–9, 1681, 1683, 1687, 1689–1701, 1703–23, 1725–43, 1745–74, 1776–91,
  1793–1861, 1863–71, 1873–82, 1893–5 **NLW**
Cop index M 1813–37 GFHS

CAERNARFON (CAERNARVON) gweler/see LLANBEBLIG

CAPEL CURIG *B*
<LIandygái/Llandegai, Trefriw, Llanrhychwyn, Llanllechid & Llanrwst 1866. PR CMB
  1730–1812 recorded in 1831 apparently lost
C 1813–1953 M 1754–1940, 1944–69 (Banns 1824–1989) B 1813–1924 **GASC** Mf M
  1754–1837 B 1813–1924 **CALL**
BT 1754–80, 1782–3, 1785–91, 1793–4, 1796–1804, 1806–41, 1843–6 **NLW**
Cop index M 1813–37 GFHS

CARNGUWCH *B*
Entries for M 1754–1812 are in PR for Edern
CB 1772–7 M 1754–1861 **GASC** CB 1813– incumbent Fac C 1813–1932 B 1813–1929
  GASC
BT 1692, 1695–9, 1702–6, 1709, 1711–16, 1718–27, 1729, ?1730, 1731, 1733, 1735–8,
  1740–2, 1744–69, 1771–1811, 1813–17, 1819–38, 1840–53, 1855–68, 1878–98, 1901
  NLW
Cop index M 1813–37 GFHS

CEIDIO *B*
<Boduan
M 1754–1810 **GASC** Fac M 1901–23 **GASC**

BT 1790, 1813, 1842, 1844–6, 1848–50, 1855–6, 1860–6, 1868–72, 1875–85, 1887–9, 1906
  NLW
Cop index M 1813–37 GFHS

CLYNNOG FAWR   *B*
C 1624–1894 M 1624–1755, 1785–1837 (Banns 1824–55) B 1624–1891 **GASC** Fac C
  1895–1981 M 1837–1968 B 1891–1981 **GASC**
BT 1689–99, 1701–35, 1737–9, 1742–74, 1776–80, 1782–6, 1788–90, 1792–1865,
  1867–85, 1887–95 **NLW**
Cop index M 1813–37 GFHS

CONWY (CONWAY)   *B*
C 1541–98, 1605–1943 M 1541–98, 1605–1973 B 1541–98, 1605–1927 **NLW** Fac C
  1943–76 B 1927–66 **NLW** Mf C 1541–1917 M 1541–1920 B 1541–1927 **CALL &**
  GASC
BT 1678, ?1690, 1691–3, 1695–1701, 1703–27, 1729–43, 1745–74, 1776–80, 1782–91,
  1793–1868, 1882–3 **NLW**
Cop PR CB 1541–1793 M 1541–1754 Alice Hadley, *Conway Parish Registers ...* (London,
  1900) Cop index M 1813–37 GFHS

CRICIETH/CRICCIETH   *B*
PR M 1754–1812 recorded in 1831 apparently lost
C 1675, 1688–1751, 1754–1987 M 1695–1751, 1754–72, 1813–1969, 1971–91 (Banns
  1823–30, 1884–1949) St Deiniol 1890–1966, 1973–86 B 1692–1751, 1754–1906 **NLW**
Mf C 1688–1883 M 1695–1772, 1813–37 B 1692–1906 **GASC**
BT 1677, 1687–92, 1695–7, 1700–2, 1705–38, 1740–6, 1748–85, 1788–1885 **NLW**
Cop PR (extracts) C 1675–1798 M 1715–67 B 1696–1807 J Jones, *Gleanings from God's*
  Acre ... (Pwllheli, 1903) Cop index M 1813–37 GFHS

DEGANNWY/DEGANWY gweler/see LLAN-RHOS

DENEIO   *B*
The parish included the town of Pwllheli
C 1686–90, 1692–4, 1696–1717, 1749, 1756–1812 M 1686–90, 1692–4, 1696–1717 B
  1686–90, 1692–4, 1696–1717, 1756–1812 **NLW** Mf **GASC** C 1813–1956 M
  1754–1804, 1806–1973 (Banns 1823–43, 1855–1963) B 1813–1963 **GASC**
BT 1677–82, 1685–6, 1689, 1691–2, 1695, 1697–8, 1700, 1702–22, 1725–35, 1738,
  1742–3, 1745, 1749–52, 1755–9, 1761–76, 1778–1862, 1882, 1885 **NLW**
Cop PR (extracts) C 1749–88 B 1765–1837 J Jones, *Gleanings from God's Acre ...* (Pwllheli,
  1903) Cop index M 1813–37 B 1813–95 GFHS

DOLBENMAEN   *B*
Entries for CB 1672–1773 and M 1672–1753 are in PR for Penmorfa
C 1672–1773, 1793–4, 1798–1803, 1807, 1809–1910 M 1672–1753, 1786–1970 B
  1672–1773, 1793–4, 1798–1803, 1807, 1809–1974 **NLW** Mf C 1793–1910 M
  1786–1837 B 1793–1907 **GASC** Fac CB 1798–1812 M 1786–1812 **GASC**

BT 1679–83, 1686, 1688–93, 1695–7, 1699–1703, 1705–18, 1720–40, 1742–3, 1745–6,
  1748–82, 1784–1886, 1901 **NLW**
Cop index M 1813–37 GFHS

DOLWYDDELAN   *B*
C 1718–1896 M 1701–14, 1721–8, 1737–1971 B 1701–14, 1721–9, 1737–1896 **GASC**
  Mf CMB 1729–1812 **CALL**
BT 1680, 1684, 1686, 1689–93, 1695–9, 1701, 1703–5, 1708–11, 1713–80, 1782–91,
  1793–1839, 1841–82 **NLW**
Cop index M 1813–37 GFHS

DWYGYFYLCHI   *B*
PR CMB 1634– recorded in 1776 and PR C 1757–1811 B 1757–1810 recorded in 1831
  apparently lost
C 1813–1979 M 1813–1947 St Seiriol, Penmaen-mawr 1883–1952 B 1813–1991 **GASC**
  Mf C 1813–67 M 1813–37 B 1813–67 **CALL**
BT 1678–81, 1683, 1686, 1690–5, 1697–1701, 1703–5, 1707–10, 1712–13, 1715–35, 1737,
  1740–8, 1750–7, 1759–61, 1763–80, 1782–91, 1793–7, 1799–1854, 1856–7, 1859–61,
  1863–71, 1882–4, 1910 **NLW**
Cop index M 1813–37 GFHS

EDERN (LLANEDERN)   *B*
C 1700–1866 M 1700–1837 B 1700–1931 **GASC** Fac C 1868–1930 M 1837–1921
  GASC
BT 1680–2, 1684–6, 1688–93, 1695, 1697, 1699–1723, 1725–46, 1748–66, 1768–1865,
  1867–8, 1877–98, 1901 **NLW**
Cop index M 1813–37 GFHS

EGLWYS-RHOS gweler/see LLAN-RHOS

ENLLI, YNYS gweler/see YNYS ENLLI

GLANOGWEN   *B*
<Llanllechid 1858
C 1853–1913 B 1856–1928 **GASC** M 1856– incumbent
BT 1882 **NLW**

GROESLON, Y gweler/see LLANDWROG

GYFFIN, Y/GYFFIN   *B*
C 1707–1901 M 1707–1970 B 1707–1887 **NLW** Mf C 1707–1901 M 1707–1837 B
  1707–1887 **CALL & GASC**
BT 1677–9, 1683, 1691–5, 1697–1701, 1703–43, 1745–80, 1782–91, 1793–1864 **NLW**
Cop index M 1813–37 GFHS

LLANAELHAEARN   *B*
PR relate also to St George, Trefor
C 1725–34, 1749–64, 1783–1926 M 1725–34, 1751–1834 B 1725–34, 1751–64, 1783–1925 **NLW** Mf **GASC** M 1837–1971 **GASC**
BT 1676, 1679–80, 1683, 1688–9, 1692–1701, 1704–5, 1707–21, 1723–6, 1728–35, 1738–43, 1745–91, 1793–1842, 1845–69 **NLW**
Cop index M 1813–37 GFHS

LLANARMON   *B*
C 1705–1993 M 1706–52, 1791–1968 (Banns 1824–1968) B 1705–1916 **NLW** Mf C 1705–1812 M 1705–52, 1791–1837 B 1705–1916 **GASC**
BT 1677–9, 1681–3, 1685–6, 1688–92, 1695, 1697–1740, 1742–6, 1748–80, 1782–1884 **NLW**
Cop PR (extracts) C 1706–1810 M 1707–40 B 1707–1807 J Jones, *Gleanings from God's Acre ...* (Pwllheli, 1903) Cop index M 1813–37 GFHS

LLANBEBLIG   *B*
The parish included the borough of Caernarfon
C 1699–1731, 1738–1974 Christ Church 1902–82 St Mary 1814–75 M 1699–1731, 1738–1898 (Banns 1823–33, 1839–66) Christ Church 1981 St David 1971–83 St Mary 1963–70 B 1699–1731, 1738–1975 corporation cemetery 1918-67 **GASC** Fac M Christ Church 1864–1930 **GASC**
BT 1678–9, 1683, 1689–1701, 1703–5, 1707–1886 **NLW** See also Waunfawr
Cop index M 1754–1837 GFHS

LLANBEDROG   *B*
C 1691–1921 M 1691–1988 B 1691–1985 **GASC** Fac C 1691–1921 M 1691–1837 B 1691–1985 **NLW**
BT 1680, 1697–1724, 1726–37, 1739–40, 1742–6, 1748–1865, 1867–85, 1887–90, 1893–9 **NLW**
Cop PR (extracts) C 1691–1812 M 1691–1801 B 1692–1868 J Jones, *Gleanings from God's Acre ...* (Pwllheli, 1903) Cop index M 1813–37 GFHS

LLANBEDRYCENNIN   *B*
C 1663–1725, 1727–99 M 1663–1725, 1727–53, 1773–99, 1813–37 (Banns 1823–8, 1906–33) B 1663–1725, 1727–99, 1813–1905 **GASC** Fac C 1813–1940 M 1837–1970 **GASC** Mf CMB 1663–1725 **NLW** Mf M 1813–37 B 1813–1905 **CALL**
BT 1676–7, ?1680, 1681, 1687, 1689–1713, 1715–43, 1745–80, 1782–91, 1793–1849, 1851–4, 1856–86, 1913 **NLW**
Cop index M 1813–37 GFHS

LLANBERIS   *B*
C 1726–1995 M 1726–1837, 1927–94 St Peris, Nantperis 1837–1986 B 1726–1969 **GASC**
BT 1677–8, 1681–3, 1689–93, 1695–1701, 1703–91, 1793–1840, 1842–51, 1854–60, 1862–7, 1889–90, 1892, 1894–7 **NLW**
Cop index M 1813–37 GFHS

* LLANDEGAI/LLANDYGÁI   *B*
C 1674–1731, 1736–1887 M 1674–1731, 1736–1864 (Banns 1836–89) B 1674–1731,
   1736–1908 **NLW** Mf C 1674–1731, 1736–1887 M 1674–1731, 1736–1858 (Banns
   1836–89) B 1674–1731, 1736–90, 1813–1908 **GASC** Mf C 1813–1909 B 1848–1917
   CALL
BT 1677–80, 1682–4, 1689–1701, 1703, 1705, 1708–15, 1717–40, 1743–7, 1749–91,
   1793–1889, 1891–2, 1901–15 **NLW**
Cop index M 1813–37 GFHS

LLANDINORWIG   *B*
<Llanddeiniolen 1858
C 1857– M 1858– B 1857– incumbent Fac C 1857–1931 M 1858–1931 **GASC**
BT 1872–3, 1882, 1892–5 **NLW**

LLANDUDNO   *B*
C 1750–1917 M 1754–1881 (Banns 1853–1912) St George 1881–1923 B 1750–1920
   GASC Mf **CALL**
BT 1677, 1680–1, 1689–1701, 1703–8, 1711–20, 1722–7, 1729–61, 1763–75, 1777–91,
   1793–1901 **NLW**
Cop index M 1813–37 GFHS

LLANDUDWEN   *B*
<Rhiw. Entries for M 1754–1810 are in PR for Ceidio
C 1815–1928 M 1754–1812, 1837–95, 1939–64 B 1825–1980 **GASC**
BT 1875–7, 1879–81, 1883–7, 1889, 1906 **NLW** See also Rhiw
Cop index M 1813–37 GFHS

LLANDWROG St Twrog   *B*
C 1593–1862 M 1593–1837 B 1593–1887 **GASC** Fac C 1863–1990 M 1837–1935 B
   1887–1989 **GASC**
BT 1676–7, 1681, 1683–4, 1687, 1689–1701, 1703–43, ?1745, 1746–65, 1767–80, 1782–91,
   1793–1855, 1860–72, 1874, 1882 **NLW**
Cop index M 1813–37 GFHS

LLANDWROG St Thomas, Y Groeslon   *B*
<Llandwrog 1858
C 1856– M 1857– incumbent B 1856–93 **GASC** Fac C 1856–1990 M 1857–1991 B
   1893–1990 **GASC**
BT 1856–75 **NLW**

LLANDYGÁI/LLANDEGAI   *B*
C 1674–1731, 1736–1887 M 1674–1731, 1736–1864 (Banns 1836–89) B 1674–1731,
   1736–1908 **NLW** Mf C 1674–1731, 1736–1887 M 1674–1731, 1736–1858 (Banns
   1836–89) B 1674–1731, 1736–90, 1813–1908 **GASC** Mf C 1813–1909 B 1848–1917
   CALL
BT 1677–80, 1682–4, 1689–1701, 1703, 1705, 1708–15, 1717–40, 1743–7, 1749–91,

1793–1889, 1891–2, 1901–15 **NLW**
Cop index M 1813–37 GFHS

LLANDYGWNNING   *B*
PR CMB 1723– recorded in 1776 apparently lost
C 1761, 1765–6, 1777, 1780–1812 M 1779–1812, 1826 B 1780–1812 **NLW** Mf CB
   1780–1812 M 1779–1812 **GASC** C 1813–1989 M 1837–1969 **GASC** Fac B 1813–1979
   GASC
BT 1676–8, 1680–1, 1686, 1688, 1696–9, 1701, 1704–19,1721–3, 1725–38, 1740, 1742–6,
   1748–1865, 1867 **NLW**
Cop ts PR CB 1780–1812 M 1779–1812 **Soc Gen** Cop index M 1813–37 GFHS

LLANDDEINIOLEN   *B*
PR CMB 1575–1643 defective
C 1575–92, 1633–46, 1660–1712, 1768–1810, 1813–32 M 1575–92, 1633–46, 1660–1712,
   1761–97, 1810–1989 (Banns 1837–1902) B 1575–92, 1633–46, 1660–1712, 1768–1810,
   1813–1999 **GASC**
BT 1676–83, 1687, 1689–1701, 1703–17, 1719–43, 1745–74, 1776–80, 1782–91,
   1793–1883 **NLW**
Cop index M 1813–37 GFHS

LLANENGAN   *B*
C 1679–91, 1700–14, 1730–1903 M 1679–91, 1700–14, 1730–52, 1755–1967 B 1679–91,
   1700–14, 1730–1937 **NLW** Mf **GASC**
BT 1677–80, 1682–3, 1687, 1689–91, 1695–1735, 1737–46, 1748–80, 1782–1885, 1887–92,
   1894–6 **NLW**
Cop index M 1813–37 GFHS

LLANFAELRHYS   *B*
Entries for CMB before 1812 are in PR for Aberdaron. See also PR for Y Rhiw. PR CB
   1751– recorded in 1776 apparently lost
C 1811, 1813–1988 M 1813–1920 B 1813–1992 **GASC** Fac C 1813–1927 B 1813–1931
   GASC
BT ?1677, 1678, 1680, ?1681, 1683, 1689, 1695, 1700, 1704–5, 1712, 1716, 1718, ?1721–2,
   1724–6, 1728–37, 1739–40, 1743–4, 1748–66, 1768–80, 1782–7, 1789–1865,1867–70,
   1872–4 **NLW**
Cop index M 1813–37 GFHS

LLANFAGLAN   *B*
PR M 1761–1812 recorded in 1831 and M 1813–37 recorded in 1934 apparently lost
C 1602–52, 1662–1812 M 1602–52, 1662–1764 B 1602–52, 1662–1812 **NLW** M
   1979–92 **GASC** Mf & Fac C 1602–1812 M 1602–1790 B 1602–1812 **GASC**
BT ?1676, 1677–9, 1681–3, 1687, 1689–1701, 1703–5, 1708–14, 1716–50, 1752, 1754–7,
   1759–74, 1776–80, 1782–91, 1793–1878, 1881–1913 **NLW**
Cop index M 1813–37 GFHS

LLANFAIRFECHAN   B
C 1634–1706, 1709–1983 M 1634–1706, 1709–1970 Christ Church 1866–1970 B
1634–1706, 1709–1992 **GASC** Mf C 1634–1908 M 1634–1837 B 1634–1900 **CALL**
BT 1676–80, 1682–4, 1686–7, 1689–1701, 1703–11, 1713–17, 1719–34, 1736–57,
1759–87, 1789–91, 1793–1898 **NLW**
Cop ms PR C 1660–1810 M 1635–1812 B 1635–1812 **Soc Gen** Cop index M 1813–37
GFHS

LLANFAIR-IS-GAER   B
Entries for C 1813–69 are in PR for Betws Garmon
C 1675–1785 with gaps, 1785–1813, 1869–1907 M 1675–1754 with gaps B 1675–1785
with gaps, 1785–1813, 1864–92 **NLW** Fac/Mf C 1675–1812, 1863–1962 M 1675–1754,
1837–1992 B 1676–1782, 1785–1812, 1864–1971 **GASC**
BT 1677–83, 1686, 1689–92, 1696–1701, 1704–18, 1720–6, 1729–52, 1754–80, 1782–8,
1790–1, 1793–1803, 1805–88 **NLW**
Cop index M 1813–37 GFHS

LLANFIHANGEL BACHELLAETH   B
C 1692–1958 M 1692–1968 B 1692–1995 **GASC** Fac CB 1692–1813 M 1692–1836
NLW
BT 1693–1721, 1723–34, 1736–40, 1742–3, 1745–6, 1748, 1750–80, 1782–1836, 1838–85,
1887–90, 1897–8 **NLW**
Cop PR (extracts) C 1693–1804 M 1723–97 B 1698–1803 J Jones, *Gleanings from God's
Acre* ... (Pwllheli, 1903) Cop index M 1813–37 GFHS

LLANFIHANGEL-Y-PENNANT   B
PR M 1755–1802 was copied by the incumbent in 1893 into the blank part of PR M
1813–37 not from the original (now lost), but from a copy made by Robert Evans,
antiquary, of Beddgelert
C 1698–1951 M 1698–1802, 1813–1971 B 1698–1959 **NLW** Mf C 1698–1951 M
1698–1802, 1813–37 B 1698–1959 **GASC**
BT 1676, 1678–80, 1683, 1688–92, 1695–7, 1699–1705, 1707–35, 1737–46, 1748–65,
1767–1885, 1888–96, 1901, 1905–6 **NLW**
Cop ms PR M 1755–1802 **NLW** Cop index M 1813–37 GFHS

LLANGELYNNIN   B
C 1733–1811, 1813–1992 M 1733–1837, 1839–1970 B 1733–1811, 1813–1907 **GASC**
Mf C 1733–1811 M 1733–1837 B 1733–1907 **CALL**
BT 1681, 1683, 1687, 1689–1701, 1703–18, 1720–80, 1782–91, 1793–1860, 1862–4, 1866
NLW
Cop index M 1813–37 GFHS

LLANGÏAN   B
PR CB 1768–99 recorded in 1934 apparently lost
C 1679–1767, 1800–1968 M 1692–1970 B 1692–1767, 1800–69 **NLW** Mf **GASC**
BT 1679, 1681–2, 1685–6, 1690–2, 1695–1732, 1734–5, 1737–40, 1743, 1745–6, 1748–73,

1775–80, 1782–1873, 1875–83, 1885–9, 1897–1901 **NLW**
Cop PR (extracts) C 1709–57 M 1710–50 B 1709–1864 J Jones, *Gleanings from God's Acre* ... (Pwllheli, 1903) Cop index M 1813–37 GFHS

LLANGWNNADL   *B*
C 1755, 1782–92, 1813–1992 M 1782–1970 B 1782–92, 1813–1969 **GASC** Fac B 1813–1969 **GASC**
BT 1677–8, 1680–2, 1689–90, 1692–3, 1695–1705, 1707–35, 1738, 1745, 1749–60, 1763–71, 1773–6, 1778–88, 1790–1868, 1873–4 **NLW**
Cop index M 1813–37 GFHS

LLANGYBI   *B*
C 1695–1751, 1754–1992 M 1695–1751, 1754–1966 (Banns 1823–1924 with gaps) B 1695–1751, 1754–1992 **NLW** Mf C 1695–1813 M 1695–1837 B 1695–1881 **GASC**
BT 1678, 1682–3, 1685–6, 1688–90, 1692, 1697–1706, 1708–34, 1737–46, 1748–80, 1782, 1784–1865, 1867–81 **NLW**
Cop PR (extracts) C 1701–1812 M 1708–49 B 1703–1874 J Jones, *Gleanings from God's Acre* ...(Pwllheli, 1903) Cop index M 1813–37 GFHS

LLANGYSTENNIN   *SA*
C 1608–33, 1636–41, 1661–1708, 1711–1934 M 1608–41, 1661–1708, 1711–1970 B 1608–33, 1636–41, 1661–1708, 1711–1958 **NLW** Mf **CALL & GASC**
BT 1674–5, 1677–81, 1684–96, 1698–1708, 1710–12, 1717, 1722–7, 1729–31, 1733–1843, 1850 **NLW** Mf **FRO & DRO**
Cop index M 1813–37 GFHS

LLANIESTYN   *B*
CB 1765–1812 **NLW** C 1813–1992 M 1754–1970 B 1813–1992 **GASC** Mf CB 1765–1812 **GASC** Fac M Banns 1824–1970 **GASC**
BT 1676–7, 1679–83, 1685–6, 1695–8, 1700–25, 1727–31, 1734–5, 1737–43, 1745–6, 1748–59, 1761–1864, 1866–70 **NLW**
Cop index M 1813–37 GFHS

LLANLLECHID   *B*
C 1690–1737, 1741–72, 1782–1856 M 1690–1737, 1739–1868 B 1690–1772, 1782–1907 **NLW** Fac **GASC**
BT 1677, 1682, 1690–1701, 1703–23, 1725–80, 1782–7, 1789–91, 1793–1855, 1864–5, 1885–8 **NLW**
Cop index M 1813–37 GFHS

LLANLLYFNI   *B*
PR CMB 1696–1738 recorded in 1934 apparently lost
C 1744–83, 1813–1915 M 1744–52, 1754–1882 B 1744–83, 1813–1924 **NLW** Fac **GASC**

BT 1679, 1681–3, 1687, 1689–1701, 1703–5, 1707–38, 1740–3, 1746–74, 1776–80, 1782–91, 1793–1859, 1863–4, 1882, 1887–8 **NLW**
Cop index M 1813–37 GFHS

LLANNOR *B*
PR at NLW is a draft of originals in GASC, with some variation in entries
C 1724–1802 B 1755–1801 **NLW** C 1756–1953 M 1754–1971 B 1756–1990 **GASC** Fac CB 1756–1812 **NLW** Fac C 1724–1802 B 1755–1801 **GASC**
BT 1677–8, 1680–3, 1685–6, 1692, 1695–6, 1698, 1700–26, ?1727, 1729, 1731–3, 1735, 1737–40, 1742–3, 1745, 1750, 1755–73, 1775–80, 1782–1862, 1883–5 **NLW**
Cop PR (extracts) C 1757–1811 B 1760–1803 J Jones, *Gleanings from God's Acre ...* (Pwllheli, 1903) Cop index M 1813–37 GFHS

LLANRUG *B*
C 1674–96, 1737–1882 M 1674–96, 1737–1922 (Banns 1849–1935) B 1674–96, 1737–1923 **GASC**
BT 1678–81, 1684, 1687, 1689–1701, 1704–5, 1707–8, 1711–39, 1741–2, 1744–74, 1776–80, 1782–7, 1789–91, 1793–1867, 1869–74, 1883–1900 **NLW**
Cop index M 1813–37 GFHS

LLAN-RHOS (EGLWYS-RHOS) *SA*
C 1758–1960 All Saints, Degannwy/Deganwy 1899–1955 St Paul, Craig-y-don 1901–45 M 1754–1993 (Banns 1889–90, 1901–33, 1946–88) All Saints 1909–71 St Paul 1909–70 (Banns 1909–65) B 1758–1961 Children 1898–1932 **GASC** Mf **CALL**
BT 1668, 1673–4, 1676, 1678, 1681–2, 1687–95, 1698–1716, 1718–1847 **NLW** Mf **FRO & DRO**
Cop index M 1813–37 GFHS

LLANRHYCHWYN *B*
Entries for CMB 1594–1812 are in PR for Trefriw. PR CMB 1733–67 recorded in 1934 apparently lost
C 1594–1666, 1767–1984 M 1594–1666, 1754–1961 B 1594–1666, 1767–1987 **GASC** Fac CMB 1594–1627 **NLW** Fac B 1813–1948 **GASC** Mf M 1754–1837 **CALL**
BT 1667, 1676, 1679–80, 1682–3, 1687, 1689, 1693–6, ?1704, 1705–10, 1712–24, 1727–80, 1782–91, 1793–1858 **NLW**
Cop index M 1813–37 GFHS

LLANWNDA *B*
C 1600–4, 1606–8, 1615–53, 1662–90, 1753–9, 1770–1902 M 1602, 1605, 1610, 1615–52, 1659–60, 1676–90, 1753–1809, 1813–37 B 1623–4, 1627–43, 1662–90, 1753–9, 1770–1873 **NLW** Fac & Mf **GASC** Fac M 1837–1970 **GASC** & **NLW** Fac B 1873–96 **GASC**
BT 1676–8, 1681, 1683, 1687, 1689–92, 1694–9, 1701, 1703–5, 1708–27, 1729–80, 1783–91, 1793–1809, 1811–78, 1881–1913 **NLW**
Cop index M 1813–37 GFHS

LLANYSTUMDWY   *B*
C 1596–1603, 1606–41, 1647–51, 1653–6, 1658–73, 1675–1724, 1726–35, 1738–66, 1783–97, 1799, 1804, 1813–1993 M 1596–1603, 1607–41, 1648–51, 1663–73, 1675–1724, 1726–30, 1733, 1735, 1738–47, 1754–1970 B 1596–1603, 1606–41, 1648–53, 1656, 1659, 1662–73, 1675–1724, 1726–35, 1738–68, 1783–97, 1799, 1803, 1813–1920 **NLW** Fac & Mf (with gaps to 1813) C 1596–1891 M 1596–1837 B 1596–1920 **GASC**
BT 1676–8, 1680–3, 1685–6, 1688–91, 1693, 1696–8, 1700, 1702, 1704–22, 1725–33, 1735, 1737–46, 1748–73, 1775–80, 1782–1864, 1867, 1872–85 **NLW**
Cop PR (extracts) C 1658–1845 M 1664–1793 B 1662–1902 J Jones, *Gleanings from God's Acre* ... (Pwllheli, 1903) Cop index M 1813–37 GFHS

LLYSFAEN gweler/see SIR DDINBYCH/DENBIGHSHIRE

MELLTEYRN & SARN   *B*
C 1741–2, 1744–52, 1763–1812 M 1741–2, 1744–52, 1763–1836 B 1742, 1744–52, 1763–1812 **NLW**   C 1813–1987 M 1837–1969 (Banns 1847–1969) B 1813–1981 **GASC**
Mf C 1741–1812 M 1741–1836 B 1742–1812 **GASC**
BT 1677, 1679, 1681, 1688–91, 1693, 1695–6, 1699–1704, 1706–12, 1714–16, 1718–19, 1721–46, 1748–73, 1775, l777–1865, 1867–82, 1884–7, 1890–2, 1895–7 **NLW**
Cop index M 1813–37 GFHS

NEFYN (NEVIN)   *B*
C 1692, 1694–1707, 1709, 1712–1813 M 1694–1707, 1712–1812 B 1694–1707, 1712–1813 **NLW** Mf **GASC** C 1813–97 M 1812–1927 B 1813–96 **GASC** Fac C 1876–1956 **GASC**
BT 1678–83, 1685–6, 1688–92, 1695–8, 1700–27, 1729–38, 1741–3, 1745–6, 1748–61, 1763–75, 1777, 1779, 1781–1865, 1867, 1889–90, 1894–5 **NLW**
Cop index M 1813–37 GFHS

NEFYN St Mary, Morfa Nefyn   *B*
C 1876– incumbent M 1873–1915 B 1873–1922 **GASC** Fac C 1876–1956 **GASC**

PENLLECH   *B*
C 1785–1930 M 1786–1922 B 1785–1949 **GASC**
BT 1676–9, 1681–2, 1689–93, 1695–1705, 1707–21, 1723–30, 1732–8, 1740, 1742–6, 1748–65, 1767–1865, 1867–84 **NLW**
Cop index M 1813–37 GFHS

PENMACHNO   *B*
PR CMB 1598– recorded in 1776 apparently lost
C 1710–1960 M 1714–1968 B 1785–1970 **GASC** Mf C 1710–1812 M 1714–58, 1813–38 B 1813–98 **CALL**
BT 1692–3, 1695–7, 1701, 1703, 1705, 1714–21, 1723–43, 1745–80, 1782–3, 1785–91, 1793–1861, 1872, 1875–82, 1888–98 **NLW**
Cop index M 1813–37 GFHS

PENMAEN-MAWR gweler/see DWYGYFYLCHI

PENMORFA   B
C 1672–1984   M 1672–1812, 1836–1970 (Banns 1954–86)   B 1672–1986 **NLW**   Fac C
   1672–1970 M 1672–1812, 1836–1970, 1972–81 B 1672–1971 **GASC**
BT 1676–7, 1679–81, 1683, 1686–92, 1695, 1697, 1701–35, 1737–40, 1742–3, 1745–6,
   1748–82, 1784–1803, 1805–86, 1901 **NLW**
Cop index M 1813–37 GFHS

PENRHOS   B
<Aber-erch 1876. Entries for CMB before 1812 are in PR for Aber-erch
C 1813–1944   M 1814–36, 1839–1924   B 1813–1930 **GASC**   Fac C 1813–1944   M
   1814–36 B 1813–1930 **NLW**
BT 1815, 1818–81, 1883, 1885 **NLW**
Cop index M 1813–37 GFHS

PENTIR   B
<Bangor. PR CMB 1574– recorded in 1776 apparently lost. For CMB 1727–99 see
   Bangor Cathedral
C 1619–52, 1666–1708 M 1619–47, 1683–1708 B 1616–44, 1664–1712 with gaps **British
   Library** Add MS 32644 CMB 1727–99 & C 1813–1992 B 1813–1910 **GASC** M 1903–
   B 1910– incumbent Fac C 1619–52, 1666–1708 M 1619–47, 1683–1708 B 1616–44,
   1664–1712 with gaps **NLW** Mf C 1619–52, 1666–1708 M 1619–47, 1683–1708 B
   1616–44, 1664–1712 with gaps **GASC** Mf B 1861–1910 **CALL**
BT 1764, 1782, 1787–91, 1793–5, 1797–1828, 1830–45, 1847–54 (see also BT for Bangor)
   NLW
Cop index M 1813–37 GFHS

PISTYLL   B
Entries for M 1754–1812 are in PR for Edern
CMB 1773–7, 1783–6, 1813–1990 M 1773–7, 1783–6, 1813–1965 B 1773–7, 1783–6,
   1813–1976 **GASC**
BT 1680, 1682, 1685–6, 1695–1725, 1727–43, 1745–6, 1748–1822, 1824–65, 1867–9,
   1877–98, 1901 **NLW**
Cop ts PR CMB 1773–7, 1783–6 **NLW** Cop index M 1813–37 GFHS

PORTHMADOG/PORTMADOC   B
<Ynyscynhaearn 1884
C 1872– incumbent M 1886–1944 (Banns 1964–80) **NLW**

PWLLHELI gweler/see DENEIO

RHIW   B
C 1782–1965 M 1782–1966 B 1782–1990 **GASC**
BT 1676, 1679, 1681–3, 1685, 1689–90, 1692, 1696, 1699–1703, 1705, 1708–27, 1730–1,
   1733–5, 1737–46, 1748–80, 1782–1885 **NLW**

Cop index M 1813–37 GFHS

SARN gweler/see MELLTEYRN & SARN

TREFLYS   *B*
PR CMB 1692– recorded in 1776 and PR CMB 1767–1812 recorded in 1831 apparently lost
CB 1813– incumbent M 1813–37, 1934 **NLW** Fac C 1813–1963 B 1813–1935 **NLW** Mf M 1813–37 **GASC**
BT 1705, 1707–35, 1737–40, 1742–6, 1749, 1751–7, 1759–80, 1782–7, 1789–90, 1792–3, 1795–1861, 1863–82, 1884–5 **NLW**
Cop index M 1813–37 GFHS

TREFOR (TREVOR) gweler/see LLANAELHAEARN

TREFRIW   *B*
PR CMB 1733–67 recorded in 1934 apparently lost
C 1594–1666, 1767–1812 M 1594–1666, 1754–1969 B 1594–1666, 1767–1892 **GASC**
Fac CMB 1594–1627 **NLW** Fac C 1813–1937 **GASC** Mf M 1754–1837 B 1813–92 **CALL**
BT 1679–81, 1683, 1687, 1689–90, 1705–10, 1712–24, 1726–80, 1782–91, 1793–1858 **NLW**
Cop index M 1813–37 GFHS

TUDWEILIOG   *B*
C 1780–1993 M 1759–1812, 1815–1971 B 1780–1983 **GASC**
BT 1690, 1698, 1701, 1704, 1710–13, 1717–19, 1721–5, 1727–36, 1738–9, 1741, 1744–6, 1749–73, 1775–88, 1790–1885, 1887–94 **NLW**
Cop index M 1813–37 GFHS

WAUNFAWR   *B*
<Llanbeblig 1881
C 1878– incumbent M 1881–1970 **GASC**
BT 1878–89, 1896 **NLW**

YNYSCYNHAEARN   *B*
The parish included the town of Porthmadog (Portmadoc). PR CMB 1692– recorded in 1776 apparently lost
C 1772–1907 M 1754–1886 B 1772–1875 **NLW** Fac C 1772–1970 M 1754–1886, 1889–1969 B 1772–1955 **GASC**
BT 1692, 1696, 1698, 1702, 1704–46, 1748–52, 1754–1865, 1867–8, 1870, 1885–92 **NLW**
Cop index M 1813–37 GFHS

YNYS ENLLI/BARDSEY ISLAND   *B*
Formerly an extra-parochial place. Entries relating to the island appear in PR for Aberdaron

DINBYCH
DENBIGHSHIRE

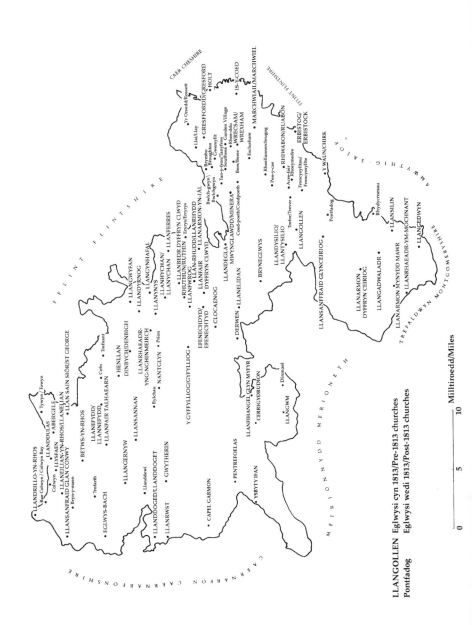

LLANGOLLEN Eglwysi cyn 1813/Pre-1813 churches
Pontfadog   Eglwysi wedi 1813/Post-1813 churches

Milltiroedd/Miles

0   5   10

ABERGELE *SA*
C 1647–1889 M 1647–8, 1659–1928 B 1647–1904 **NLW** Mf **CACB DRO & FRO**
BT 1665–8, 1670, 1672–5, 1677, 1679–80, 1682, 1684–7, 1689–96, 1698–1701, 1704,
1706–15, 1722–1842, 1844–5, 1848–51 **NLW** Mf 1783–1851 **DRO & FRO**
Cop ms PR (extracts) CMB 1647–1883 **NLW** PR CMB 1647–1812 with index CFHS

ACRE-FAIR gweler/see RHOSYMEDRE

BAE COLWYN/COLWYN BAY *SA*
<Llandrillo-yn-Rhos 1893
C 1893–1955 M 1891–1952 (Banns 1893–1936) B 1931–64 **DRO** Mf (excluding Banns)
  CACB CALL FRO & NLW

BERS/BERSE (BERSE DRELINCOURT) *SA*
<Wrecsam/Wrexham 1742
C 1860–1957 M 1890–1983 (Banns 1890–1957, 1962–89) **DRO** Mf (excluding Banns)
  FRO & NLW

BETWS-YN-RHOS (BETWS ABERGELE) *SA*
C 1705–1992 M 1705–1989 (Banns 1865–1991) B 1705–1992 **DRO** Mf (excluding
  Banns) **CACB CALL FRO & NLW**
BT 1663–8, 1670, 1672–4, 1676–9, 1681–2, 1684, 1686–94, 1696, 1698–1703, 1705–16,
1718, 1720–1833 **NLW** Mf **DRO & FRO**
Cop PR & BT CMB 1663–1812 with index CFHS

BROUGHTON *SA*
<Wrecsam/Wrexham 1909
C 1890–1937 M 1909–93 (Banns 1909–76) B 1889–1996 **DRO** Mf C 1890–1925 M
1909–54 B 1889–1927 **FRO & NLW**

BRYMBO *SA*
<Wrecsam/Wrexham 1844
C 1838–1945 M 1839–1971 (Banns 1872–1935, 1949–73) B 1838–1968 **DRO** Mf
  (excluding Banns) **FRO & NLW**
BT 1839–44, 1846–55 **NLW** Mf **DRO & FRO**

BRYNEGLWYS *SA*
C 1687–1867 M 1691–1970 B 1687–1944 **DRO** Mf **FRO & NLW**
BT 1662–3, 1666, 1670–84, 1686–96, 1699–1701, 1703–7, 1710, 1712, 1714–20, 1722,
1724–6, 1728–42, 1745–1808, 1810, 1812–50 **NLW** Mf **DRO & FRO**
Cop PR & BT CMB 1662–1812 with index CFHS

BRYN-Y-MAEN *SA*
<Llandrillo-yn-Rhos (Colwyn & Bae Colwyn/Colwyn Bay), Llaneilian-yn-Rhos/Llanelian
& Llansanffraid Glan Conwy 1900

C 1898– B 1896– incumbent M 1900–70 **DRO** Mf C 1898–1991 B 1896–1991 **DRO** Mf C 1898–1991 M 1900–70 B 1896–1991 **CACB CALL FRO & NLW**

BWLCH-GWYN/BWLCHGWYN *SA*
<Brymbo, co Denbigh, & Llanfynydd, co Flint 1880
C 1880–1990 M 1882–1969, 1973–83 B 1881–1990 **DRO** Mf **FRO & NLW**

BYLCHAU *SA*
<Henllan & Llansannan 1855
C 1857–1994 M 1858–1969 B 1858–1994 **DRO** Mf **CACB CALL FRO & NLW**

CAPEL GARMON (ST GERMAIN) *SA*
<Llanrwst 1863
C 1702–49, 1754–1910 M 1707–48, 1754–1969 B 1702–49, 1754–1869 **DRO** Mf **CACB CALL FRO GASC & NLW**
BT 1696–7, 1790–1853 **NLW** Mf **DRO & FRO**
Cop PR & BT C 1696–1842 M 1696–1812 B 1696–1841 CFHS

CEFN *SA*
<Llanelwy/St Asaph (Meiriadog/Meriadog & Wicwer/Wigfair) 1865
C 1865–1980 M 1865–1971 **DRO** Mf **FRO & NLW** B 1866– incumbent

CEGIDOG gweler/see LLAN SAIN SIÔR/ST GEORGE

CERRIGYDRUDION *SA*
C 1590–1846 M 1591–1970 (Banns 1824–67) B 1590–1851 **DRO** Mf C 1847–1988 B 1851–1988 **DRO** Mf C 1590–1988 M 1591–1970 B 1590–1988 **CACB CALL FRO & NLW**
BT 1665–8, 1670–2, 1674–7, 1679–96, 1698–1702, 1704–16, 1718, 1720–30, 1732–58, 1760–1840 **NLW** Mf **DRO & FRO**
Cop ms PR C 1813–31 B 1816–31 **NLW** PR C 1590–1846 M 1591–1812 B 1590–1812 with index CFHS

★ CHIRK/Y WAUN *SA*
C 1678–80, 1705–1956 M 1611–44, 1648–50, 1661, 1678, 1684, 1719–1971 B 1611–43, 1678–81, 1708–1975 **NLW** Mf/Fac **DRO** Mf **FRO** Mf C 1678–1845 M 1611–1971 B 1611–1812 **WAS**
BT 1663, 1666–8, 1670–3, 1679, 1681–2, 1685–6, 1693, 1697–8, 1702, 1704–1852 **NLW** Mf 1666–1852 **DRO & FRO**
Cop ms PR (extracts) C 1705–21 B 1708–96 **Soc Gen** PR & BT CMB 1611–1812 with index CFHS

CLOCAENOG *SA*
C 1672–1961 M 1676–95, 1709–1965 B 1672–1933 **DRO** Mf **FRO & NLW**
BT 1676–7, 1679–80, 1682–3, 1685–90, 1692–4, 1697–1708, 1711–32, 1736, 1742–63,

1765–72, 1774–1863 **NLW** Mf 1813–63 **DRO & FRO**
Cop PR CMB 1672–1812 with index CFHS

COED-POETH/COEDPOETH gweler/see MWYNGLAWDD/MINERA

COLWYN *SA*
<Llandrillo-yn-Rhos, Llaneilian-yn-Rhos/Llanelian & Llysfaen 1844
C 1838–1914 M St Catherine 1840–1970 St John 1905–71 (Banns 1905–35) B 1846–1952
DRO Mf (excluding Banns) **CACB CALL FRO & NLW**

⋆ COLWYN BAY/BAE COLWYN *SA*
<Llandrillo-yn-Rhos 1893
C 1893–1955 M 1891–1952 (Banns 1893–1936) B 1931–64 **DRO** Mf (excluding Banns)
CACB CALL FRO & NLW

CYFFYLLIOG gweler/see GYFFYLLIOG, Y

DENBIGH gweler/see DINBYCH

DERWEN *SA*
C 1633–1891 M 1632–1968 B 1633–1916 **DRO** Mf **FRO & NLW**
BT 1677–80, 1683, 1686–96, 1698–1716, 1727–32, 1736, 1742–72, 1774–1842, 1844–51
NLW Mf **DRO & FRO**
Cop PR CMB 1632–1812 with index CFHS

DINBYCH/DENBIGH *SA*
C 1683–1983 M 1686–1876 (Banns 1850–1974) St Mary 1876–1981 St David 1897–1980
St Marcella (Eglwys Wen/Whitchurch) 1928–70 B 1683–1984 **DRO** Mf (excluding
Banns) **FRO & NLW**
BT 1671–4, 1679–87, 1689–96, 1699, 1705–8, 1713, 1722–37, 1739–1842 **NLW** Mf **DRO
& FRO**
Cop PR CMB 1683–1812 with index CFHS

DINMAEL *SA*
<Llangwm 1878
M 1879–1969 **DRO** B see Llangwm Mf M 1879–1969 **CACB CALL FRO & NLW**

EFENECHDYD/EFENECHTYD *SA*
C 1693–1995 M 1693–1811, 1813–1960 (Banns 1813–17, 1882–9) B 1694–1995 **DRO**
Mf C 1693–1983 M 1693–1960 B 1694–1981 **FRO** C 1693–1812 M 1693–1960 B
1694–1812 **NLW**
BT 1680, 1687–9, 1692–4, 1696–1711, 1713–19, 1721–2, 1724–32, 1734, 1736, 1740,
1742–9, 1751, 1753–64, 1766–72, 1774–1836, 1855–9, 1861–4 **NLW** Mf **DRO & FRO**
Cop ts PR C 1693–1761 M 1693–1754 B 1694–1789 **Soc Gen** PR CMB 1693–1812
with index CFHS

EGLWYS-BACH *SA*
Included township of Maenan, co Caernarfon
C 1601–62, 1695–1872 M 1601–62, 1695–1837 (Banns 1833–1918) B 1601–1929
DRO Mf (excluding Banns) **CACB CALL FRO GASC & NLW**
BT 1666–8, 1670, 1673, 1675–9, 1681, 1683, 1687, 1690, 1693, 1696, 1699–1705, 1707, 1709, 1711–21, 1723–40, 1742–1844, 1846–50 **NLW** Mf 1670–1850 **DRO & FRO**
Cop PR & BT C 1601–62, 1666–1729, 1760–1812 M 1601–62, 1668–1812 B 1601–62, 1666–1812 with index CFHS Cop index M 1813–37 GFHS

ERBISTOG/ERBISTOCK *SA*
Partly in Flintshire
C 1680–1918 M 1679–1970 B 1679–1991 **DRO** Mf **FRO & NLW** Mf C 1680–1918 M 1679–1837 B 1679–1875 **WAS**
BT 1663, 1670–4, 1681–4, 1686–96, 1706–8, 1714, 1717–20, 1722–3, 1725–45, 1747–8, 1750–1835 **NLW** Mf 1671–1835 **DRO & FRO**
Cop PR (extracts) C 1680–1795 M 1682–1713 B 1680–1778 *Archaeologia Cambrensis* (1888) PR CMB 1679–1812 with index CFHS

ERYRYS/ERRYRYS *SA*
<Llanarmon-yn-Iâl 1861
C 1862– B 1865– incumbent M 1864–1970 **DRO** Fac C 1862–1978 B 1865–1977 **DRO & FRO** Mf M 1864–1970 **FRO & NLW**

ESCLUSHAM *SA*
<Wrecsam/Wrexham 1879
C 1879–1952 M 1880–1971 (Banns 1879–1963) B 1879–1952 **DRO** Mf (excluding Banns) **FRO & NLW**

FOELAS gweler/see PENTREFOELAS

FRONCYSYLLTAU/FRONCYSSYLLTE gweler/see LLANGOLLEN

GARDEN VILLAGE *SA*
<Wrecsam/Wrexham 1928
C 1929–75 M 1950–86 (Banns 1950–86) **DRO** Mf (excluding Banns) **FRO & NLW**

GLAN CONWY gweler/see LLANSANFFRAID GLAN CONWY

GLYNCEIRIOG gweler/see LLANSANFFRAID GLYNCEIRIOG

GLYNTRAEAN gweler/see PONTFADOG

GRESFFORDD/GRESFORD *SA*
Included townships of Marford & Hoseley, co Flint
C 1661–1976 M 1672–1988 (Banns 1776–1836, 1848–1988) B 1660–1979 **DRO** Mf (excluding Banns) **FRO & NLW** Mf C 1870–1976 M 1884–1971 B 1887–1979 **WAS**

BT 1670–4, 1677–83, 1688–91, 1694, 1718, 1725–32, 1734–1842, ?1843, 1847, 1849–59, 1861–8, 1870–98 **NLW** 1843–4 **DRO** Mf 1670–1897 **DRO & FRO**
Cop PR CMB 1660–1812 with index CFHS

GWERSYLLT *SA*
<Gresffordd/Gresford & Wrecsam/Wrexham 1851
C 1851–1985 M 1851–1994 (Banns 1852–1994) B 1851–1975 **DRO** Mf C 1851–1934 M 1851–1931 B 1851–1924 **FRO & NLW**

GWYTHERIN *SA*
C 1718–48, 1750–3, 1756–83, 1785–1812 M 1718–48, 1750–3, 1756–1813, 1837–1970 (Banns 1814–22) B 1718–48, 1750–3, 1756–83, 1785–1812 **NLW** Mf **CACB DRO & FRO** C 1813–1992 M 1813–37 B 1813–1994 **DRO** Mf **FRO & NLW**
BT 1667–74, 1676, 1679–91, 1693–5, 1698–1725, 1727–40, 1742–51, 1753–66, 1769–1835 **NLW** Mf 1671–1835 **DRO & FRO**
Cop PR & BT CMB 1667–1812 with index CFHS

GYFFYLLIOG, Y/GYFFYLLIOG (CYFFYLLIOG) *SA*
C 1617–25, 1636–50, 1658–1851 M 1617–25, 1637–50, 1658–1717, 1721–1967 (Banns 1824–1940) B 1617–25, 1636–50, 1658–1953 **DRO** Mf (excluding Banns) **FRO & NLW**
BT 1663, 1676–7, 1682–3, 1686–90, 1692–1708, 1710–19, 1721–3, 1725–32, ?1734, 1736, 1742–72, 1774–1861 **NLW** Mf **DRO & FRO**
Cop PR CMB 1617–1812 with index CFHS

HENLLAN *SA*
C 1684–1983 M 1684–1961 (Banns 1834–1903) B 1684–1939 **DRO** Mf (excluding Banns) **FRO & NLW**
BT 1668, 1674, 1681–2, 1692, 1694, 1696, 1698, 1703–4, 1707–37, 1739–1849 **NLW** Mf **DRO & FRO**
Cop PR CMB 1684–1812 with index CFHS

HOLT *SA*
C 1661–1966 M 1661–1971 B 1662–1997 **DRO** Mf C 1661–1966 M 1661–1971 B 1662–1924 **FRO NLW & WAS**
BT 1600, 1616, 1620–1, 1623, 1625–7, 1629–35, 1637–9, 1641, 1663, 1666, 1668–71, 1673–80, 1682, 1698–1700, 1715–24, 1726–45, 1747–53, 1755–1849 **Ches RO** 1850–60, 1862–4, 1866–9 **NLW** Mf 1600–1849 **FRO** 1850–60, 1862–4, 1866–9 **DRO & FRO**
Cop PR CB 1661–1812 M 1661–1837 with index CFHS

IS-Y-COED *SA*
<Holt 1826
C 1749–1946 M 1750–5, 1798–1970 (Banns 1824–1960) B 1750–1927 **DRO** Mf (excluding Banns) **FRO & NLW**
BT 1749, 1813–49 **Ches RO** 1850–60 **NLW** Mf 1749, 1813–49 **FRO**
Cop PR C 1749–1813 M 1750–1837 B 1750–1813 with index CFHS

KEGIDOG gweler/see LLAN SAIN SIÔR/ST GEORGE

LLAI/LLAY   *SA*
<Gresffordd/Gresford 1925
C 1925–61 M 1925–71 (Banns 1925–69) **DRO** Mf (excluding Banns) **FRO & NLW**

LLANARMON DYFFRYN CEIRIOG   *SA*
C 1625–92 with gaps, 1696–1991 M 1624–92 with gaps, 1696–1813, 1824–1970 B
1624–92 with gaps, 1696–1980 **DRO** Mf **FRO & NLW**
BT 1668, 1677, 1679, 1681–1709, 1714–16, 1718, 1720–3, 1725–42, 1744, 1746–53,
1755–1835 **NLW** Mf **DRO & FRO**
Cop PR C 1625–1813 MB 1624–1813 with index CFHS

LLANARMON MYNYDD MAWR   *SA*
C 1695–1700, 1720–1987 M 1699, 1720–1836, 1839–1923 B 1695–1700, 1720–1989
DRO Mf **FRO NLW & PCAO**
BT 1672–3, 1681–3, 1690, 1704–5, 1708–9, 1714, 1716–17, 1719, 1721, 1723–35,
1737–45, 1747–67, 1769–80, 1782–1800, 1802–50 **NLW** Mf **DRO & FRO**
Cop ms/ts PR C 1695–1836 M 1699–1836 B 1695–1812 **DRO** PR & BT CB
1681–1812 M 1683–1812 CFHS

LLANARMON-YN-IÂL   *SA*
Included township of Bodidris, co Flint
C 1683–1943 M 1676–8, 1692–1969 (Banns 1843–1910) B 1677–1937 **DRO** Mf
(excluding Banns) **FRO & NLW**
BT 1666–7, 1670–3, 1675–7, 1679, 1683–96, 1698–1708, 1710–12, 1714–16, 1719–23,
1725–1836, 1851 **NLW** Mf 1667–1836 **DRO & FRO**
Cop PR CMB 1676–1812 with index CFHS

LLANBEDR DYFFRYN CLWYD   *SA*
C 1650–1894 M 1683–1968 B 1650–1888 **DRO** Mf **FRO & NLW**
BT 1676, 1683, 1687–90, 1692–1702, 1704–19, 1722–3, 1726–32, 1736, 1742–72,
1774–1816, 1818–60 **NLW** Mf 1813–60 **DRO & FRO**
Cop ts PR C 1656–1891 M 1690–1868 B 1652–1883 **Soc Gen** PR CMB 1650–1812
with index CFHS

LLANDEGLA   *SA*
C 1710–1896 M 1710–52, 1754–1812, 1814–1970 (Banns 1824–1913) B 1710–1810,
1813–81 **DRO** Mf (excluding Banns) **FRO & NLW**
BT 1663, 1668, 1670–3, 1676–96, 1698–1758, 1760–3, 1765, 1767–1851 **NLW** Mf **DRO
& FRO**
Cop PR & BT CMB 1710–1812 with index CFHS

LLANDRILLO-YN-RHOS   *SA*
Included township of Eirias, co Caernarfon

C 1693–1859 M 1693–1921 (Banns 1902–29) B 1693–1910 **DRO** Mf (excluding Banns) **CACB CALL FRO & NLW**
BT 1663, 1672–4, 1680–1, 1691, 1700, 1704–5, 1707, 1712–16, 1718, 1720–6, 1728–1835, 1837–8 **NLW** Mf 1702–1838 **DRO & FRO**
Cop ts PR CMB 1693–1713 **NLW** PR & BT CMB 1663–1837 with index CFHS

LLANDYRNOG   *SA*
C 1664–1753 with gaps, 1755–1866 M 1664–1732 with gaps, 1734–1905, 1907–70, 1972–86 (Banns 1823–1959) B 1664–1753 with gaps, 1755–1969 **DRO** Mf C 1664–1753 with gaps, 1755–1866 M 1664–1732 with gaps, 1734–1905, 1907–70 B 1664–1753 with gaps, 1755–1969 **FRO & NLW**
BT 1676, 1678, 1687, 1695–8, 1700–5, 1709–10, 1714–16, 1727–31, 1736, 1742–72, 1774–1838, 1840–5, 1856 **NLW** Mf **DRO & FRO**
Cop PR CMB 1664–1812 with index CFHS

LLANDYSILIO/LLANTYSILIO   *SA*
C 1677–1717, 1721–55, 1759–1992 M 1677–1717, 1721–82, 1784–1970 B 1678–1717, 1721–55, 1759–1969 **DRO** Mf **FRO & NLW**
BT 1671–2, 1674–7, 1680–7, 1691–6, 1698–1701, 1703–98, 1802–3, 1805–36 **NLW** Mf 1675–1836 **DRO & FRO**
Cop PR & BT CMB 1671–1812 with index CFHS

LLANDDEWI   *SA*
<Llangernyw 1867
C 1867–1949 M (Banns 1867–1940) B 1873–1955 **DRO** M 1871–1955 **NLW** Mf C 1867–1949 B 1873–1955 **FRO & NLW** Mf M 1871–1955 **CACB CALL DRO & FRO**

LLANDDOGED/LLANDDOGET   *SA*
Pages from first PR with entries for 1637–9 have been re-used to supply BT for 1702–3
C 1600–37, 1641–1933 M 1600–32, 1660–1752, 1754–1812, 1814–1967 B 1602–37, 1642–1990 **DRO** Mf **CACB CALL FRO GASC & NLW**
BT 1673, 1675–6, 1682–96, 1698, 1702–3, 1707–9, 1712, 1718–1856 **NLW** Mf **DRO & FRO**
Cop PR CB 1600–1812 M 1600–1837 with index CFHS Cop index M 1813–37 GFHS

LLANDDULAS   *SA*
C 1761–1947 M 1755–1971 (Banns 1824–1940) B 1761–1941 **DRO** Mf (excluding Banns) **CACB CALL FRO & NLW**
BT 1665, 1673, 1677, 1679–83, 1685–90, 1692–3, 1695–6, 1707, 1710–16, 1718–19, 1722–1839 **NLW** Mf 1682–1839 **DRO & FRO**
Cop PR & BT CMB 1665–1812 CFHS

LLANEFYDD/LLANNEFYDD   *SA*
PR CMB 1721–1812 recorded in 1936 apparently lost
C 1813–1989 M 1754–1964 B 1813–61 **DRO** Mf **CACB CALL FRO & NLW**

BT 1665–7, 1672–3, 1676–95, 1698–1700, 1702, 1704–14, 1716, 1718, 1720–9, 1731–9, 1741–1818, 1820–36 **NLW** Mf **DRO & FRO**
Cop PR & BT CMB 1665–1812 with index CFHS

LLANEILIAN-YN-RHOS/LLANELIAN   *SA*
C 1589–1623, 1627–33, 1637–1715, 1719–1987 M 1589–1619, 1627–1811, 1813–1981 B 1589–98, 1627–1992 **DRO** Mf **CACB CALL FRO & NLW**
BT 1666, 1671–2, 1674, 1677–8, 1680, 1682–91, 1693, 1701, 1703, 1706, 1708–11, 1714–16, 1718–19, 1721–1840 **NLW** 1841–3 **DRO** Mf 1672–1840 **DRO & FRO**
Cop PR CMB 1589–1812 with index CFHS

LLANELIDAN   *SA*
C 1686–1995 M 1697–1970 (Banns 1824–1965) B 1695–1862 **DRO** Mf (excluding Banns) **FRO & NLW**
BT 1676–7, 1682, 1686–90, 1692–9, 1701–32, 1736, 1742–1836, 1850–68, 1870–1 **NLW** Mf **DRO & FRO**
Cop ts PR (extracts) C 1686–1770 M 1703–42 B 1694–1766 **Soc Gen** PR CMB 1686–1812 with index CFHS

LLANFAIR DYFFRYN CLWYD   *SA*
C 1680–3, 1691–1979 M 1691–1971 (Banns 1871–1966) B 1680–3, 1691–1940 Ancient churchyard 1927–62 **DRO** Mf (excluding Banns) **FRO & NLW**
BT 1683, 1689–1700, 1702–13, 1715–17, 1719–32, 1736, 1742–72, 1774–6, 1778–1864 **NLW** Mf 1813–64 **DRO & FRO**
Cop PR CMB 1680–1812 with index CFHS

LLANFAIR TALHAEARN   *SA*
C 1669–1999 M 1671–1716, 1718–1961 (Banns 1824–1907) B 1669–1999 **DRO** Mf C 1669–1854 M 1671–1716, 1718–1961 B 1669–1868 **CACB CALL FRO & NLW**
BT 1668, 1670–3, 1675, 1677–82, 1684, 1687–90, 1692–6, 1699–1715, 1720–95, 1797–1852 **NLW** Mf 1668–1851 **DRO & FRO**
Cop PR CMB 1669–1812 with index CFHS

LLANFERRES   *SA*
C 1586–1810, 1813–1998 M 1588–1990 (Banns 1918–98) B 1587–1810, 1813–1997 **DRO** Mf C 1586–1810, 1813–1945 M 1588–1990 B 1587–1810, 1813–59 **FRO & NLW**
BT 1666, 1673–7, 1680–8, 1690–3, 1695–6, 1699–1700, 1703–10, 1712, 1714, 1718–31, 1733–42, 1744–77, 1779–1837 **NLW** 1841–2 **DRO** Mf **DRO & FRO**
Cop ts PR C 1611–1845 M 1612–1834 B 1611–1897 **Soc Gen** PR CB 1587–1810 M 1588–1837 with index CFHS

LLANFIHANGEL GLYN MYFYR   *SA*
Included township of Cefn-post, co Merioneth
C 1662–78, 1689–1991 M 1663–77, 1692–1717, 1729–1960 (Banns 1823–1963) B 1662–1991 **DRO** Mf (excluding Banns) **CACB CALL FRO & NLW** Fac C 1689–1728 M 1692–1717 B 1678–1729 **NLW**

BT 1663, 1667–8, 1670, 1672–6, 1678–9, 1681–8, 1690–2, 1694–5, 1698–1702, 1704–15, 1718–1837, 1842–3 **NLW** Mf **DRO & FRO**
Cop PR CMB 1662–1812 with index CFHS

LLANFWROG   *SA*
C 1638–1936 M 1638–1945 (Banns 1848–1949) B 1638–1934 **DRO** Mf (excluding Banns) **FRO & NLW**
BT 1676–8, 1682–3, 1686–90, 1692–6, 1698–1700, 1702–32, 1734, 1736, 1742, 1744, 1746–51, 1753–6, 1758–72, 1774–1860 **NLW** Mf 1813–60 **DRO & FRO**
Cop ts PR CB 1638–1755 M 1638–1750 **Soc Gen** Cop PR CB 1638–1812 M 1638–1837 with index CFHS

LLANGADWALADR   *SA*
C 1736–69, 1776–1995 M 1739–1967 B 1736–70, 1776–1947 **DRO** Mf C1736–1990 M 1739–1967 B 1736–1947 **FRO NLW & PCAO**
BT 1666–7, 1670–1, 1673, 1679, 1681–7, 1689–90, 1692–1708, 1710–11, 1713–15, 1717, 1719–37, 1739–1835, 1837–41, 1843–54 **NLW** Mf **DRO & FRO**
Cop ms PR CB 1736–70, 1776–1813 M 1739–1836 **NLW** ms/ts PR CB 1736–1911 M 1739–1915 **DRO** PR CMB 1736–1813 with index CFHS

LLANGEDWYN   *SA*
C 1672–1738, 1745–97, 1813–1931 M 1697–1738, 1745–1952 B 1675–1738, 1745–97, 1813–1937 **NLW** Mf **DRO & FRO**
BT 1667–70, 1674, 1676–9, 1681–2, 1684–6, 1688, 1690, 1693–6, 1698–1722, 1724–49, 1751–1817, 1819–39 **NLW** Mf **DRO & FRO**
Cop ms BT CMB 1797–1812 **NLW** ts C 1672–1847 M 1697–1844 B 1676–1868 (PR 1672–1868 & BT 1797–1812) **DRO** PR C 1672–1813 M 1697–1812 B 1675–1812 with index CFHS

LLANGERNYW   *SA*
C 1570–1617, 1627–38 (misc entries 1642–71), 1682–1734, 1779–1812, 1825–34, 1858–76 M 1570–1617, 1627–38, 1682–97, 1704–22, 1731–4, 1754–1812 B 1570–1617, 1627–38, 1684–1725, 1731–4, 1779–1812, 1825–34, 1858–79 **NLW** Mf **CACB DRO & FRO** C 1730–79, 1813–1998 M 1730–78, 1813–1970 B 1730–79, 1813–1998 **DRO** Mf C 1730–79, 1813–96 M 1730–78, 1813–1970 B 1730–79, 1813–97 **FRO & NLW**
BT 1667, 1672–5, 1677, 1682–6, 1689–96, 1698–1701, 1703–6, 1708–16, 1718, 1720–69, 1771–1842 **NLW** Mf 1672–1842 **DRO & FRO**
Cop PR CMB 1682–1747 (extracts) *Denbighshire Historical Society Transactions,* 18 (1969) PR CMB 1570–1812 with index CFHS

LLANGOLLEN   *SA*
C 1623–60, 1670–96, 1699–1706, 1708–1964 Trefor/Trevor 1868–1992 M 1587–1625, 1670–92, 1699–1705, 1708–1986 (Banns 1823–1942, 1960–86) Froncysylltau/Froncyssyllte 1932–75 Trefor/Trevor 1925–86 B 1597–1634, 1655–64, 1670–94, 1699–1706, 1708–1971 **DRO** Mf (excluding Banns) **FRO & NLW**
BT 1662, 1671–7, 1679–80, 1682–5, 1689–90, 1699, 1701–1806, 1808–35 **NLW** 1836–46

DRO Mf 1662–1835 **DRO & FRO**
Cop ts PR C 1670–1780 M 1699–1786 B 1670–1790 **Soc Gen** PR C 1623–1812 M 1587–1812 B 1597–1812 with index CFHS

LLANGWM   *SA*
C 1738–1977 M 1738–1965 (Banns 1831–1940) B 1738–1974 **DRO** Mf (excluding Banns) **CACB CALL FRO & NLW**
BT 1665, 1667–70, 1672–3, 1675–8, 1680–96, 1698–1704, 1706–7, 1710–13, 1716–18, 1720–59, 1761–74, 1776–1801, 1803–19, 1821–41 **NLW** Mf 1669–1841 **DRO & FRO**
Cop PR CMB 1738–1812 with index CFHS

LLANGWYFAN   *SA*
C 1723–1991 M 1729–1968 B 1728–1992 **DRO** Mf **FRO & NLW**
BT 1676, 1682–3, 1687, 1689, 1692–4, 1696–1713, 1715–17, 1721–2, ?1724, 1727–32, 1734, 1736, 1742–72, 1774–1856 **NLW** Mf **DRO & FRO**
Cop PR & BT CB 1676–1812 M 1683–1837 with index CFHS

LLANGYNHAFAL   *SA*
C 1704–1938 M 1704–1936 (Banns 1784–1952) B 1704–1940 **DRO** Mf (excluding Banns) **FRO & NLW**
BT 1676–8, 1682–3, 1687–9, 1692–4, 1696–1732, 1734, 1736, 1742–56, 1758–72, 1774, 1777–1873 **NLW** Mf **DRO & FRO**
Cop ts PR CB 1706–79 M 1706–47 **Soc Gen** PR & BT CMB 1676–1812 with index CFHS

LLANHYCHAN/LLANYCHAN   *SA*
C 1696–1991 M 1696–1812, 1814–33, 1838–1970 B 1696–1812, 1814–1991 **DRO** Mf **FRO & NLW**
BT 1676–7, 1680, 1682, 1692–9, 1701–13, 1715–16, 1727–32, 1734–6, 1743–72, 1774–87, 1790–1843, 1855, 1857–8, 1862 **NLW** Mf **DRO & FRO**
Cop ts BT CM 1677–96 B 1676–96 & PR CB 1696–1837 M 1696–1833 **NLW & Soc Gen** ts PR (extracts) C 1750–1874 M 1751–1805 B 1750–1832 **Soc Gen** PR & BT C 1677–1813 MB 1677–1812 with index CFHS

* LLANNEFYDD/LLANEFYDD   *SA*
PR CMB 1721–1812 recorded in 1936 apparently lost
C 1813–1989 M 1754–1964 B 1813–61 **DRO** Mf **CACB CALL FRO & NLW**
BT 1665–7, 1672–3, 1676–95, 1698–1700, 1702, 1704–14, 1716, 1718, 1720–9, 1731–9, 1741–1818, 1820–36 **NLW** Mf **DRO & FRO**
Cop PR & BT CMB 1665–1812 with index CFHS

LLANRWST   *SA*
Included township of Gwedir/Gwydir (or Trewydir), co Caernarfon
C 1613–16, 1627–8, 1632–1947 St Mary 1891–1956 M 1615, 1626–8, 1632–90, 1692–1715, 1717–1973 (Banns 1812–17, 1822–1970) St Mary 1884–1955 B 1615, 1627–9, 1632–1879 St Mary 1891–1942 **DRO** Mf (excluding Banns) **CACB CALL**

FRO GASC & NLW
BT 1665, 1670, 1672–3, 1675, 1678–9, 1683–4, 1691, 1694, 1696, 1698–1700, 1702, 1705–6, 1708–9, 1711, 1713–18, 1720–31, 1733–5, 1737–1855, 1867–77 **NLW** Mf **DRO & FRO**
Cop PR CMB 1613–1812 with index CFHS Cop index M 1813–37 GFHS

LLANRHAEADR-YM-MOCHNANT *SA*
Included seven townships in Montgomeryshire
C 1678–92, 1695–1847 M 1682–91, 1697–1919 (Banns 1845–85) B 1678–92, 1695–1930 **DRO** Mf (excluding Banns) **FRO NLW & PCAO**
BT 1663, 1670, 1674–7, 1679, 1681–3, 1691, 1694–6, 1709–13, 1716–1835, 1837–44 **NLW** Mf **DRO & FRO**
Cop ts PR C 1679–1812 (extracts), 1813–46 M 1675–1839 B 1679–1858 (extracts) **DRO** PR CB 1678–92, 1759–1812 M 1678–1812 with index CFHS

LLANRHAEADR-YNG-NGHINMEIRCH *SA*
C 1683–1908 M 1683–1971 B 1683–1863 **DRO** Mf **FRO & NLW**
BT 1676, 1679, 1688, 1693–4, 1696–8, 1700–32, 1734, 1736, 1742–3, 1745–72, 1774–6, 1778–1842, 1844–6, 1848–52, 1854–6, 1858, 1863 **NLW** Mf **DRO & FRO**
Cop PR & BT CB 1676–1812 with index CFHS

LLAN-RHUDD/LLANRHYDD *SA*
C 1608–1954 M 1610–1970 (Banns 1852–1958) B 1610–1991 **DRO** Mf (excluding Banns) **FRO & NLW**
BT 1676–8, 1680, 1682–3, 1687–90, 1692–9, 1701–7, 1709–19, 1721–32, 1734, 1736, 1742–55, 1757–72, 1774–1861 **NLW** Mf 1813–61 **DRO & FRO**
Cop PR C 1608–1812 MB 1610–1812 with index CFHS

LLAN SAIN SIÔR/ST GEORGE (CEGIDOG) *SA*
C 1694–1941 M 1696–1971 (Banns 1830–1940) B 1694–1927 **DRO** Mf (excluding Banns) **CACB CALL FRO & NLW**
BT 1663, 1665–6, 1668, 1680–1, 1684–6, 1703–4, 1706–8, 1711, 1714–23, 1726–34, 1736–46, 1748–1846 **NLW** Mf **DRO & FRO**
Cop PR CB 1694–1751 M 1696–1750 with index F A Crisp, *The Parish Registers of Kegidog alias St George...* (1890) ms PR (extracts) CMB 1694–1874 **NLW** PR CMB 1694–1812 with index CFHS

LLANSANFFRAID GLAN CONWY *SA*
PR 1729–40 was destroyed by fire with the rectory in 1740. CMB 1741–4 are loose copies
C 1660–1730, 1741–1913 M 1695–1729, 1741–1970 (Banns 1836–1937) B 1662–1729, 1741–1993 **DRO** Mf (excluding Banns) **CACB CALL FRO & NLW** Mf C 1660–1913 M 1695–1837 B 1662–1901 **GASC**
BT 1662, 1664–8, 1671–8, 1681, 1683–6, 1688–93, 1695, 1698–1705, 1708, 1710, 1713–16, 1718–25, 1727–30, 1733–4, 1736–1835, 1838–40 **NLW** Mf **DRO & FRO**
Cop PR CMB 1660–1812 with index CFHS Cop index M 1813–37 GFHS

LLANSANFFRAID GLYNCEIRIOG   *SA*
C 1768–1898 M 1754–1970 (Banns 1824–1954) B 1768–1891 **DRO** Mf (excluding Banns) **FRO & NLW**
BT 1661–4, 1667–8, 1670–1, 1673–4, 1677, 1679, 1681–2, 1684–6, 1689, 1691–2, 1694–1702, 1704–5, 1715–19, 1724, 1726, 1729–30, 1734, 1736–50, 1753–9, 1761–3, 1765–1837, 1841–7, 1849–51 **NLW** Mf 1662–1847 **DRO & FRO**
Cop ms PR CB 1768–1805 **NLW** PR CB 1768–1814 M 1754–1814 with index CFHS

LLANSANNAN   *SA*
C 1730–79, 1813–1998 M 1730–78, 1813–1970 (Banns 1852–1998) B 1730–79, 1813–1998 **DRO** Mf C 1730–79, 1813–88 M 1730–78, 1813–1970 B 1730–79, 1813–88 **CACB CALL FRO & NLW**
BT 1666–8, 1670–1, 1673, 1679, 1681, 1683–5, 1688, 1690–1, 1693–5, 1699–1700, 1702, 1704–7, 1709–14, 1720, 1722–5, 1727–1832 **NLW** Mf 1667–1832 **DRO & FRO**
Cop CMB 1666–1812 (BT 1666–1726 & PR 1727–1812) R Ellis, *The Registers of the Parish of Llansannan* (Liverpool, 1904) & CFHS

LLANSILIN   *SA*
Included township of Sychdyn, co Salop
C 1668, 1706–43, 1751–4, 1759–1856 M 1668, 1706–1967 B 1668, 1706–1932 **NLW** C 1856– incumbent M (Draft banns) 1896–1913 **DRO** Mf C 1856–1992 **NLW** Mf C 1668–1992 M 1668–1967 B 1668–1932 **DRO & FRO**
BT 1666–8, 1670–4, 1676–7, 1679–87, 1689–91, 1698–1708, 1710–45, 1747–59, 1761–1846 **NLW** Mf **DRO & FRO**
Cop ms PR C 1668–1838 M 1668–1837 B 1668–1876 **NLW** ms/ts CMB 1666–1913 (PR 1668–1913 & BT 1666–1759) **DRO** PR & BT CMB 1666–1812 with index CFHS

★ LLANTYSILIO/LLANDYSILIO   *SA*
C 1677–1717, 1721–55, 1759–1992 M 1677–1717, 1721–82, 1784–1970 B 1678–1717, 1721–55, 1759–1969 **DRO** Mf **FRO & NLW**
BT 1671–2, 1674–7, 1680–7, 1691–6, 1698–1701, 1703–98, 1802–3, 1805–36 **NLW** Mf 1675–1836 **DRO & FRO**
Cop PR & BT CMB 1671–1812 with index CFHS

★ LLANYCHAN/LLANHYCHAN   *SA*
C 1696–1991 M 1696–1812, 1814–33, 1838–1970 B 1696–1812, 1814–1991 **DRO** Mf **FRO & NLW**
BT 1676–7, 1680, 1682, 1692–9, 1701–13, 1715–16, 1727–32, 1734–6, 1743–72, 1774–87, 1790–1843, 1855, 1857–8, 1862 **NLW** Mf **DRO & FRO**
Cop ts BT CM 1677–96 B 1676–96 & PR CB 1696–1837 M 1696–1833 **NLW & Soc Gen** ts PR (extracts) C 1750–1874 M 1751–1805 B 1750–1832 **Soc Gen** PR & BT C 1677–1813 MB 1677–1812 with index CFHS

LLANYNYS   *SA*
C 1626–1727 with gaps, 1739–1891 M 1626–1734 with gaps, 1739–1971 B 1626–1734 with gaps, 1739–1903 **DRO** Mf **FRO & NLW**

BT 1686–9, 1692–4, 1696–1714, 1717–31, 1742–56, 1758–70, 1772, 1774, 1776–1805, 1807–66 **NLW** Mf 1813–66 **DRO & FRO**
Cop ts PR CMB 1626–1837 **Soc Gen** ts PR/BT CB 1626–1840 M 1626–1837 **NLW** PR CMB 1626–1812 with index CFHS

* LLAY/LLAI   *SA*
<Gresffordd/Gresford 1925
C 1925–61 M 1925–71 (Banns 1925–69) **DRO** Mf (excluding Banns) **FRO & NLW**

LLYSFAEN   *SA*
A detached part of Caernarfonshire until 1922. PR CB 1761–1809 recorded in 1831
  apparently lost
C 1661–1760, 1809–57 M 1663–1752, 1755–1938 B 1661–1760, 1809–1931 **DRO** Mf
  CACB CALL FRO & NLW Fac CB 1661–1760 M 1663–1752 **NLW**
BT 1662–8, 1670–5, 1679–83, 1685–91, 1694–6, 1698–1708, 1710–15, 1718, 1720–1844
  NLW Mf **FRO & NLW**
Cop PR CMB 1661–1812 with index CFHS

MARCHWIAIL/MARCHWIEL   *SA*
C 1653–1942 M 1666–1812, 1814–1970 B 1662–1908 **DRO** Mf **FRO & NLW** Mf C
  1813–1942 M 1814–1970 B 1813–1908 **WAS**
BT 1661–3, 1667–8, 1670, 1672–3, 1677–82, 1684, 1690, 1692–3, 1698, 1700–1, 1703–15,
  1718, 1720–1, 1723–83, 1785–1830, 1832–71 **NLW** Mf 1667–1871 **DRO & FRO**
Cop PR CMB 1653–1812 with index CFHS

MWYNGLAWDD/MINERA   *SA*
<Wrecsam/Wrexham 1844
C 1786–1894 M 1845–1927 (Banns 1845–91, 1894–1939) B 1847–1915 St Tudfil, Coed-
  poeth/Coedpoeth C 1895–1935 M 1895–1971 (Banns 1869–92, 1895–1939, 1969–92) B
  1896–1961**DRO** Mf (excluding Banns) **FRO & NLW**
BT 1772–1816, 1842–4, 1850–9 **NLW** Mf 1772–85 **DRO**
Cop ms PR C 1786–95 **DRO** PR & BT C 1772–1820 with index CFHS

NANTGLYN   *SA*
PR M 1775–92 recorded in 1831 as 'in the possession of one Owen Morris, late parish clerk,
  from whom it cannot be obtained'
C 1719–94, 1813–1993 M 1720–53, 1755–73, 1792–1967 (Banns 1871–1958) B 1719–94,
  1813–1958 **DRO** Mf (excluding Banns) **FRO & NLW**
BT 1663–8, 1670, 1673–4, 1676–7, 1680–94, 1696, 1698–1707, 1711, 1721–3, 1725–6,
  1729–35, 1737–68, 1770–1854 **NLW** Mf **DRO & FRO**
Cop ms PR CB 1719–94 M 1720–53 **DRO** ts PR CB 1720–79 M 1720–45 **Soc Gen**
PR & BT CMB 1663–1812 with index CFHS

ORSEDD, YR/ROSSETT   *SA*
<Gresffordd/Gresford (Trefalun/Allington, Burton, Marford & Hoseley) 1840

C 1840–1944 M 1841–1939 B 1841–1916 **DRO** Mf **FRO & NLW**
BT 1847, 1849–57 **NLW** Mf **DRO & FRO**

PENTREFOELAS (FOELAS) *SA*
<Llanefydd/Llannefydd & Ysbyty Ifan 1772
C 1782–1928 M 1772–1966 B 1773–1881 **DRO** Mf **CACB CALL FRO & NLW**
BT 1773–99, 1813–56 **NLW** Mf **DRO & FRO**
Cop PR C 1782–1812 M 1772–1837 B 1773–1812 CFHS

PEN-Y-CAE *SA*
<Rhiwabon/Ruabon, Rhosllannerchrugog & Rhosymedre 1879
C 1880–1919 M 1880–1971 B 1881–1952 **DRO** Mf **FRO & NLW**

PONTFADOG (GLYNTRAEAN) *SA*
<Llangollen 1848
C 1847–1951 M 1848–1970 (Banns 1906–13) **DRO** B 1849– incumbent Mf C
   1847–1951 M 1848–1970 **FRO & NLW**
BT 1847–52 **NLW** Mf **DRO & FRO**

PRION *SA*
<Llanrhaeadr-yng-Nghinmeirch 1860
M 1861–1936 **DRO** C 1859– B 1861– incumbent Mf M 1861–1936 **FRO & NLW**

★ ROSSETT/YR ORSEDD *SA*
<Gresffordd/Gresford (Trefalun/Allington, Burton, Marford & Hoseley) 1840
C 1840–1944 M 1841–1939 B 1841–1916 **DRO** Mf **FRO & NLW**
BT 1847, 1849–57 **NLW** Mf **DRO & FRO**

RUABON gweler/see RHIWABON

★ RUTHIN/RHUTHUN *SA*
C 1592–1964 M 1594–1970 (Banns 1857–1959) B 1592–1991 **DRO** Mf (excluding
   Banns) **FRO & NLW**
BT 1680, 1682–3, 1687, 1689–1719, 1722–30, 1734, 1736, 1742–72, 1774, 1776–1860
   NLW Mf 1813–60 **DRO & FRO**
Cop ms PR CB 1828–34 **DRO** ts PR C 1609–85 M 1608–47 B 1614–1720 **Soc Gen**
   PR CMB 1592–1812 with index CFHS

RHIWABON/RUABON *SA*
C 1559–1945 M 1599–1964 (Banns 1838–1917, 1932–72) B 1599–1963 **NLW** Mf
   (excluding Banns) **DRO & FRO** Fac C 1828–1945 M 1827–1964 B 1832–1963 **DRO**
BT 1663–8, 1670–2, 1674, 1676, 1679–85, 1690–2, 1694–5, 1698–9, 1701, 1704–9, 1716,
   1718–1861, 1863–7 **NLW** Mf 1663–1861 **DRO & FRO**
Cop PR C 1559–1853 M 1599–1843 B 1599–1847 with index CFHS

RHOS-DDU *SA*
<Wrecsam/Wrexham, Gresffordd/Gresford & Gwersyllt 1886
C 1886–1975 Rhosnesni 1963–75 Rhosrobin 1963–75 M 1887–1990 (Banns 1937–42, 1952–79) **DRO** Mf C 1886–1975 M 1887–1990 **FRO & NLW**

RHOSLLANNERCHRUGOG *SA*
<Rhiwabon/Ruabon 1844
C 1853–1906 M 1854–1930 (Banns 1854–1943, 1948–52) B 1853–1920 **DRO** Mf (excluding Banns) **FRO & NLW**

RHOSNESNI gweler/see RHOS-DDU

RHOSROBIN gweler/see RHOS-DDU

RHOSYMEDRE *SA*
<Rhiwabon/Ruabon 1844
C 1837–1992 M 1844–1988 (Banns 1880–7, 1892–1932, 1954–61) Acre-fair 1964–84 B 1839–1974 **DRO** Mf (excluding Banns) **FRO & NLW**
BT 1851 **NLW**

RHUTHUN/RUTHIN *SA*
C 1592–1964 M 1594–1970 (Banns 1857–1959) B 1592–1991 **DRO** Mf (excluding Banns) **FRO & NLW**
BT 1680, 1682–3, 1687, 1689–1719, 1722–30, 1734, 1736, 1742–72, 1774, 1776–1860 **NLW** Mf 1813–60 **DRO & FRO**
Cop ms PR CB 1828–34 **DRO** ts PR C 1609–85 M 1608–47 B 1614–1720 **Soc Gen** PR CMB 1592–1812 with index CFHS

RHYDYCROESAU *L*
<Llansilin, co Denbigh, & Llanyblodwel, Croesoswallt/Oswestry & Selatyn, co Salop 1844
C 1838– M 1845– B 1839– incumbent

★ ST GEORGE/LLAN SAIN SIÔR (CEGIDOG) *SA*
C 1694–1941 M 1696–1971 (Banns 1830–1940) B 1694–1927 **DRO** Mf (excluding Banns) **CACB CALL FRO & NLW**
BT 1663, 1665–6, 1668, 1680–1, 1684–6, 1703–4, 1706–8, 1711, 1714–23, 1726–34, 1736–46, 1748–1846 **NLW** Mf **DRO & FRO**
Cop PR CB 1694–1751 M 1696–1750 with index F A Crisp, *The Parish Registers of Kegidog alias St George...* (1890) ms PR (extracts) CMB 1694–1874 **NLW** PR CMB 1694–1812 with index CFHS

ST GERMAIN gweler/see CAPEL GARMON

SOUTHSEA   *SA*
<Wrecsam/Wrexham 1884. PR B 1909–47 apparently lost
C 1914–61   M 1922–83 (Banns 1922–48) Tan-y-fron 1944–80   B 1947–73 **DRO**   Mf
(excluding Banns) **FRO & NLW**

TAN-Y-FRON gweler/see SOUTHSEA

* TOWYN/TYWYN   *SA*
<Abergele 1873
C 1873–1965   M 1877–1966 (Banns 1877–1969) **DRO**   B 1875– incumbent   Mf C
1873–1965 M 1877–1966 **CACB CALL FRO & NLW**

TREFNANT   *SA*
<Henllan 1855
C 1855–1920   M 1855–1975 (Banns 1855–1969) **DRO**   B 1857– incumbent   Mf C
1855–1920 M 1855–1975 **FRO & NLW**

TREFOR/TREVOR gweler/see LLANGOLLEN

TROFARTH   *SA*
<Betws-yn-Rhos, Llansanffraid Glan Conwy & Llangernyw 1873. PR CB 1873–1991 M
1963–91 were stolen from the church in 1991
M 1874–1963 **DRO**   CMB 1991– incumbent   Mf M 1874–1963 **CACB CALL FRO &
NLW**

TYWYN/TOWYN   *SA*
<Abergele 1873
C 1873–1965   M 1877–1966 (Banns 1877–1969) **DRO**   B 1875– incumbent   Mf C
1873–1965 M 1877–1966 **CACB CALL FRO & NLW**

WAUN, Y/CHIRK   *SA*
C 1678–80, 1705–1956   M 1611–44, 1648–50, 1661, 1678, 1684, 1719–1971   B 1611–43,
1678–81, 1708–1975 **NLW**   Mf/Fac **DRO**   Mf **FRO**   Mf C 1678–1845   M 1611–1971   B
1611–1812 **WAS**
BT 1663, 1666–8, 1670–3, 1679, 1681–2, 1685–6, 1693, 1697–8, 1702, 1704–1852 **NLW**
Mf 1666–1852 **DRO & FRO**
Cop ms PR (extracts) C 1705–21 B 1708–96 **Soc Gen**   PR & BT CMB 1705–1812 with
index CFHS

WRECSAM/WREXHAM   *SA*
Included township of Abenburyfechan, co Flint
C 1618–45, 1652–1988   M 1632–44, 1662–6, 1668–1994 (Banns 1826–1983)   B 1620–45,
1650, 1654, 1662–1977 All Saints M 1986–92 St John C 1977–85   M 1975–85 St Mark
C 1870–1933 St Michael M 1979–86 St Peter C 1973–85   M 1979 (Banns 1978–83)
DRO   Mf (excluding M 1989–94 and Banns) **FRO & NLW**   Mf C 1826–1916   M
1813–1913   B 1822–8, 1833–1911 **WAS**   Fac C 1906–38   M 1901–32   B 1897–1944 St

Mark C 1870–1933 **WAS**

BT 1662–74, 1676–80, 1682, 1684–5, 1687–8, 1703–11, 1718–1858 **NLW** 1858–70 **DRO**
Mf 1662–1823 **DRO**

Cop PR (extracts) C 1618–1818 M 1637–1823 B 1621–1824 A N Palmer *History of the Town of Wrexham* (Wrexham, 1893) ts PR C 1620–1746 M 1638–1737 B 1625–1775 **Soc Gen** PR C 1618–1812 M 1632–1813 B 1620–1812 with index CFHS ts index C 1813–24 **DRO & FRO**

YSBYTY IFAN   *SA*

Included township of Eidda, co Caernarfon

C 1732–1855 M 1732–1968 B 1732–1958 **DRO** Mf **CACB CALL FRO GASC & NLW** Fac C 1732–1855 M 1732–1842 B 1732–1958 **GASC**

BT 1677, 1679–86, 1688–91, 1695–6, 1698–1700, 1703, 1714, 1725–6, 1729–30, 1732–7, 1739–43, 1745, 1747–1804, 1806–51 **NLW** Mf **DRO & FRO**

Cop PR & BT CMB 1677–1812 with index CFHS Cop index M 1813–37 GFHS

FFLINT
FLINTSHIRE

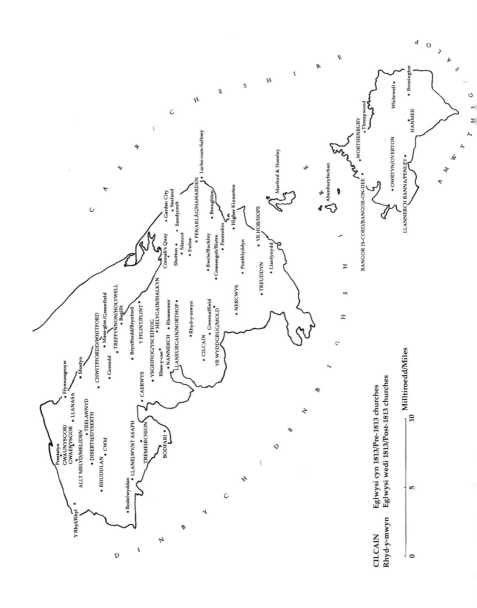

CILCAIN   Eglwysi cyn 1813/Pre-1813 churches
Rhyd-y-mwyn Eglwysi wedi 1813/Post-1813 churches

0   5   10   Milltiroedd/Miles

ALLT MELYD/MELIDEN *SA*
C 1602–26, 1685–7, 1690–1734, 1741–1973 M 1603–26, 1687, 1692–1734, 1742–1982
(Banns 1824–91, 1893–1983) B 1602–26, 1686–7, 1690–1734, 1741–1996 **FRO** Mf C
1602–1973 M 1603–1982 B 1602–1960 **DRO & NLW**
BT 1668, 1672–3, 1677, 1679, 1681, 1683, 1686, 1692, 1698–1700, 1703–39, 1741–1834,
1851 **NLW** Mf 1673–1851 **FRO & DRO**
Cop PR CB 1602–19 M 1603–17 *Northern Flintshire,* 1 (1913) ts PR/BT CB 1602–1718
M 1603–1718 **NLW** PR CMB 1602–1812 with index CFHS

BAGILLT *SA*
<Treffynnon/Holywell 1844
C 1839–1954 M 1841–1943 (Banns 1915–47) B 1839–1944 **FRO** Mf (excluding Banns)
DRO & NLW
BT 1839–57 **NLW** Mf **FRO & DRO**

BANGOR IS-COED/BANGOR-ON-DEE (BANGOR MONACHORUM) *SA*
Included townships of Eutun/Eyton, Royton, Pickhill and Seswick, co Denbigh
C 1675–1939 M 1675–1900 B 1675–1887 **FRO** Mf **DRO & NLW**
BT 1614, 1622–30, 1632–3, 1635–6, 1664, 1666–8, 1670–1, 1673, 1675–7, 1679–85,
1690–1, 1694–1700, 1703–11, 1713–32, 1734–8, 1740–2, 1744–1848 **Ches RO** 1849
NLW Mf 1614–1848 **FRO**
Cop PR C1675–1813 MB 1675–1812 with index CFHS

* BISTRE/CROESESGOB *SA*
<Yr Wyddgrug/Mold 1844
C 1842–80, 1882–1964 M 1842–1974 (Banns 1898–1974) B 1843–1950 **FRO** Mf
(excluding Banns) **DRO & NLW**

BODELWYDDAN *SA*
<Llanelwy/St Asaph 1860
C 1860– B 1861– incumbent M 1860–1959 (Banns 1936–52) **FRO** Mf M 1860–1959
DRO & NLW

BODFARI *SA*
Included township of Aberchwiler/Aberwheeler, co Denbigh
C 1571–1643, 1648–1986 M 1571–1640, 1670–1970 (Banns 1823–1972) B 1571–1642,
1655–1915 **FRO** Mf (excluding Banns) **DRO & NLW**
BT 1662–3, 1665, 1668, 1672–3, 1676–7, 1681–6, 1707–12, 1715, 1717–20, 1722–33,
1735–1836 **NLW** Mf 1665–1836 **FRO & DRO**
Cop PR C 1571–1643, 1648–1812 M 1571–1640, 1670–1812 B 1571–1643, 1655–1812
with index CFHS

BRONINGTON (NEW FENS CHAPEL) *SA*
<Hanmer 1836
C 1837–1972 M 1852–1970 (Banns 1857–1968) B 1837–1921 **FRO** Mf (excluding Banns)
DRO & NLW

BROUGHTON   *SA*
<Penarlâg/Hawarden 1824
C 1824–1970 M 1841–1990 (Banns 1841–1916, 1956–91) B 1824–1962 **FRO**   Mf
  (excluding Banns) **DRO & NLW**
BT 1824–72 **FRO**

BRYNFFORDD/BRYNFORD   *SA*
<Treffynnon/Holywell & Ysgeifiog/Ysceifiog 1853. PR CB 1853–76 apparently lost
C 1877– incumbent M 1855–1965 B 1877–1917 **FRO**   Mf M 1855–1965 B 1877–1917
  DRO & NLW

BWCLE/BUCKLEY   *SA*
<Penarlâg/Hawarden 1822
C 1822–1966 M 1841–1992 (Banns 1841–1956) B 1822–1978 **FRO**   Mf C 1822–1921 M
  1841–1951 B 1822–1958 **DRO & NLW**
BT 1867–72 **FRO**

CAERFALLWCH gweler/see RHOSESMOR

CAERWYS   *SA*
C 1673–1957 M 1673–1983 (Banns 1949–84) B 1673–1936 **FRO**   Mf (excluding Banns)
  DRO & NLW Fac CB 1673–1790 M 1673–1754 **NLW**
BT 1666–8, 1672–4, 1676–8, 1680–95, 1699–1702, 1704, 1707–9, 1713–38, 1740–1842
  NLW Mf 1667–1842 **FRO & DRO**
Cop PR CMB 1673–1812 with index CFHS

CILCAIN   *SA*
C 1577–1875 M 1576–1971 B 1584–1875 **FRO**   Mf **DRO & NLW**
BT 1662–3, 1665–8, 1672–4, 1676–91, 1693–6, 1698–1700, 1702–53, 1755–1842 **NLW**
  Mf **FRO & DRO**
Cop PR CB 1576–1812 M 1583–1843 with index CFHS

CONNAH'S QUAY   *SA*
<Llaneurgain/Northop 1844
C 1837–1979 M 1839–1981 (Banns 1876–1910, 1924–73) B 1837–1933 **FRO**   Mf
  (excluding Banns) **DRO & NLW**

CROESESGOB/BISTRE   *SA*
<Yr Wyddgrug/Mold 1844
C 1842–80, 1882–1964 M 1842–1974 (Banns 1898–1974) B 1843–1950 **FRO**   Mf
  (excluding Banns) **DRO & NLW**

CWM   *SA*
PR CB 1791–1812 recovered from a London bookseller in 1890 (see *Flintshire Observer*, 9
  Jan 1890)
C 1727–63, 1765–1939 M 1727–1971 B 1727–63, 1765–1913 **FRO**   Mf **DRO & NLW**

BT 1666–8, 1670–5, 1677–83, 1685–90, 1692, 1694–6, 1698–1700, 1702–13, 1718–23, 1726, 1728–43, 1745–1838 **NLW** 1841, 1845–50 **FRO** Mf 1666–1837 **FRO & DRO**
Cop ms PR CB 1727–84 M 1727–54 **NLW** PR CB 1727–1812 M 1727–1837 with index CFHS

CHWITFFORDD/WHITFORD *SA*
C 1643–1938 M 1656–1926 (Banns 1823–67) B 1662–1882 **FRO** Mf (excluding Banns) **DRO & NLW** Fac CMB 1742–78 **NLW**
BT 1664–5, 1673, 1675, 1677, 1681–3, 1687, 1691–2, 1695–6, 1698–1702, 1704–17, 1719–20, 1722, 1724–1837 **NLW** Mf 1734–1837 **FRO & DRO**
Cop PR CMB 1643–1812 with index CFHS

DISERTH/DYSERTH *SA*
C 1602–26, 1636, 1678–1702, 1705–1811, 1813–1974 M 1603–26, 1635–6, 1681–1702, 1706–54, 1756–1970 (Banns 1851–1974) B 1602–25, 1636–7, 1678–1702, 1705–1811, 1813–1935 **FRO** Mf (excluding Banns) **DRO & NLW**
BT 1671–2, 1681, 1683, 1687–90, 1692–4, 1696, 1698–1700, 1702–12, 1716–54, 1756, 1758–1815, 1817–24, 1828–30 **NLW** Mf **FRO & DRO**
Cop PR CMB 1602–1812 with index CFHS

EWLOE *SA*
<Hawarden 1938
M 1938–87 (Banns 1938–88) **FRO**

FENS CHAPEL gweler/see BRONINGTON

FFLINT, Y/FLINT *SA*
See also entries relating to Flint in early PR for Llaneurgain/Northop
C 1598–1685, 1707–1929 M 1598–1685, 1707–20, 1727–1955 (Banns 1823–1968) B 1598–1724, 1727–1900 **FRO** Mf (excluding Banns) **DRO & NLW**
BT 1662–3, 1670–1, 1673–4, 1676, 1678–96, 1698–1702, 1704–32, 1734–9, 1741–5, 1747–53, 1755–60, 1762–3, 1766–77, 1779–1837 **NLW** Mf 1663–1837 **FRO & DRO**
Cop PR (extracts) C 1599–1684 M 1607–79 B 1612–85 Henry Taylor, *Historic Notices ... of Flint* (London, 1883) PR CB 1598–1812 M 1598–1837 with index CFHS

FFYNNONGROYW *SA*
<Llanasa 1883
C 1884–1968 M 1884–1967 **FRO** Mf **DRO & NLW**

GARDEN CITY gweler/see SHOTTON

GORSEDD *SA*
<Chwitffordd/Whitford & Ysceifiog 1853
CB 1853– incumbent M 1854–1970 **FRO** Mf **DRO & NLW**

* GREENFIELD/MAES-GLAS   *SA*
<Treffynnon/Holywell 1871
M 1913–84 (Banns 1913–74) **FRO** B see Treffynnon/Holywell Mf M 1913–71 **DRO &**
NLW

GWAUNYSGOR/GWAENYSGOR   *SA*
C 1538–1760, 1768–1983 M 1538–1995 B 1538–1757, 1768–1990 **FRO** Mf C
1538–1983 M 1538–1970 B 1538–1990 **DRO & NLW**
BT 1664–7, 1670, 1672–7, 1680–3, 1687, 1689–92, 1694–6, 1703–4, 1706, 1708, 1712–17,
1719–38, 1740–3, 1745–9, 1751–4, 1757–97, 1799–1810, 1812–21, 1823–4, 1827–40,
1850 **NLW** Mf 1672–1850 **FRO & DRO**
Cop ts PR C 1714–60 M 1715–54 B 1713–57 **FRO & NLW** PR CMB 1538–1812 with
index CFHS

GWERNAFFIELD (WAUN)   *SA*
<Yr Wyddgrug/Mold 1844
C 1838–1988 M 1839–1988 (Banns 1880–1981) **FRO** B 1839– incumbent Mf C
1838–1988 M 1839–1988 **DRO & NLW**
BT 1838–43, 1850–1 **NLW** Mf **FRO & DRO**

* HALKYN/HELYGAIN   *SA*
C 1595–1706, 1720–1993 M 1595–1641, 1667–1706, 1720–1989 (Banns 1858–1980) B
1594–1643, 1666–1706, 1720–1911 **FRO** Mf (excluding Banns) **DRO & NLW**
BT 1667, 1670–1, 1673–9, 1681–90, 1693–4, 1698–1700, 1702–14, 1719–43, 1747–54,
1756–1850 **NLW** Mf 1670–1850 **FRO & DRO**
Cop PR & BT CB 1595–1840 M 1595–1837 with index CFHS

HANMER   *SA*
The following PRs were lost when the church was destroyed by fire in 1889: B 1784–1813
(replaced by copying burial entries in BTs), M 1787–1813, 1837–88, and B 1856–84
C 1563–1642, 1646–9, 1653–1960 M 1563–1642, 1646–9, 1653–1787, 1813–37 (Banns
1824–81, 1889–1934) B 1563–1642, 1646–9, 1653–1856, 1884–1935 **FRO** Mf
(excluding Banns) **DRO & NLW**
BT 1586, 1593, 1599, 1601, 1604–5, 1611, 1613–15, 1622–3, 1626–31, 1633–6, 1639–41,
1662, 1666, 1668–9, 1671–7, 1679–84, 1688–91, 1695–1735, 1737–43, 1745–6, 1748–71,
1773–1838 **Ches RO** 1850 **NLW** Mf 1586–1838 **FRO**
Cop ts PR (extracts) CB 1563–1850 M 1563–1749, 1813–50 ts PR M 1749–87 **Soc Gen**
PR CB 1563–1812 M 1563–1787 with index CFHS

* HAWARDEN/PENARLÂG   *SA*
C 1586–1960 RAF Sealand 1958–77 Mancot 1960–93 M 1586–1994 (Banns 1823–47,
1969–83) B 1586–1969 **FRO** Mf C 1586–1960 M 1586–1994 B 1586–1938 **DRO &**
NLW
BT 1755–1836, 1838–72 **FRO**
Cop ms PR C 1586–1763 M 1586–1754 B 1586–1766 **FRO** PR C 1585–1850 M
1585–1837 B 1585–1840 with index CFHS

HELYGAIN/HALKYN *SA*
C 1595–1706, 1720–1993 M 1595–1641, 1667–1706, 1720–1989 (Banns 1858–1980) B
1594–1643, 1666–1706, 1720–1911 **FRO** Mf (excluding Banns) **DRO & NLW**
BT 1667, 1670–1, 1673–9, 1681–90, 1693–4, 1698–1700, 1702–14, 1719–43, 1747–54,
1756–1850 **NLW** Mf 1670–1850 **FRO & DRO**
Cop PR & BT CB 1594–1840 M 1595–1837 with index CFHS

HIGHER KINNERTON *C*
<Dodleston, co Chester. PR 1570–1903 and BT 1584–1872 with gaps for Dodleston are in
Ches RO. Mf BT are in FRO
C 1868–1966 M 1894–1947 **Ches RO** B 1894– incumbent

HOB, YR/HOPE *SA*
C 1668–1904 M 1668–1907 (Banns 1825–93) B 1668–1943 **FRO** Mf (excluding Banns)
DRO & NLW
BT 1662–6, 1671–4, 1677–83, 1685, 1687, 1690, 1695–6, 1698–9, 1704–11, 1713,
1715–21, 1723–1847, 1851 **NLW** Mf **FRO & DRO**
Cop PR CMB 1668–1812 with index CFHS

* HOLYWELL/TREFFYNNON *SA*
C 1677–1995 M 1677–1997 (Banns 1823–1984) B 1677–1978 **FRO** Mf C 1677–1968 M
1677–1978 B 1677–1978 **DRO & NLW**
BT 1667, 1671–80, 1682, 1685–8, 1690, 1694–6, 1698–1700, 1702–5, 1721–5, 1728–66,
1770–1866 **NLW** Mf **FRO & DRO**
Cop ts PR C 1728–37 B 1718–23 **Soc Gen** PR C 1677–1840 M 1677–1812 B
1677–1841 with index CFHS

HOPE gweler/see HOB, YR

IS-COED/ISCOYD Whitewell church *C*
<Malpas, co Chester, 1880. BT 1584–1893 with gaps, and Mf of PR 1561–1949 for Malpas
are in Ches RO. Mf BT are in FRO
CB 1885– M 1886– incumbent

KINNERTON, HIGHER gweler/see HIGHER KINNERTON

LACHE-CUM-SALTNEY *C*
<Chester St Mary, co Chester, & Penarlâg/Hawarden, co Flint, 1855
C 1853–1964 M 1857–1972 Saltney Ferry 1925–55 **Ches RO**
BT 1873–98 **Ches RO** Mf **FRO**

LLANASA *SA*
C 1629–1863 M 1629–1882 (Banns 1823–1904) B 1629–1890 **FRO** Mf (excluding Banns)
DRO & NLW
BT 1663–5, 1667–8, 1670–3, 1675, 1677, 1679–1700, 1702–5, 1707–31, 1733–45,

1747–1837 **NLW** Mf 1670–1837 **FRO & DRO**
Cop PR CMB 1629–1812 with index CFHS

LLANELWY/ST ASAPH   *SA*
Included townships of Meiriadog/Meriadog & Wicwer/Wigfair, co Denbigh, which became
the parish of Cefn 1865. PR M include marriages in the cathedral. C 1864– and B 1859–
are in the cathedral
C 1593–1668, 1677–1971 H M Stanley Hospital 1949–93 M 1603–68, 1671–1983 (Banns
1932–78) B 1594–1668, 1671–1952 **FRO** Mf (excluding Banns) **DRO & NLW** Fac C
1593–1668 M 1603–68 B 1594–1868 **NLW**
BT 1667–8, 1672–7, 1680, 1682, 1686, 1690, 1696, 1704–18, 1722–9, 1731–1836 **NLW**
Mf **FRO & DRO**
Cop PR CMB 1593–1812 with index CFHS

LLANEURGAIN/NORTHOP   *SA*
C 1590–1980 M 1590–1993 (Banns 1823–1977) M Northophall 1986–91 B 1590–1957
FRO Mf C 1590–1980 M 1590–1982 B 1590–1957 **DRO & NLW**
BT 1662–4, 1666–7, 1670–3, 1675–92, 1696, 1698–1706, 1708–23, 1725–6, 1728–1809,
1811–52 **NLW** Mf 1791–1852 **FRO & DRO**
Cop PR CMB 1590–1812 with index CFHS

LLANFYNYDD   *SA*
<Yr Hob/Hope 1845. PR MB 1843–92 destroyed in church fire 1892
C 1843–1914 M 1893–1997 **FRO** B 1893– incumbent Mf C 1843–1914 M 1893–1970
DRO & NLW

LLANNERCH BANNA/PENLEY   *SA*
<Ellesmere, co Salop, 1869. PR C 1813–73 recorded in 1936 apparently lost. PR for
Ellesmere C 1654–1891 M 1654–1940 B 1654–1898 are in SRR, and BT 1630–1880
with gaps in Lichfield RO
C 1657–61 B 1659–60 Private hands Fac **FRO** C 1752–1812, 1873–1968 M 1753,
1867–1970 B 1753–1923 **FRO** Mf **DRO & NLW**
BT 1663, 1752–1896 **Lichfield RO** Fac C 1813–64 **FRO**
Cop ts PR C 1752–1812 M 1753 B 1753–1812 & BT C 1813–64 with index **FRO &
SRR** PR & BT C 1657–61, 1752–1864 M 1753 B 1659–60, 1753–1812 with index
CFHS

MAES-GLAS/GREENFIELD   *SA*
<Treffynnon/Holywell 1871
M 1913–84 (Banns 1913–74) **FRO** B see Treffynnon/Holywell Mf M 1913–71 **DRO &
NLW**

MANCOT gweler/see PENARLÂG/HAWARDEN

MARFORD & HOSELEY
Flintshire townships in Gresffordd/Gresford, co Denbigh. From 1840 in parish of Yr
Orsedd/Rossett, co Denbigh

* MELIDEN/ALLT MELYD   SA
   C 1602–26, 1685–7, 1690–1734, 1741–1973 M 1603–26, 1687, 1692–1734, 1742–1982
   (Banns 1824–91, 1893–1983) B 1602–26, 1686–7, 1690–1734, 1741–1996 **FRO** Mf C
   1602–1973 M 1603–1982 B 1602–1960 **DRO & NLW**
   BT 1668, 1672–3, 1677, 1679, 1681, 1683, 1686, 1692, 1698–1700, 1703–39, 1741–1834,
   1851 **NLW** Mf 1673–1851 **FRO & DRO**
   Cop PR CB 1602–19 M 1603–17 *Northern Flintshire,* 1 (1913) ts PR/BT CB 1602–1718
   M 1603–1718 **NLW** Cop PR CMB 1602–1812 with index CFHS

* MOLD/YR WYDDGRUG   SA
   C 1612–1973 St John 1880–1947 M 1604–5, 1614–1985 (Banns 1843–74, 1907–51,
   1964–91) St John 1886–1946 B 1612–1988 **FRO** Mf (excluding Banns) **DRO & NLW**
   BT 1664–9, 1672–82, 1684–7, 1689–90, 1693–6, 1698–1701, 1703–26, 1728–49, 1751–4,
   1756–1856 **NLW** Mf 1678–1856 **FRO & DRO**
   Cop PR CMB 1604–1812 with index CFHS

  MOSTYN   SA
  <Chwitffordd/Whitford 1844
  C 1846–1916 M 1845–1948 B 1845–1907 **FRO** Mf **DRO & NLW**

  NANNERCH   SA
  Included township of Penbedw, co Denbigh
  C 1664–1892 M 1664–1970 B 1664–1889 **NLW** Mf/Fac **FRO** Mf **DRO**
  BT 1667–8, 1670–3, 1679–87, 1699, 1707–8, 1710–15, 1717–59, 1761, 1763, 1765–1851
    NLW Mf 1672–1851 **FRO & DRO**
  Cop PR CMB 1664–1812 with index CFHS

  NERCWYS (NERQUIS)   SA
  <Yr Wyddgrug/Mold
  C 1665–1724, 1732–1960 M 1669–1724, 1732–1970 B 1669–1724, 1732–1856 **FRO** Mf
    DRO & NLW
  BT 1670–3, 1676–84, 1687–9, 1691–3, 1695, 1697–8, 1700–8, 1710–92, 1794–1846,
    1848–51 **NLW** Mf **FRO & DRO**
  Cop PR CMB 1665–1812 with index CFHS

  NEWMARKET gweler/see TRELAWNYD

* NORTHOP/LLANEURGAIN   SA
   C 1590–1980 M 1590–1993 (Banns 1823–1977) M Northophall 1986–91 B 1590–1957
    FRO Mf C 1590–1980 M 1590–1982 B 1590–1957 **DRO & NLW**
   BT 1662–4, 1666–7, 1670–3, 1675–92, 1696, 1698–1706, 1708–23, 1725–6, 1728–1809,
    1811–52 **NLW** Mf 1791–1852 **FRO & DRO**

Cop PR CMB 1590–1812 with index CFHS

OWRTYN/OVERTON   *SA*
<Bangor 1868
C 1602–39, 1654–1723, 1727–1859 M 1602–44, 1654–1724, 1727–1934 B 1602–51,
1654–1957 **FRO** Mf **DRO & NLW**
BT 1604, 1615, 1617, 1620, 1623–9, 1633, 1635, 1639, 1666–9, 1671, 1674–7, 1680–5,
1688–91, 1694–1700, 1702–3, 1705, 1707–23, 1725–37, 1739–1838 **Ches RO** Mf **FRO**
Cop ms PR (extracts) CM 1721–80 B 1681–1780 **NLW** PR CMB 1602–1812 with index
CFHS

PENARLÂG/HAWARDEN   *SA*
C 1586–1960 RAF Sealand 1958–77 Mancot 1960–93 M 1586–1994 (Banns 1823–47,
1969–83) B 1586–1969 **FRO** Mf C 1586–1960 M 1586–1994 B 1586–1938 **DRO &
NLW**
BT 1755–1836, 1838–72 **FRO**
Cop ms PR C 1586–1763 M 1586–1754 B 1586–1766 **FRO** PR C 1585–1850 M
1585–1837 B 1585–1840 with index CFHS

★ PENLEY/LLANNERCH BANNA   *SA*
<Ellesmere, co Salop, 1869. PR C 1813–73 recorded in 1936 apparently lost. PR for
Ellesmere C 1654–1891 M 1654–1940 B 1654–1898 are in SRR, and BT 1630–1880
with gaps in Lichfield RO
C 1657–61 B 1659–60 Private hands Fac **FRO** C 1752–1812, 1873–1968 M 1753,
1867–1970 B 1753–1923 **FRO** Mf **DRO & NLW**
BT 1663, 1752–1896 **Lichfield RO** Fac C 1813–64 **FRO**
Cop ts PR C 1752–1812 M 1753 B 1753–1812 & BT C 1813–64 with index **FRO &
SRR** PR & BT C 1657–61, 1752–1864 M 1753 B 1659–60, 1753–1812 with index
CFHS

PENTROBIN (PENYMYNYDD)   *SA*
<Penarlâg/Hawarden 1843
C 1843–1902 M 1881–1983 **FRO** B 1843– incumbent Mf B 1843–1983 **FRO** Mf C
1843–1902 M 1881–1983 B 1843–1983 **DRO & NLW**
BT 1843–72 **FRO**

PONTBLYDDYN   *SA*
<Yr Wyddgrug/Mold 1836
C 1836–1965 M 1839–1971 B 1836–1946 **FRO** Mf C 1836–1965 M 1839–1948 B
1836–1946 **DRO & NLW**
BT 1836–8, 1840–3, 1851 **NLW** Mf 1836–43 **FRO & DRO**

PRESTATYN   *SA*
<Allt Melyd/Meliden & Llanasa 1860
C 1861–1949 M 1863–1971 (Banns 1863–1971) B 1864–1950 **FRO** Mf (excluding Banns)
DRO & NLW

RHES-Y-CAE   *SA*
<Helygain/Halkyn, Cilcain & Ysgeifiog/Ysceifiog 1848
C 1849–1993 M 1865–1971 B 1849–1992 **FRO** Mf **DRO & NLW**

RHOSESMOR (CAERFALLWCH)   *SA*
<Llaneurgain/Northop 1876
C 1876–1975 M 1877–1971 (Banns 1901–67) B 1876–1951 **FRO** Mf (excluding Banns)
DRO & NLW

RHUDDLAN   *SA*
C 1681–1748, 1759–1918 M 1682–1748, 1754–1940 (Banns 1824–1954) B 1681–1748,
1759–1934 **FRO** Mf (excluding Banns) **DRO & NLW**
BT 1681–2, 1684, 1686–7, 1689–92, 1694–6, 1698–1718, 1720–6, 1728–56, 1759–1834
NLW Mf **FRO & DRO**
Cop ts PR (extracts) C 1681–1717 M 1686–1712 B 1681–1742 **Soc Gen** PR CB
1681–1812 M 1682–1837 with index CFHS

RHYD-Y-MWYN   *SA*
<Cilcain, Helygain/Halkyn, Yr Wyddgrug/Mold & Llaneurgain/Northop 1865
C 1864–1978 M 1866–1970 B 1863–1977 **FRO** Mf **DRO & NLW**

RHYL, Y/RHYL   *SA*
<Rhuddlan 1835
C 1841–1948 M Holy Trinity 1844–1970 (Banns 1892–1977) St Thomas 1889–1982
(Banns 1899–1926, 1950–75) St Ann 1909–79 (Banns 1928–69) St John 1937–74 (Banns
1937–95) B 1859–1965 **FRO** Mf C 1841–1921 M Holy Trinity 1844–1963 St Thomas
1889–1924 St Ann 1909–27 B 1859–1965 **DRO & NLW**

* ST ASAPH/LLANELWY   *SA*
Included townships of Meiriadog/Meriadog & Wicwer/Wigfair, co Denbigh, which became
the parish of Cefn 1865. PR M include marriages in the cathedral. C 1864– and B 1859–
are in the cathedral
C 1593–1668, 1677–1971 H M Stanley Hospital 1949–93 M 1603–68, 1671–1983 (Banns
1932–78) B 1594–1668, 1671–1952 **FRO** Mf (excluding Banns) **DRO & NLW** Fac C
1593–1668 M 1603–68 B 1594–1868 **NLW**
BT 1667–8, 1672–7, 1680, 1682, 1686, 1690, 1696, 1704–18, 1722–9, 1731–1836 **NLW**
Mf **FRO & DRO**
Cop PR CMB 1593–1812 with index CFHS

SALTNEY gweler/see LACHE-CUM-SALTNEY

SANDYCROFT   *SA*
<Penarlâg/Hawarden 1913
C 1913–52 **FRO** Mf **DRO & NLW** M 1935– incumbent

SEALAND   *SA*
<Penarlâg/Hawarden 1867. For PR RAF Sealand gweler/see Penarlâg/Hawarden
C 1867–1948 M 1868–1990 (Banns 1868–1992) **FRO**
BT 1867–72 **FRO**

SHOTTON   *SA*
<Penarlâg/Hawarden 1902
C 1902–80 M 1902–92 (Banns 1968–81) Garden City 1964–84 **FRO** Mf (excluding
Banns) **DRO & NLW**

THREAPWOOD   *C*
<Worthenbury, co Flint, & Malpas, co Chester, 1817. Formerly an extra-parochial place.
The Flintshire part of the parish was transferred to Cheshire in 1896
C 1817–1944 M 1837– B 1829– incumbent
BT 1817–40 **Ches RO** Mf **FRO**

TREFFYNNON/HOLYWELL   *SA*
C 1677–1995 M 1677–1997 (Banns 1823–1984) B 1677–1978 **FRO** Mf C 1677–1968 M
1677–1978 B 1677–1978 **DRO & NLW**
BT 1667, 1671–80, 1682, 1685–8, 1690, 1694–6, 1698–1700, 1702–5, 1721–5, 1728–66,
1770–1866 **NLW** Mf **FRO & DRO**
Cop ts PR C 1728–37 B 1718–23 **Soc Gen** PR C 1677–1840 M 1677–1812 B
1677–1841 with index CFHS

TRELAWNYD (NEWMARKET)   *SA*
C 1696–1719, 1752–1909 M 1699–1719, 1752–1970 (Banns 1824–1934) B 1696–1719,
1752–1904 **FRO** Mf (excluding Banns) **DRO & NLW**
BT 1663, 1670, 1672–5, 1677–84, 1687, 1694, 1696, 1698–1703, 1707–8, 1710, 1712–18,
1720–43, 1745–62, 1764–1812, 1814–24, 1827–40, 1858 **NLW** Mf **FRO & DRO**
Cop PR C 1696–1713 M 1699–1713 B 1696–1714 *Northern Flintshire*, 1 (1913) ms PR C
1752–1909 M 1752–1910 B 1752–1912 **NLW** PR C 1700–1812 M 1700–1836 B
1699–1812 with index CFHS

TREMEIRCHION   *SA*
C 1599–1992 M 1599–1988 (Banns 1824–1929) B 1599–1966 **FRO** Mf (excluding Banns)
DRO & NLW Fac CB 1599–1810 M 1599–1753 **NLW**
BT 1665–8, 1670–4, 1677–84, 1686–91, 1693, 1695–6, 1698–1713, 1715–17, 1719–1839
NLW Mf 1665–1835 **FRO & DRO**
Cop ts PR C 1604–1758 M 1604–1753 B 1604–1760 **Soc Gen** PR CMB 1599–1812
with index CFHS

TREUDDYN   *SA*
<Yr Wyddgrug/Mold
C 1611–92, 1695–1728, 1732–1923 M 1618–92, 1696–1727, 1732–1908 (Banns 1824–99)
  B 1613–92, 1695–1728, 1732–1857 **FRO** Mf (excluding Banns) **DRO & NLW**
BT 1667, 1670–4, 1676–89, 1691, 1693–6, 1699, 1701–8, 1710–19, 1721–1834, 1838–50
  NLW Mf 1672–1834 **FRO & DRO**
Cop PR CMB 1611–1812 with index CFHS

WAUN gweler/see GWERNAFFIELD

WHITEWELL gweler/see IS-COED/ISCOYD

★ WHITFORD/CHWITFFORDD   *SA*
  C 1643–1938 M 1656–1926 (Banns 1823–67) B 1662–1882 **FRO** Mf (excluding Banns)
  DRO & NLW Fac CMB 1742–78 **NLW**
  BT 1664–5, 1673, 1675, 1677, 1681–3, 1687, 1691–2, 1695–6, 1698–1702, 1704–17,
  1719–20, 1722, 1724–1837 **NLW** Mf 1734–1837 **FRO & DRO**
  Cop PR CMB 1643–1812 with index CFHS

WORTHENBURY   *SA*
<Bangor 1689
C 1597–1749, 1755–1936 M 1598–1749, 1754–1970 B 1597–1749, 1755–1939 **FRO** Mf
  DRO & NLW
BT 1599, ?1600, 1601, 1603–5, 1611, 1613–15, 1618–19, 1622–9, 1631, 1633–5, 1639,
  1662, 1664, 1666–72, 1674, 1676–7, 1679–85, 1688–91, 1695–1700, 1702–14, 1718–35,
  1737–46, 1754, 1756–69, 1771–94, 1796–1815, 1817–42, 1844–8 **Ches RO** 1850–9,
  1861–70, 1873–4, 1876 **NLW** Mf 1599–1806 **FRO** 1850–9, 1861–70, 1873–4, 1876
  FRO & DRO
Cop PR C 1597–1813 M 1598–1820 B 1597–1812 with index CFHS

WYDDGRUG, YR/MOLD   *SA*
C 1612–1973 St John 1880–1947 M 1604–5, 1614–1985 (Banns 1843–74, 1907–51,
  1964–91) St John 1886–1946 B 1612–1988 **FRO** Mf (excluding Banns) **DRO & NLW**
BT 1664–9, 1672–82, 1684–7, 1689–90, 1693–6, 1698–1701, 1703–26, 1728–49, 1751–4,
  1756–1856 **NLW** Mf 1678–1856 **FRO & DRO**
Cop PR CMB 1604–1812 with index CFHS

YSGEIFIOG/YSCEIFIOG   *SA*
C 1662–1996 M 1662–1960 (Banns 1823–1905, 1914–17) B 1662–1910 **FRO** Mf
  (excluding Banns) **DRO & NLW**
BT 1666–8, 1670–9, 1681–92, 1694–6, 1699–1712, 1714–15, 1717–18, 1720–36,
  1739–1841 **NLW**
Cop PR CMB 1662–1812 with index CFHS

MAESYFED
RADNORSHIRE

NANTMEL Eglwysi cyn 1813/Pre-1813 churches
Evancoyd Eglwysi wedi 1813/Post-1813 churches

0   5   10 Milltiroedd/Miles

ABATY CWM-HIR/ABBEY CWMHIR   *SB*
An ancient chapel of ease with CMB before 1831 entered in PR Llanbister
C 1831–1981 M 1831–1971 (Banns 1833–1960) B 1831–1978 **NLW** Mf **PCAO**
BT 1831–7, 1841–3, 1864–7 **NLW**

ABEREDW   *SB*
PR C 1690–1719 M 1700–19 B 1695–1719 recorded in 1831 apparently lost
C 1740–1991 M 1740–1971 (Banns 1813–1953) B 1740–1992 **NLW** Mf **PCAO**
BT 1687, 1706–7, 1710, 1713–35, 1737–9, 1742–7, 1749, 1751–4, 1756–8, 1760–95,
    1797–1810, 1813–34, 1836–43 **NLW**
Cop ms PR C 1740–1900 M 1740–1968 B 1740–1901 ms BT CMB 1687, 1701–8,
    1713–21 **Soc Gen**

BEGUILDY gweler/see BUGEILDY   *SB*

BETWS CLEIRWY/BETWS CLYRO   *SB*
An ancient chapelry with CMB entered in PR Cleirwy/Clyro

BETWS DISERTH   *SB*
C 1731–1980 M 1731–52, 1755–1839, 1964 (Banns 1824–1956) B 1731–1958 **NLW**
    Mf/Fac (except M 1964) **PCAO**
BT 1687, 1707, 1714–18, 1720–47, 1749–84, 1786–95, 1797–1809, 1813–38, 1840–4,
    1846, 1865–7 **NLW**

BLEDDFA   *SB*
C 1603–86, 1719–95, 1801–1986 M 1603–86, 1719–54, 1775–95, 1813–1971 (Banns
    1824–1983) B 1603–86, 1719–95, 1801–1984 **NLW** Mf **PCAO**
BT 1701, 1707, 1710, 1714–23, 1726–95, 1797–1809, 1813–14, 1816–41, 1843, 1864–7
    NLW

BOCHRWD/BOUGHROOD   *SB*
C 1689–1709, 1711–1979 M 1695–1708, 1711–1971 (Banns 1824–70) B 1689–1709,
    1711–19, 1729–1973 **NLW** Mf **PCAO**
BT 1687, 1701, 1713–20, 1723, 1725–95, 1797–1809, 1813–35, 1838–40, 1845–7 **NLW**

BRYN-GWYN   *SB*
PR M 1798–1812 recorded in 1900 inventory apparently lost
C 1614–29, 1632–4, 1664–73, 1687–92, 1715–19, 1721–2, 1725–76, 1782–1982 M
    1614–29, 1632–4, 1664–73, 1687–92, 1715–19, 1721–2, 1725–98, 1813–1971 (Banns
    1824–1981) B 1614–29, 1632–4, 1664–73, 1687–92, 1715–19, 1721–2, 1725–76,
    1782–1981 **NLW** Mf **PCAO**
BT 1687, 1707, 1713–17, 1719–95, 1797–1809, 1813–46, 1849–52 **NLW**

BUGEILDY/BEGUILDY   *SB*
C 1703–1986 M 1703–1983 (Banns 1850–1934) B 1703–1959 **NLW** Mf **PCAO**
BT 1701, 1706–7, 1710, 1713–34, 1736–95, 1797–1809, 1813–39, 1841–4 **NLW**

CASGOB/CASCOB   *SB*
PR 1624–67 recorded in 1831 apparently lost
C 1678–1985   M 1678–1812, 1815–35, 1837–1900, 1905–71 (Banns 1824–1912)   B
  1678–1986 **NLW** Mf **PCAO**
BT 1701, 1707–10, 1713–21, 1723–51, 1753–78, 1780–94, 1796–1809, 1813–53 **NLW**

CEFN-LLYS   *SB*
C 1671–1901   M 1671–1812, 1815–1971 (Banns 1824–1901)   B 1671–1947 **NLW**   Mf C
  1671–1901   M 1671–1812, 1815–1954   B 1671–1947 **PCAO**
BT 1701, 1708, 1713–25, 1727–77, 1779–1809, 1813–39, 1842–3, 1864–7, 1869 **NLW**
Cop ts PR M 1815–47 **PCAO**

CLAS-AR-WY, Y/GLASBURY All Saints   *SB*
<Y Clas-ar-Wy/Glasbury St Peter 1882 (see under Brycheiniog/Brecknockshire). It has no
separate register of burials
C 1882–1989   M 1883–1971 **NLW** Mf **PCAO**

CLEIRWY/CLYRO   *SB*
Earliest PR includes C (& births) 1667–87 of one family
C 1688–1988   M 1688–1971   B 1688–1989 **NLW**   Mf C 1688–1988   M 1688–1920   B
  1688–1989 **PCAO**
BT 1714–18, 1720–1, 1724–6, 1728–36, 1738–47, 1749–95, 1797–1809, 1813–65, 1867–72
  NLW

COLFA/COLVA   *SB*
PR CB 1797–1812 recorded in 1831 apparently lost
C 1663–1794, 1813–1988   M 1663–1753, 1756–1811, 1813–1971 (Banns 1825–44)   B
  1663–1794, 1813–1991 **NLW** Mf **PCAO**
BT 1687, 1690, 1705, 1707, 1713–63, 1765–83, 1785–1806, 1808–9, 1813–38, 1840–50
  NLW

CREGRINA (CRAIG FURUNA)   *SB*
Diocesan records suggest that *c*1790 this parish had registers going back to 1647
C 1685–1729, 1754–1989   M 1685–1729, 1754–1836, 1841–1971 (Banns 1824–1990)   B
  1685–1729, 1754–1991 **NLW** Mf **PCAO**
BT 1713–14, 1716–45, 1748–58, 1760–6, 1768–70, 1772–95, 1797–1809, 1813–48 **NLW**
Cop ts PR CB 1754–1812 M 1754–1967 **PCAO**

CWM-BACH LLECHRYD   *SB*
<Diserth 1886–7
C 1886–1997   M 1888–1997   B 1887–1992 **NLW** Mf M 1888–1971   B 1887–1992 **PCAO**

CWMTEUDDWR gweler/see LLANSANFFRAID CWMTEUDDWR

DISERTH   *SB*
Pre-1734 registers destroyed by fire (1831 survey)
C 1734–1991 M 1734–1839 (Banns 1789–1816, 1823–86) B 1734–1915 **NLW** Mf
  PCAO
BT 1687, 1701, 1715–26, 1728–1809, 1813–38, 1840–4, 1846, 1865–7 **NLW**
Cop ts PR CB 1734–1812 M 1734–56 **NLW & Soc Gen**

DISGOED/DISCOED   *H*
A chapelry in the parish of Llanandras/Presteigne. CB 1805–12 entered in PR
  Llanandras/Presteigne
C 1680–1805 M 1680–1811, 1814–1933 (Banns 1755–1811, 1822–1951) B 1680–1805
  HRO Mf **PCAO**
BT 1662–70, 1672, 1674–99, 1701–43, 1745–1804, 1812–17, 1819–34, 1836–8, 1840,
  1842–4, 1846–9, 1851–1861 **HRO** Mf **PCAO**

EGLWYS NEWYDD, YR/NEWCHURCH   *SB*
PR M 1814–35 recorded in 1900 inventory apparently lost
C 1708–1981 M 1708–48, 1755–1811, 1837–1971 (Banns 1825–1981) B 1708–1981 **NLW**
  Mf **PCAO**
BT 1701, 1708, 1712–26, 1728–63, 1765–83, 1785–97, 1799–1806, 1808–9, 1813–16,
  1818–53 **NLW**

EVANCOYD   *SB*
<Pencraig/Old Radnor 1866
C 1867–1992 M 1872–1971 (Banns 1872–1991) B 1871–1991 **NLW** Mf **PCAO**

* GLADESTRY/LLANFAIR LLYTHYFNWG   *SB*
C 1683–1946 M 1683–1971 B 1683–1929 **NLW** Mf **PCAO**
BT 1687, 1713–57, 1759–95, 1797–1809, 1813, 1815, 1822–32, 1834–9, 1841–7, 1849–52
  NLW

* GLASBURY/Y CLAS-AR-WY All Saints   *SB*
<Y Clas-ar-Wy/Glasbury St Peter 1882 (see under Brycheiniog/Brecknockshire). It has no
  separate register of burials
C 1882–1989 M 1883–1971 **NLW** Mf **PCAO**

GLASGWM   *SB*
C 1679–1797, 1813–1992 M 1679–1971 B 1679–1797, 1813–1991 **NLW** Mf **PCAO**
BT 1687, 1690, 1704–7, 1709, 1713–21, 1723–76, 1778–83, 1785–8, 1790–5, 1797–1806,
  1808–9, 1813–45 **NLW**

* HEYOPE/LLANDDEWI-YN-HEIOB   *SB*
PR CMB 1711–33 recorded in 1831 apparently lost
C 1679–1711, 1733–97, 1805–11, 1813–1986 M 1679–1711, 1733–69, 1781–1835,
  1838–1959, 1962–71 (Banns 1824–1987) B 1679–1711, 1733–97, 1805–11, 1813–1986
  NLW Mf **PCAO**

BT 1687, 1701, 1708, 1710, 1714–19, 1721–95, 1797–1809, 1813–36, 1839–40, 1842–6, 1848–53 **NLW**

* KNIGHTON/TREFYCLAWDD *SB*
C 1599–1964 M 1599–1971 (Banns 1946–78) B 1599–1959 **NLW** Mf **PCAO**
BT 1662–1833, 1836, 1838–46 **HRO** Mf **PCAO**

LLANANDRAS/PRESTEIGNE *H*
Included several townships in co Hereford
C 1561–1912 M 1561–1922 (Banns 1824–1948) B 1561–1904 **HRO** Mf **PCAO**
BT 1659–99, 1701–43, 1745–1833, 1836–56, 1880–1 **HRO** Mf 1659–1856 **PCAO**

LLANANNO *SB*
C 1721–1987 M 1721–1971 (Banns 1824–1941) B 1721–1983 **NLW** Mf **PCAO**
BT 1687, 1701, 1705–8, 1710, 1713–29, 1731–65, 1767–83, 1785–9, 1791–1809, 1813–14, 1817–47 **NLW**
Cop ts index PR C 1813–37 M 1721–1871 B 1813–50 **NLW & PCAO**

LLANBADARN FAWR *SB*
C 1696–1778, 1781–1911 M 1696–1795, 1797–1971 B 1696–1778, 1781–1919 **NLW** Mf
  C 1696–1778, 1781–1911 M 1696–1795, 1797–1928 B 1696–1778, 1781–1919 **PCAO**
BT 1701, 1705–8, 1713, 1715–71, 1773–95, 1797–1809, 1813–18, 1823–49, 1864–5 **NLW**
Cop ts PR M 1717–1928 **PCAO**

LLANBADARN FYNYDD *SB*
C 1678–1709, 1721–1997 M 1678–1709, 1721–1971 (Banns 1831–1939) B 1678–1709, 1721–1958 **NLW** Mf C 1678–1709, 1721–1892 M 1678–1709, 1721–1971 (Banns 1831–1939) B 1678–1709, 1721–1958 **PCAO**
BT 1687, 1707–8, 1710–11, 1713, 1715–65, 1767–95, 1797–1809, 1813–14, 1816–48 **NLW**
Cop ts PR C 1813–37 M 1678–1870 B 1813–70 with index **NLW & PCAO**

LLANBADARN GARREG/LLANBADARN-Y-GARREG *SB*
Earliest PR includes C 1732–51 of one family
C 1750–1992 M 1750–5, 1779, 1783–1812, 1814–34, 1839–1971 B 1750–1812, 1814–1991 **NLW** Mf **PCAO**
BT 1704, 1713–19, 1721–55, 1757–66, 1769, 1773, 1775, 1777–1809, 1813–38, 1840–8 **NLW**

LLANBEDR CASTELL-PAEN/LLANBEDR PAINSCASTLE *SB*
C 1726–1981 M 1726–1971 (Banns 1836–1980) B 1726–1980 **NLW** Mf **PCAO**
BT 1687, 1707, 1709–10, ?1713, 1714–18, 1721–33, 1736–44, 1746–95, 1797–1809, 1813–50 **NLW**

LLANBISTER *SB*
PR CMB 1682–1704 recorded in 1831 apparently lost
C 1705–1964 M 1705–1971 (Banns 1854–1901) B 1705–1994 **NLW** Mf C 1705–1964 M

1705–1971 (Banns 1854–1901) B 1705–1812 **PCAO**
BT 1705–8, 1710, 1713–95, 1797–1809, 1813–37, 1840 **NLW** Mf 1785–1840 **Soc Gen**
Cop ts PR CMB 1687–98 **NLW** ts PR index C 1813–37 M 1704–1871 **NLW & PCAO**

LLANDEGLAU/LLANDEGLEY   *SB*
Diocesan records suggest that *c*1790 this parish had registers going back to 1672
C 1727–1914 M 1727–1971 B 1727–1990 **NLW** Mf **PCAO**
BT 1706, 1713–16, 1718, 1720–32, 1734–62, 1765–1805, 1807–9, 1813–59, 1868 **NLW**

LLANDEILO GRABAN   *SB*
PR CMB 1660–1812 recorded in 1935 apparently lost
C 1813–1992 M 1813–1971 B 1813–1992 **NLW** Mf M 1813–1971 **PCAO**
BT 1687, 1706, 1708, 1714–19, 1721–8, 1730–95, 1797–1805, 1807–9, 1813–42, 1844,
   1846–53 **NLW**

LLANDRINDOD   *SB*
C 1734–1901 M 1734–1971 B 1734–1947 **NLW** Mf **PCAO**
BT 1701, 1707, 1714–18, 1720–3, 1725–6, 1728–30, 1732, 1734–43, 1745–95, 1797–1809,
   1813–38, 1840–1, 1843, 1864–7, 1869–70 **NLW**

LLANDDEWI FACH   *SB*
C 1775–1981 M 1754–1971 (Banns 1829–1900, 1980) B 1775–1960 **NLW** Mf **PCAO**
BT 1687, 1713–21, 1724–33, 1735–63, 1765–95, 1797–1809, 1813–17, 1819–35, 1837–41
   NLW

LLANDDEWI-YN-HEIOB/HEYOPE   *SB*
PR CMB 1711–33 recorded in 1831 apparently lost
C 1679–1711, 1733–97, 1805–11, 1813–1986 M 1679–1711, 1733–69, 1781–1835,
   1838–1959, 1962–71 (Banns 1824–1987) B 1679–1711, 1733–97, 1805–11, 1813–1986
   NLW Mf **PCAO**
BT 1687, 1701, 1708, 1710, 1714–19, 1721–95, 1797–1809, 1813–36, 1839–40, 1842–6,
   1848–53 **NLW**

LLANDDEWI-YN-HWYTYN/WHITTON   *SB*
C 1600–22, 1625–1986 M 1600–22, 1625–1971 (Banns 1824–1986) B 1600–22,
   1625–1986 **NLW** Mf (except Banns) **PCAO**
BT 1687, 1690, 1706–8, 1715–33, 1735–70, 1772–95, 1797–1809, 1813–14, 1816–18,
   1820–41 **NLW**

LLANDDEWI YSTRADENNI   *SB*
C 1732–51, 1758–1946 M 1732–51, 1754–1971 (Banns 1826–1957) B 1732–51,
   1758–1981 **NLW** Mf **PCAO**
BT 1690–1, 1705–8, 1713–27, 1729–54, 1756–95, 1797–1805, 1807–9, 1813–37, 1839–51,
   1855–9 **NLW**
Cop ts PR CMB 1732–91 **PCAO**

LLANELWEDD   *SB*
C 1773–1981 M 1796–1971 B 1773–1982 **NLW** Mf **PCAO**
BT 1714, 1717–25, 1727–9, 1731–62, 1764–7, 1769–95, 1797–1805, 1807–9, 1813–16,
1818, 1820–3, 1825–7, 1829–55, 1867–71 **NLW**

LLANFAIR LLYTHYFNWG/GLADESTRY   *SB*
C 1683–1946 M 1683–1971 B 1683–1929 **NLW** Mf **PCAO**
BT 1687, 1713–57, 1759–95, 1797–1809, 1813, 1815, 1822–32, 1834–9, 1841–7, 1849–52
NLW

LLANFAREDD   *SB*
C 1698–1713, 1730–1984 M 1698–1713, 1730–1971 B 1698–1713, 1730–1979 **NLW** Mf
  C 1698–1713, 1730–1984 M 1698–1713, 1730–1960 B 1698–1713, 1730–1979 **PCAO**
BT 1706–8, 1713–15, 1717–18, 1720–54, 1756–8, 1760–95, 1797–1809, 1813–36, 1838–43
NLW

LLANFIHANGEL DYFFRYN ARWY/MICHAELCHURCH-ON-ARROW   *H*
C 1741–1988 M 1741–1811, 1813–1964 B 1741–1993 **HRO** Mf CB 1741–1812 M
1741–1964 **PCAO**
BT 1662–7, 1669–1743, 1745–1833, 1836–41, 1849–52 **HRO** Mf **PCAO**

LLANFIHANGEL HELYGEN   *SB*
A note in BT Llanllŷr/Llanyre 1713 says that 'there was no register ever kept at
Llanvyhangell it being no burial place but what there happens is inserted in the registers of
Nantmell and Llanyre'
C 1732–78 with gaps, 1781–99, 1806–1991 M 1737, 1755–96, 1805–10, 1814–34,
1841–1971 B 1811, 1828–1990 **NLW** Mf C 1732–78 with gaps, 1781–99, 1806–1991 M
1737, 1755–96, 1805–10, 1814–34 B 1811, 1828–1990 **PCAO**
BT 1736, 1784–8, 1790, 1792–8, 1801–8, 1814–15, 1817, 1821, 1823–37, 1839–45 **NLW**
Cop ts PR C 1736–1990 M 1736–1834 B 1736–1828 **PCAO**

LLANFIHANGEL NANT MELAN   *SB*
C 1700–1929 M 1700–1809, 1813–1971 (Banns 1823–39, 1888–1975) B 1700–1991 **NLW**
Mf **PCAO**
BT 1705–7, 1709, 1713–18, 1720–70, 1772–95, 1797–1809, 1813–19, 1821–3, 1825–33,
1836, 1838–41, 1843–64, 1866–7, 1871–2 **NLW**

LLANFIHANGEL RHYDIEITHON/LLANFIHANGEL RHYDITHON   *SB*
C 1725, 1732–47, 1749–55, 1758–1944 M 1732–47, 1749–1837, 1839–1971 B 1732–47,
1749–55, 1758–1990 **NLW** Mf **PCAO**
BT 1687, 1704–8, 1710, 1714–95, 1797–1809, 1813–55 **NLW**

LLANGYNLLO   *SB*
C 1744–1986 M 1744–1971 (Banns 1823–1912) B 1744–1925 **NLW** Mf **PCAO**
BT 1687, 1690, 1702, 1705–11, 1713–68, 1770–1809, 1813–54 **NLW**

Cop ts PR C 1813–46 M 1776–1875 (Banns 1823–37, 1921–36) B 1813–93 **NLW &
PCAO**

LLANLLŶR (-YN-RHOS)/LLANYRE   *SB*
PR CB 1735–59 M 1735–59, 1772–94 recorded in 1831 apparently lost
C 1760–1903 M 1759–72, 1783, 1795–1971 B 1760–1963 **NLW** Mf C 1760–1903 M
1759–72, 1783, 1795–1837 B 1760–1963 **PCAO**
BT 1705, 1713–16, 1718–25, 1727–55, 1757, 1759–77, 1779–95, 1797–1809, 1813–18,
1823–36, 1839–43, 1864–7 **NLW**
Cop ts PR M 1795–1902 **PCAO**

LLANSAINTFFRAID-IN-ELWELL gweler/see LLANSANFFRAID-YN-ELFAEL

LLANSANFFRAID CWMTEUDDWR   *SB*
PR CMB 1682–[1736] recorded in 1831 apparently lost
C 1737–1811, 1813–97 M 1737–1837, 1972–8 Nant-gwyllt 1875–1971 B 1737–1811,
1813–1936 **NLW** Mf **PCAO**
BT 1687, 1690, 1701, 1706–8, 1710, 1713–17, 1719–24, 1726–64, 1766–95, 1797–1809,
1813–36, 1838, 1864–73 **NLW**

LLANSANFFRAID-YN-ELFAEL/LLANSAINTFFRAID-IN-ELWELL   *SB*
Diocesan records suggest that *c*1790 this parish had registers going back to 1603
C 1767–1930 M 1813–1957 (Banns 1824–1972) B 1767–1980 **NLW** Mf/Fac **PCAO**
BT 1701, 1707, 1713–14, 1716–95, 1797–1809, 1813–15, 1818–55, 1864 **NLW**

LLANSTEFFAN/LLANSTEPHAN   *SB*
C 1696–1981 M 1697–1971 (Banns 1884–1962) B 1696–1980 **NLW** Fac/Mf **PCAO**
BT 1690, 1707, 1713, 1715–29, 1731–63, 1765–95, 1797–1809, 1813–42, 1844, 1865–7,
1869 **NLW**

★ LLANYRE/LLANLLŶR (-YN-RHOS)   *SB*
PR CB 1735–59 M 1735–59, 1772–94 recorded in 1831 apparently lost
C 1760–1903 M 1759–72, 1783, 1795–1971 B 1760–1963 **NLW** Mf C 1760–1903 M
1759–72, 1783, 1795–1837 B 1760–1963 **PCAO**
BT 1705, 1713–16, 1718–25, 1727–55, 1757, 1759–77, 1779–95, 1797–1809, 1813–18,
1823–36, 1839–43, 1864–7 **NLW**
Cop ts PR M 1795–1902 **PCAO**

LLOWES   *SB*
PR CMB 1661–94 recorded in 1831 apparently lost
C 1701–1954 M 1701–53, 1760–1971 (Banns 1823–67) B 1701–1955 **NLW** Mf **PCAO**
BT 1714–15, 1719–1809, 1813–17, 1819–41 **NLW**

MAESYFED/NEW RADNOR   *SB*
C 1644–1903 M 1644–1971 (Banns 1823–1942) B 1644–1918 **NLW** Mf C 1644–1878 M
1644–1971 (Banns 1823–1942) B 1644–1918 **PCAO**

BT 1660, 1662–6, 1668–88, 1690–6, 1698, 1700–4, 1706–46, 1748–1833, 1836–7, 1843–6
HRO Mf **PCAO**
Cop ts PR CMB 1644–1708 with index **NLW & Soc Gen**

* MICHAELCHURCH-ON-ARROW/LLANFIHANGEL DYFFRYN ARWY   *H*
C 1741–1988 M 1741–1964 B 1741–1993 **HRO** Mf CB 1741–1812 M 1741–1964
PCAO
BT 1662–7, 1669–1743, 1745–1833, 1836, 1838–41, 1849–50, 1852 **HRO** Mf **PCAO**

NANT-GWYLLT gweler/see LLANSANFFRAID CWMTEUDDWR

NANTMEL   *SB*
C 1742–1992 M 1742–1980 (Banns 1823–1998) B 1742–1992 **NLW** Mf C 1742–1992 M
1742–1980 (Banns 1823–1939) B 1742–1992 **PCAO**
BT 1705, 1709, 1713, 1715–19, 1721–4, 1726–40, 1743–95, 1797–1809, 1813–37,
1839–43, 1864–73 **NLW**

* NEWBRIDGE-ON-WYE/PONTNEWYDD-AR-WY   *SB*
<Llanafan Fawr, co Brecknock and Llanllŷr/Llanyre, co Radnor 1882
C 1883–1966 M 1883–1982 (Banns 1883–1996) B 1884–1992 **NLW** Mf (except Banns)
PCAO
Cop ts PR C 1883–1956 ts PR M 1883–1971 with index **PCAO**

* NEWCHURCH/YR EGLWYS NEWYDD   *SB*
PR M 1814–35 recorded in 1900 inventory apparently lost
C 1708–1981 M 1708–48, 1755–1811, 1837–1971 (Banns 1825–1981) B 1708–1981 **NLW**
Mf **PCAO**
BT 1701, 1708, 1712–26, 1728–63, 1765–83, 1785–97, 1799–1806, 1808–9, 1813–16,
1818–53 **NLW**

* NEW RADNOR/MAESYFED   *SB*
C 1644–1903 M 1644–1971 (Banns 1823–1942) B 1644–1918 **NLW** Mf C 1644–1878 M
1644–1971 (Banns 1823–1942) B 1644–1918 **PCAO**
BT 1660, 1662–88, 1668–88, 1690–6, 1698, 1700–4, 1706–46, 1748–1833, 1836–7, 1843–6
HRO Mf **PCAO**
Cop ts PR CMB 1644–1708 with index **NLW & Soc Gen**

NORTON (NORTYN)   *SB*
C 1704–1922 M 1704–1971 (Banns 1824–1982) B 1704–1984 **NLW** Mf (except Banns
1925–82) **PCAO**
BT 1631, 1660–2, 1664–6, 1669–1717, 1719–47, 1749–78, 1780–1834, 1836–41, 1843–65,
1871–3 **HRO** Mf **PCAO**

PENCRAIG/OLD RADNOR *H*
Included the township of Lower Harpton, co Hereford
C 1682–1864 M 1682–1961 (Banns 1824–1937) B 1682–1945 **HRO** Mf C 1682–1864 M
  1682–1753, 1804–1837 (Banns 1824–1937) B 1682–1893 **PCAO** Mf CB 1682–1735,
  1806–12 M 1682–1735, 1761–1803 **NLW**
BT 1660–4, 1666, 1690, 1692–4, 1696–1735, 1737–44, 1754–1833, 1836–51, 1853,
  1855–6, 1862–6, 1868–70 **HRO** Mf 1660–1849 **PCAO**

★ PILLETH/PYLLALAI *SB*
Earliest registers destroyed by fire 1772
C 1766, 1771–1811, 1813–1980 M 1772–1812, 1814–36, 1838–87 B 1772–1811,
  1816–1964 **NLW** Mf **PCAO**
BT 1687, 1690, 1698, 1706–8, 1710, 1714–26, 1728, 1731–51, 1753–61, 1763–95,
  1797–1809, 1813–17, 1819–55 **NLW**

PONTNEWYDD-AR-WY/NEWBRIDGE-ON-WYE *SB*
<Llanafan Fawr, co Brecknock and Llanllŷr/Llanyre, co Radnor 1882
C 1883–1966 M 1883–1982 (Banns 1883–1996) B 1884–1992 **NLW** Mf (except Banns)
  PCAO
Cop ts PR C 1883–1956 ts PR M 1883–1971 with index **PCAO**

★ PRESTEIGNE/LLANANDRAS *H*
Included several townships in co Hereford
C 1561–1912 M 1561–1922 (Banns 1824–1948) B 1561–1904 **HRO** Mf **PCAO**
BT 1659–99, 1701–43, 1745–1833, 1836–56, 1880–1 **HRO** Mf 1659–1856 **PCAO**

PYLLALAI/PILLETH *SB*
Earliest registers destroyed by fire 1772
C 1766, 1771–1811, 1813–1980 M 1772–1812, 1814–36, 1838–87 B 1772–1811,
  1816–1964 **NLW** Mf **PCAO**
BT 1687, 1690, 1698, 1706–8, 1710, 1714–26, 1728, 1731–51, 1753–61, 1763–95,
  1797–1809, 1813–17, 1819–55 **NLW**

RHAEADR GWY/RHAYADER *SB*
Some CMB 1737–8, 1743 are entered in earliest extant vestry book (pp 256, 258)
C 1751–1992 M 1761–1980 (Banns 1828–1968) B 1759–1903, 1909–92 **NLW** Mf
  PCAO
BT 1779–1809, 1813–38, 1864–9, 1871–2 **NLW**
Cop ts PR CB 1759–1812 M 1761–1971 **PCAO**

RHIWLEN/RHULEN *SB*
PR C 1783–1812 B 1786–1812 recorded in 1831 apparently lost. M 1801–12 entered in
  PR Glasgwm
C 1813–1987 M 1773–1836, 1842–1971 B 1813–1988 **NLW** Mf (except B) **PCAO**
BT 1687, 1699, 1707, 1713–43, 1745–50, 1752–3, 1755–61, 1764–6, 1768–76, 1779–80,

1782–95, 1799–1806, 1808–9, 1813–17, 1819, 1821, 1823, 1825–9, 1833–6, 1838–45, 1847–50 **NLW**

Cop ts PR M 1773–81 (Banns 1785–1809) **PCAO**

SAINT HARMON   *SB*

PR CB 1794–1812 recorded in 1831 apparently lost. Diocesan records suggest that *c*1790 this parish had registers going back to 1696

C 1751–4, 1757–79, 1821–65 M 1751–3, 1758–1971 B 1751–4, 1757–78, 1813–89 **NLW** Mf **PCAO**

BT 1687, 1701, 1704–5, 1710, 1713–15, 1717–95, 1797–1809, 1813–41, 1865 **NLW**

TREFYCLAWDD/KNIGHTON   *SB*

C 1599–1964 M 1599–1971 (Banns 1946–78) B 1599–1959 **NLW** Mf **PCAO**

BT 1662–1833, 1836, 1838–46 **HRO** Mf **PCAO**

★ WHITTON/LLANDDEWI-YN-HWYTYN   *SB*

C 1600–22, 1625–1986 M 1600–22, 1625–1971 (Banns 1824–1986) B 1600–22, 1625–1986 **NLW** Mf (except Banns) **PCAO**

BT 1687, 1690, 1706–8, 1715–33, 1735–70, 1772–95, 1797–1809, 1813–14, 1816–18, 1820–41 **NLW**

MEIRIONNYDD
MERIONETH

TAL-Y-LLYN   Eglwysi cyn 1813/Pre-1813 churches
Corris   Eglwysi wedi 1813/Post-1813 churches

Milltiroedd/Miles

0   5   10

ABERDYFI/ABERDOVEY   *B*
<Tywyn/Towyn 1844
C 1846– B 1846– incumbent M 1846–1933 **GASD** Fac C 1846–1929 B 1846–1939
  GASD Fac M 1846–1933 **NLW**
BT 1846–57, 1876, 1883 **NLW**

ABERMAW gweler/see LLANABER

BALA, Y Christ Church   *SA*
<Llanycil 1855
M 1880–1970 **GASD**

BARMOUTH gweler/see LLANABER

BETWS GWERFUL GOCH   *SA*
C 1685–1981 M 1695–1960 B 1685–1969 **GASD** Mf **DRO & FRO** Fac C 1685–1846
  M 1695–1837 B 1685–1870 **NLW**
BT 1670–3, 1676–8, 1681–4, 1686–91, 1693–6, 1698–1701, 1703–4, 1706–8, 1710–21,
  1723–1836 **NLW** Mf 1802–36 **DRO & FRO**
Cop PR & BT CB 1670–1812 M 1671–1812 with index CFHS Cop index M 1754–1837
  GFHS

BLAENAU FFESTINIOG   *B*
<Ffestiniog 1844
CM 1844– incumbent B 1844–94 **GASD**
BT 1893 **NLW**

BONT-DDU, Y   *B*
<Llanaber 1887
C 1860– M 1888– B 1887– incumbent
BT 1887–8, 1890–1, 1893, 1901 **NLW**

BRITHDIR   *B*
<Dolgellau 1896
C 1898–1985 M 1899–1970 (Banns 1899–1970) **GASD**

BRYNCOEDIFOR   *B*
<Dolgellau 1853
C 1852–1987 M 1858–1970 (Banns 1889–1972) **GASD** B 1852–1994 **NLW**
BT 1852–7, 1876–1905 **NLW**

CORRIS   *B*
<Tal-y-llyn, co Merioneth, & Llanwrin, co Montgomery 1861
CM 1862– B 1861– incumbent Fac C 1862–1928 M 1862–1930 (Banns 1894–1929) B
  1861–1929 **GASD**
BT 1888–9, 1907–8 **NLW**

CORWEN   *SA*
C 1719–1963 M 1722–1968 (Banns 1902–36) B 1719–1964 **GASD** Mf /Fac C
   1719–1889 M 1722–1935 B 1719–1935 **DRO & FRO**
BT 1667–8, 1670–9, 1681–7, 1690–2, 1694–6, 1699–1716, 1718–23, 1725–30, 1732–7,
   1739–1834 **NLW** Mf **DRO & FRO**
Cop PR & BT CMB 1677–1812 with index CFHS Cop index M 1754–1837 GFHS

DOLGELLAU   *B*
C 1640–1812 M 1640–52, 1655–67, 1670, 1674–1753 B 1640–50, 1653, 1656–8, 1660–7,
   1669–71, 1673–1812 **NLW** C 1813–1978 M 1754–1971 (Banns 1823–33, 1851–1976) B
   1813–1989 **GASD** Fac CB 1640–1812 M 1640–1753 **GASD**
BT 1677–8, 1683–5, 1687–91, 1693–8, 1700–19, 1721–4, 1727, 1729–33, 1735, 1742–5,
   1747–88, 1790–1870, 1884–94 **NLW**
Cop index M 1754–1837 GFHS

FRON-GOCH   *SA*
<Llanfor, Llandderfel & Llanycil 1859
C 1859–1969 M 1862-1961 (Banns 1865–1961) B 1865–1979 **GASD**

FFESTINIOG   *B*
C 1695–1811, 1813–1909 St Martha 1959–90 M 1695–1915, 1918–90 St Martha 1954–69,
   1971–90 B 1695–1811, 1813–1956 **GASD** Fac CMB 1695–1791 **NLW**
BT 1676–80, 1683–4, 1687, 1689–92, 1696, 1698–9, 1701–3, 1705–11, 1713–24, 1726–7,
   1729–34, 1737–8, 1740, 1742–1851 **NLW**
Cop index M 1754–1837 GFHS

GLYNDYFRDWY St Thomas   *SA*
<Corwen 1859
C 1859– M 1860– B 1862– incumbent Fac M 1860–1930 **DRO FRO & GASD**

GWYDDELWERN   *SA*
C 1691–1704, 1720–1936 M 1696–1705, 1720–1970 (Banns 1823–1939) B 1695–1706,
   1720–1980 **NLW** Mf (excluding Banns) **DRO FRO & GASD**
BT 1662–3, 1665–8, 1670–1, 1673, 1675–83, 1685, 1695–6, 1698, 1701–3, 1706, 1709–10,
   1716–17, 1720–1837 **NLW** Mf **DRO & FRO**
Cop PR & BT CMB 1662–1812 with index CFHS Cop index M 1754–1837 GFHS

HARLECH gweler/see LLANDANWG

LLANABER   *B*
The parish included the town of Abermaw/Barmouth. PR CMB 1726– recorded in 1776
   apparently lost
C 1750–1978 M 1755–1886 (Banns 1897–1966) Caerdeon 1888–1969 St John 1895–1971
   St Mary 1954–71 B 1750–1956 **GASD** Fac C 1813–97 M 1755–1812, 1837–86 B
   1813–1915 **NLW**
BT 1676–9, 1681, 1683–4, 1694, 1696–8, 1700, 1706, 1708, 1714–16, 1719, 1729–34,

1738, 1740, 1742–75, 1777–1844, 1887–91 **NLW**
Cop index M 1754–1837 GFHS

LLANBEDR   *B*
CB 1627–1812 M 1627–1754, 1813–38 **GASD** M 1754–1811 **NLW** Fac C 1627–1812
  M 1627–1754, 1813–38 B 1627–1812 **NLW** B 1813-64 **GASD**
BT 1676–80, ?1681, 1684–92, 1694–7, 1699–1700, 1702–8, 1710–24, 1726–7, 1729–34,
  1738, 1740, 1742–90, 1792–1808, 1810–53, 1870–95, 1909–10, 1912–13 **NLW**
Cop index M 1754–1837 GFHS

LLANDANWG   *B*
The parish included the town of Harlech. PR CMB 1695–1725 recorded in 1934
  apparently lost
C 1725–1812 M 1725–1838 St Tanwg 1904–70 B 1725–1902 **GASD** Mf CMB
  1695–1725 **GASD** Fac CB 1695–1812 M 1695–1754 **NLW**
BT 1676–8, 1680–1, 1684–5, 1687–91, 1694–8, 1700–3, 1705–7, 1709–24, 1726–34, 1738,
  1740, 1742–56, 1758–1852, 1869–70, 1872–97 **NLW**
Cop ms PR (extracts) M 1754–1808 **NLW** Cop index M 1754–1837 GFHS

LLANDECWYN   *B*
PR CMB 1668–1802 damaged and defective
C 1668–94, 1728–66, 1768–1992 M 1668–94, 1728–1966 B 1668–94, 1728–66,
  1768–1950 **GASD**
BT 1676–8, 1680–1, 1683–91, 1693–1700, 1702–17, 1719–23, 1725–7, 1729–34, 1737–8,
  1740, 1742–56, 1758–1886 **NLW**
Cop PR (extracts) CMB 1678–1735 *Merioneth Historical and Record Society Journal,* 4 (1962)
  Cop index M 1754–1837 GFHS

LLANDRILLO-YN-EDEIRNION   *SA*
C 1686–1716, 1720–1921 M 1686–1716, 1720–1971 B 1686–1716, 1720–1994 **GASD**
  Mf C 1686–1921 M 1686–1971 B 1686–1868 **DRO & FRO** Fac B 1868–1983 **DRO
  & FRO**
BT 1662–3, 1665–8, 1670–93, 1695–6, 1698–1709, 1713–16, 1719–21, 1723–1822,
  1824–33, 1851 **NLW** Mf **DRO & FRO**
Cop PR & BT CB 1662–1812 M 1662–1825 with index CFHS Cop index M 1754–1837
  GFHS

LLANDDERFEL   *SA*
C 1598–1613, 1615–1994 M 1598–1613, 1615–1912 B 1598–1613, 1615–1992 **GASD**
  Mf C 1785–1888 B 1781–1866 **DRO & FRO**
BT 1662–6, 1668, 1670–87, 1689–96, 1698–1702, 1704–17, 1719, 1721–4, 1726–1811,
  1813–35, 1837–9 **NLW** Mf **DRO & FRO**
Cop ts PR (extracts) CMB 1602–1721, 1757 **Soc Gen** Cop index M 1754–1837 GFHS

LLANDDWYWE   *B*
C 1674–82, 1684–1711, 1743–1812 M 1674–82, 1684–1711, 1743–88, 1813–37 B

1674–82, 1684–1711, 1743–1812 **NLW** C 1813–1978 M 1838–1969 B 1813–1989 **GASD** Mf CB 1674–1812 M 1674–1788, 1813–37 **GASD**
BT 1677–8, 1680, 1683–5, 1687–96, 1698–1715, 1717–24, 1726–7, 1729–34, 1738, 1742–3, 1745–50, 1752–6, 1758–1836, 1905–6, 1910, 1913–14 **NLW**
Cop index M 1754–1837 GFHS

LLANEGRYN   *B*
C 1723–65, 1773–1878 M 1723–1970 B 1723–65, 1773–1940 **GASD**
BT 1676, 1678–9, 1681, ?1683, 1684, 1687–90, 1692–8, 1700–1, 1703–4, ?1706–7, 1708–24, 1727, 1729, 1731–2, 1734, 1740, 1742–9, 1751–1865 **NLW**
Cop index M 1754–1837 GFHS

LLANELLTUD/LLANELLTYD   *B*
C 1681–1718, 1730–1976 M 1681–1718, 1730–1984 (Banns 1824–1966) B 1681–1718, 1730–1990 **GASD**
BT 1676–8, 1680–1, 1683–91, 1693–1703, 1705–19, 1721–4, 1726–7, 1729–31, 1733–4, 1738, 1740, 1744, 1746, 1748–1836, 1874–92, 1894–6, 1899–1900 **NLW**
Cop index M 1754–1837 GFHS

LLANENDDWYN   *B*
C 1694–1700, 1702–9, 1718–1901 M 1694–1700, 1702–9, 1718–1837 B 1694–1700, 1702–9, 1718–1913 **NLW** M 1837–1971 **GASD** Fac C 1694–1901 M 1694–1837 B 1694–1913 **GASD**
BT 1677–81, 1683–91, 1693–9, 1701–15, 1717–24, 1727, 1729, 1731–4, 1738, 1740–1836, 1905–8, 1910, 1913 **NLW**
Cop index M 1754–1837 GFHS

LLANFACHRETH   *B*
C 1635–90, 1720–1927 M 1635–90, 1720–1982 (Banns 1824–1941, 1961–82) B 1635–90, 1720–1855 **GASD** Fac C 1635–1927 M 1635–1837 B 1635–1855 **NLW**
BT 1676, 1678, 1680–1, 1683–1703, 1705–7, 1709–24, 1726, 1729–34, 1738, 1740, 1742, 1744, 1746, 1748, 1750–3, 1756–1833, 1835–6, 1888–92, 1905 **NLW**
Cop index M 1754–1837 GFHS

LLANFAIR (LLANFAIR JUXTA HARLECH)   *B*
PR CB 1695–1812 M 1695–[1774] recorded in 1934 apparently lost
CB 1746–56 M 1746–53 **NLW** C 1813–1993 M 1754–1966 B 1813–1971 **GASD** Mf CB 1695–1812 M 1695–1753 **GASD** Fac CB 1695–1812 M 1695–1753 **NLW**
BT 1676–9, 1683–91, 1694–5, 1698–1711, 1713–14, 1716–24, 1726, 1729–34, 1738, 1740, 1742–1838, 1894–5, 1900–10 **NLW**
Cop index M 1754–1837 GFHS

LLANFAWR gweler/see LLANFOR

LLANFIHANGEL-Y-PENNANT   *B*
PR M 1754–1812 entries are copies made in 1902 when the original PR was destroyed in a flood
C 1770–1995 M 1754–1969 B 1770–1964 **GASD**
BT 1676, 1678–80, 1683–4, 1686–9, 1691, 1693–6, 1703–12, 1714–16, 1720–4, 1727–34, 1737–8, 1740, 1742–5, 1747–57, 1759–63, 1765–70, 1772–9, 1781–1865 **NLW**
Cop index M 1754–1837 GFHS

LLANFIHANGEL-Y-TRAETHAU   *B*
PR CB 1690–1813 M 1690–1754 damaged and defective
C 1690–1928 M 1690–1970 (Banns 1831–1934) B 1690–1992 **GASD**
BT 1676, 1678–81, 1683–97, 1699–1704, 1706–17, 1719–20, 1722–4, 1726–7, 1729–34, 1737–8, 1740, 1742–56, 1758–1858, 1872 **NLW**
Cop PR (extracts) CMB 1692–1712 *Merioneth Historical and Record Society Journal,* 4 (1962)
Cop index M 1754–1837 GFHS

LLANFOR (LLANFAWR)   *SA*
C 1722–1992 M 1722–1954 B 1722–1966 **GASD** Fac C 1722–1812 M 1722–1835 B 1722–1858 **NLW**
BT 1666–8, 1670, 1672–4, 1676–95, 1698–1833, 1835 **NLW**
Cop PR CMB 1722–1812 with index CFHS Cop index M 1754–1837 GFHS

LLANFROTHEN   *B*
C 1677–1995 M 1677–1965 B 1677–1971 **GASD** Fac CB 1772–1812 **NLW**
BT 1677–8, 1681, 1689–90, 1693–5, 1703, 1705, 1707–23, 1727, 1729–34, 1737–8, 1740, 1742–50, 1752, 1754–1848 **NLW**
Cop index M 1754–1837 GFHS

LLANGAR   *SA*
C 1614–1710, 1721–1848 M 1614–1710, 1721–1970 B 1614–1710, 1721–1919 **GASD**
Mf C 1614–1848 M 1614–1837 B 1614–1919 **DRO & FRO** Fac C 1614–1848 M 1614–1837 B 1614–1919 **NLW** Fac M 1837–1933 **DRO & FRO**
BT 1664, 1666–8, 1671, 1673–6, 1678–86, 1688–96, 1698, 1700–2, 1705–16, 1718–1831 **NLW** Mf **DRO & FRO**
Cop ts PR CB 1614–1806 M 1615–1708, 1724–1811 **Soc Gen** Cop PR C 1614–1849 M 1615–1812 B 1614–1806 with index CFHS Cop index M 1754–1837 GFHS

LLANGELYNNIN   *B*
C 1618–92, 1702–20, 1722–1861 M 1618–65, 1678–92, 1702–20, 1722–76, 1778–1865 B 1618–92, 1702–20, 1722–1919 **NLW** Mf **GASD**
BT 1676, 1678–9, 1684, 1686–7, 1689, 1692, 1694–7, 1700–2, 1704, 1706–24, 1726–7, 1729–34, 1738, 1740, 1742–50, 1752–76, 1778–1847 **NLW**
Cop index M 1754–1837 GFHS

LLANGELYNNIN *B*
Society of Friends burial ground, Llwyn-du
BT 1876–8, 1880, 1883–4 **NLW**

LLANGYWER/LLANGOWER *SA*
C 1603–50, 1654, 1662–79, 1727–1812 M 1627–38, 1665, 1676–7, 1727–1815 B 1626,
1628–46, 1672–7, 1727–1812 **NLW** C 1813–1978 M 1816–1964 B 1813–1993 **GASD**
Mf C 1603–1812 M 1627–1815 B 1626–1812 **GASD**
BT 1668, 1671–9, 1681, 1684–6, 1688, 1690–6, 1699–1702, 1704–41, 1743–1837, 1850,
1852 **NLW**
Cop index M 1754–1837 GFHS

LLANSANFFRAID GLYNDYFRDWY *SA*
C 1767–1898 M 1770–1816, 1818–37 B 1767–1905 **GASD** Mf **DRO & FRO** Fac M
1837–1930 **DRO FRO & GASD** Fac C 1767–87, 1813–98 M 1767–87, 1818–37 B
1767–87, 1813–1905 **NLW**
BT 1682, 1685–6, 1785–96, 1798, 1811–39 **NLW** Mf 1685–1839 **DRO & FRO**
Cop PR & BT CMB 1682–1812 with index CFHS Cop index M 1754–1837 GFHS

LLANUWCHLLYN *SA*
C 1697–1763, 1770–1812 M ?1697–1751, 1785–1837 B 1697–1763, 1770–1845 **NLW** C
1813–1926 M 1837–1964 B 1845–1972 **GASD** Fac C 1697–1812 M ?1697–1837 B
1697–1845 **GASD**
BT 1668, 1671–8, 1681–2, 1684, 1686, 1695–6, 1698, 1700–4, 1706–1825, 1827–37, 1850,
1852 **NLW** Mf **DRO FRO & GASD**
Cop index M 1754–1837 GFHS

LLANYCIL *SA*
C 1615–1890 M 1615–1969 (Banns 1890–1951) B 1615–1966 **GASD**
BT 1663, 1666–77, 1680–1, 1685–92, 1695–6, 1699–1702, 1704–18, 1720–1833 **NLW** Mf
DRO & FRO
Cop index M 1754–1837 GFHS

LLANYMAWDDWY *B*
C 1627–87 with gaps, 1735–55, 1770–1811, 1813–1993 M 1627–87 with gaps, 1735–1970
B 1627–87 with gaps, 1735–55, 1770–1811, 1813–99 **NLW** Mf CB 1627–1811 M
1627–1970 **GASD**
BT 1666–7, 1672–4, 1684–8, 1700–7, 1709, 1711–13, 1715, 1717–21, 1725–1830,
1832–42, 1881–5 **NLW**
Cop index M 1754–1837 GFHS

LLAWRYBETWS *SA*
<Llanfor, Llandderfel & Gwyddelwern 1864
C 1864– M 1865– B 1864– incumbent Fac M 1865–1930 **GASD**

MAENTWROG *B*
C 1695–1926 M 1695–1970 B 1695–1880 **GASD** Fac CMB 1695–1800 **NLW**
BT 1676–80, 1683, ?1686, 1687, 1691–3, 1696, 1698–1709, 1711, 1713–25, 1729–34,
 ?1737, 1738, 1740, 1742–55, 1757–64, 1766–1851, 1893 **NLW**
Cop index M 1754–1837 GFHS

MALLWYD *B*
C 1568–78, 1580–6, 1600–24, 1630–4, 1658–67, 1669–1894 M 1568–78, 1580–6,
 1600–24, 1630–4, 1658–67, 1669–1967 B 1568–78, 1580–6, 1600–24, 1630–4, 1658–67,
 1669–1876 **NLW** Mf **GASD**
BT 1667–8, 1672–5, 1678, 1680–2, 1684, 1688–96, 1700–8, 1710–11, 1714, 1716–20,
 1722–3, 1725–49, 1750–63, 1765–1814, 1816–32, 1834–8, 1882–5 **NLW**
Cop PR CMB 1568–1610 *Montgomeryshire Collections,* 30 & 32 (1898–1902) Cop index M
 1754–1837 GFHS

PENNAL *B*
C 1721–1991 M 1721–1970 (Banns 1824–43) B 1721–1940 **GASD** Fac C 1721–1812 M
 1721–1843 B 1721–1862 **NLW**
BT 1676–81, 1683–4, 1686–1701, 1703–7, 1709, 1713–16, 1718, 1720–5, 1727, 1729–34,
 1737–8, 1740, 1742–87, 1790–1837, 1839–40, 1882 **NLW**
Cop index M 1754–1837 GFHS

PENRHYNDEUDRAETH *B*
<Llanfihangel-y-traethau, Llandecwyn & Llanfrothen 1858
C 1858–1994 M 1858–1970 (Banns 1927–50) B 1858–1976 **GASD**
BT 1895–6, 1905–6, 1908, 1910 **NLW**

RHOSYGWALIAU *SA*
<Llanfor 1856
C 1838–1980 M 1839–1969 B 1842–1984 **GASD**

TAL-Y-LLYN *B*
C 1683–1962 M 1683–1969 (Banns 1914–57) B 1683–1978 **GASD** Fac C 1811–20 M
 1811–37 B 1811–1901 **NLW**
BT 1676–8, 1680–1, 1684, 1687–98, 1700–24, 1726–7, 1729–34, 1737–8, 1740, 1742–1883
 NLW
Cop index M 1754–1837 GFHS

TOWYN gweler/see TYWYN

TRAWSFYNYDD *B*
C 1730–1934 M 1730–1850 B 1730–1845 **GASD** Fac CMB 1685–1729 **GASD** Fac M
 1754–1850 **NLW**
BT 1680–1, 1687–91, 1693–4, 1696–7, 1699–1700, 1702, 1705–8, 1710–13, 1717–24,
 1726–7, 1729–34, 1737–8, 1740, 1742–1839, 1887–90 **NLW**
Cop index M 1754–1837 GFHS

TYWYN/TOWYN   *B*
C 1663–1715, 1721–1852 M 1663–1715, 1721–1918 B 1663–1715, 1721–1903 **GASD**
BT 1678–9, 1687–92, ?1693, 1695–1713, 1715–19, 1721, 1723–4, 1726, 1729–34, 1737–8, 1740, 1742–1837, 1839 **NLW**
Cop index M 1754–1837 GFHS

MÔN
ANGLESEY

LLANGEFNI   Eglwysi cyn 1813/Pre-1813 churches
Bryngwran   Eglwysi wedi 1813/Post-1813 churches

Milltiroedd/Miles

0   5

ABERFFRO/ABERFFRAW B
C 1719–1999 M 1719–1970 (Banns 1850–1951) B 1719–1999 ACRO Fac NLW
BT 1675–9, 1682–6, 1689, 1692–3, 1695–1703, 1705–9, 1712–27, 1729–35, 1737–63,
1765–6, 1768–91, 1793, 1795–1839, 1845–7, 1849–71 NLW
Cop index M 1754–1837 GFHS

AMLWCH B
PR CMB 1630–1705 damaged
CMB 1630, 1634, 1636, 1638–41, 1643, 1645, 1664, 1666–7, 1692–1729 C 1732–1801,
1805–1925 M 1732–1869 (Banns 1823–60) B 1732–1801, 1805–52 NLW B 1846–1946
Fac C 1692–1801, 1805–1925 M 1692–1729, 1732–1869 (Banns 1823–60) B 1692–1851
ACRO
BT 1675, 1678, 1682–6, 1689, 1692–9, 1701–4, 1706–31, 1733–5, 1737–51, 1753–66,
1768–70, 1772–93, 1795–1858 NLW
Cop ts BT 1801–4 ACRO index M 1754–1837 GFHS

BAE TREARDDUR gweler/see CAERGYBI/HOLYHEAD

BEAUMARIS gweler/see BIWMARES

BETWS-Y-GROG gweler/see CEIRCHIOG

BIWMARES/BEAUMARIS B
C 1649–59, 1668–1739, 1741–1894, 1900–48 M 1653–6, 1668–70, 1675, 1677–1971 B
1653, 1655, 1668–71, 1676–1739, 1741–1956 NLW Fac C 1655–1947 M 1655–1971 B
1655–1957 ACRO
BT 1699, 1703, 1713–25, 1727–9, 1731, 1734, 1737, 1741–2, 1745–72, 1774–5, 1777–91,
1793–4, 1796–1848 NLW
Cop ts PR C 1723–81 M 1724–53 B 1724–81 NLW & Soc Gen index M 1754–1837
GFHS

BODEDERN B
CMB 1695–1712, 1722–33, 1739–48 CB 1762–1812 M 1837–1985 (Banns 1823–44)
Caergeiliog C 1946–55, 1981–97 ACRO C 1813–53 M 1754–1837 B 1813–1913 NLW
Mf CMB 1695–1712, 1722–33, 1739–48 NLW Mf C1813–53 M 1754–1837 B
1813–1913 ACRO
BT 1678–80, 1682–3, 1686, 1689–90, 1693–1700, 1702, 1706–11, 1713–31, 1733–5,
1737–66, 1768–91, 1793–1836, 1838–62, 1871, 1881–3, 1885–1900 NLW
Cop index M 1754–1837 GFHS

BODEWRYD B
<Llaneilian
C 1776–1991 M 1755–6, 1773–1812, 1814–31, 1840–1970 B 1776–1991 ACRO Fac C
1776–1812 M 1755–6, 1773–1831 NLW
BT 1817–21, 1823, 1834–85, 1887, 1904, 1906 NLW
Cop index M 1754–1837 GFHS

BODWROG   *B*
PR CMB 1617–84 recorded in 1934 apparently lost
C 1758–77, 1813–1991 M 1754–1837 (Banns 1823–1984) B 1758–77, 1813–1993 **ACRO**
  Fac CB 1758–77 M1754–1837 **NLW**
BT 1682–5, 1689–90, 1692–1713, 1715–24, 1728–31, 1733, 1735, 1737–53, 1755–66,
  1768–91, 1793–1862, 1864–7, 1870–5 **NLW**
Cop index M 1754–1837 GFHS

BRYNGWRAN   *B*
<Llechylched
BT 1843 **NLW**

CAERGEILIOG gweler/see BODEDERN

CAERGYBI/HOLYHEAD   *B*
C 1737–1903 M 1737–1915 B 1737–1893 **NLW** C 1903–74 M 1915–91 (Banns
  1976–89) St Seiriol 1899–1987 St Ffraid, Bae Trearddur/Trearddur Bay 1956–92 B
  1893–1931 **ACRO** Fac C 1737–1903 M 1737–1915 B 1737–1893, 1931–90 **ACRO**
BT 1682, 1689–90, 1693–1706, 1708–9, 1711–16, 1718–22, 1724, 1726–30, 1733–4,
  1737–91, 1793, 1795, 1797–1836, 1845–6, 1859 **NLW**
Cop ts CMB 1682–1840 with index (BT 1682–1735 & PR 1737–1840) **NLW & Soc Gen**
Cop index M 1754–1837 GFHS

CEIDIO gweler/see RHODOGEIDIO

CEIRCHIOG/BETWS-Y-GROG (HOLYROOD CHURCH)   *B*
<Llanbeulan. Church closed *c*1843 and PR CB 1813– were subsequently used to record
baptisms (from 1895) and burials (from 1891) at Llechylched. PR M 1754–1811 recorded
in 1831 apparently lost
M 1813–42 B 1813–46, 1891–1997 Fac C 1813–42 **ACRO**
BT 1676–8, 1686, 1690, 1692–4, 1697–1702, 1704, 1707–9, 1711–12, 1714–19, 1722,
  1724, 1726–7, 1729–31, 1733–5, 1737–8, 1740–51, 1753–63, 1765–6, 1768–91, 1793–7,
  1799, 1802–46, 1891 **NLW**
Cop index M 1754–1837 GFHS

CEMAIS gweler/see LLANBADRIG

CERRIGCEINWEN   *B*
C 1721–1991 M 1721–1971 B 1721–1992 **ACRO** Fac CB 1721–1812 M 1721–1837
  NLW
BT 1676, 1678–80, 1683–5, 1689–90, 1692, 1694–7, 1699–1701, 1706–31, 1733–5, 1737,
  1739–55, 1757–66, 1768–80, 1782–91, 1793–1843, 1845–8, 1851–4, 1866–7, 1882–91
  NLW
Cop index M 1754–1837 GFHS

COEDANA   *B*
PR C 1783–1812 M 1783–1811 B 1786–1812 recorded in 1831 apparently lost
C 1813–1990 M 1813–1970 (Banns 1823–1991) B 1813–1995 **ACRO**   Fac M 1813–36
NLW
BT 1685–6, 1689, 1693, 1695–1702, 1704–11, 1713–16, 1718–26, 1728, 1731, 1733–42,
1744–5, 1747–56, 1758–9, 1762–6, 1768–73, 1775–7, 1779–83, 1785–91, 1793–1882,
1884–93, 1906 **NLW**
Cop index M 1754–1837 GFHS

EGLWYS AIL gweler/see LLANGADWALADR

GAERWEN gweler/see LLANFIHANGEL YSGEIFIOG

GWREDOG   *B*
An ancient chapelry of Llantrisaint without pre-1813 registers. For entries C 1834– B 1863–
see Rhodogeidio
M 1839–63 **ACRO**   Fac **NLW**   Fac C 1834–1947 B 1863–1991 **ACRO**
BT see Rhodogeidio

HENEGLWYS   *B*
C 1693–1993 M 1693–1790, 1813–1970 (Banns 1823–1993) B 1693–1900, 1932–52
ACRO   Fac C 1693–1763, 1777–1825 M 1693–1763, 1777–90, 1793–1812 B
1693–1763, 1777–1900 **NLW**
BT 1677–80, 1682–4, 1686–7, 1692–8, 1700–7, 1712–31, 1733–5, 1737–59, 1761–6,
1768–73, 1775–80, 1782–91, 1793–1896 **NLW**
Cop index M 1754–1837 GFHS

★ HOLYHEAD/CAERGYBI   *B*
C 1737–1903 M 1737–1915 B 1737–1893 **NLW**   C 1903–74 M 1915–91 (Banns
1976–89) St Seiriol 1899–1987 St Ffraid, Trearddur Bay 1956–92 B 1893–1931 **ACRO**
Fac C 1737–1903 M 1737–1915 B 1737–1893, 1931–90 **ACRO**
BT 1682, 1689–90, 1693–1706, 1708–9, 1711–16, 1718–22, 1724, 1726–30, 1733–4,
1737–91, 1793, 1795, 1797–1836, 1845–6, 1859 **NLW**
Cop ts CMB 1682–1840 with index (BT 1682–1735 & PR 1737–1840) **NLW & Soc Gen**
Cop index M 1754–1837 GFHS

LLANALLGO   *B*
Entries for CMB 1725–63 are in PR for Llaneugrad. CB 1838–51 apparently lost
C 1725–63, 1813–38, 1852–1992 M 1725–87, 1833–1970 B 1725–63, 1825–37,
1852–1992 **ACRO**   Fac C 1813–38, 1852–1903 M 1754–89 with index, 1833–6 B
1827–35, 1852–1918 **NLW**
BT 1682–6, 1689–90, 1692, 1694–5, 1697–8, 1701–11, 1714–27, 1729–31, 1733, 1735,
1737–52, 1754–73, 1775–7, 1779–91, 1793–1835, 1837, 1841, 1844, 1847, 1852–71,
1883, 1885–7, 1889–90 **NLW**
Cop index M 1754–1837 GFHS

LLANBABO   *B*
Early PR (CB 1740–1814 & M 1754–73) are in poor condition
C 1740–1976 M 1754–73 with gaps, 1773–1812, 1814–1964 B 1740–1986 **ACRO** Fac
    CB 1777–1810 M 1814–37 **NLW**
BT 1683, 1685–6, 1689–90, 1692–6, 1698–1702, 1705–12, 1715–20, 1722, 1724–6,
    1728–31, 1733–5, 1737–66, 1768–91, 1793–1863, 1865–70 **NLW**
Cop ms PR CB 1777–1810 **ACRO** index M 1754–1837 GFHS

LLANBADRIG   *B*
C 1731–1992 M 1731–1837 Cemais 1837–1971 St Padrig 1885–1964 B 1731–1992
    ACRO Fac C 1731–1813 M 1731–1837 B 1731–1861 **NLW**
BT 1680, 1682–6, 1689–90, 1693–5, 1700–11, 1713–15, 1717–31, 1733–5, 1737–66,
    1768–70, 1772–1837, 1840, 1842–54, 1869–79, 1882–4, 1889–97, 1899–1904, 1909–11
    NLW 1831 **ACRO** Fac 1812–35 **ACRO**
Cop PR index M 1754–1837 GFHS PR & BT CMB 1754–1812 GFHS ts BT C 1870–9
    ACRO

LLANBEDR-GOCH   *B*
C 1754–1987 M 1754–81, 1784–1836 B 1754–1986 **ACRO** Fac C 1767–1921 M
    1754–81, 1784–1836 B 1767–1921 **NLW**
BT 1680, 1682–6, 1689–90, 1692–4, 1696–1720, 1722–31, 1733–5, 1737–51, 1753–66,
    1768–87, 1789–91, 1793–1833, 1836–41, 1844–53, 1866 **NLW**
Cop index M 1754–1837 GFHS

LLANBEULAN   *B*
PR CMB 1748– recorded in 1776 apparently lost
C 1775–1959 M 1754–1889, 1893–1952 B 1775–1812 **NLW** Fac & Mf **ACRO**
BT 1676–9, 1682–6, 1689–90, 1692–1704, 1706–16, ?1717, 1719–31, 1734–5, 1737–45,
    1747–63, 1765–6, 1768–91, 1793–1852, 1855–9, 1864–77, 1879–91, 1894–5, 1898, 1900
    NLW
Cop index M 1754–1837 GFHS

LLANDEGFAN   *B*
CB 1547–53, 1557–63, 1571–3, 1575–6, 1594–1640, 1642–4, 1646–9, 1651–3, 1657–8,
    1660–6, 1668, 1672, 1733–41, 1751–2, 1755–87, 1789–1976 M 1547–53, 1557–63,
    1571–3, 1575–6, 1594–1640, 1642–4, 1646–9, 1651–3, 1657–8, 1660–6, 1668, 1672,
    1733–41, 1751–2, 1754–1971 **NLW** Mf **ACRO**
BT 1686, 1692–6, 1698–1701, 1703–27, 1730–1, 1733–4, 1738, 1740–3, 1745, 1747–52,
    1755, 1757–66, 1769–75, 1778–91, 1793–1829, 1831–60 **NLW**
Cop ms PR CMB 1547–1672 **NLW** index M 1754–1837 GFHS

LLANDRYGARN   *B*
C 1739–1934 M 1739–1837 (Banns 1823–1988) B 1739–1993 **ACRO** Fac CB 1739–1812
    M 1739–1837 **NLW**
BT 1679, 1683, 1685–6, 1689–90, 1692–1724, 1727–31, 1733–5, 1738–62, 1764–6,

1768–80, 1782–91, 1793–1862, 1864–5, 1867, 1869–75, 1877–83 **NLW**
Cop index M 1754–1837 GFHS

LLANDYFRYDOG   *B*
PR CMB 1589–1633 recorded in 1934 apparently lost
C 1690–1709, 1725–1811, 1813–1943   M 1690–1709, 1727–1837 (Banns 1824–39, 1877,
  1939–62) B 1690–1709, 1727–1811, 1813–1914 **NLW**   Mf (excluding Banns) **ACRO**
BT 1678, 1683–6, 1690, 1692–5, 1697–1720, 1722–3, 1725–31, 1733–5, 1737–58, 1760–6,
  1768–89, 1791, 1793–1899 **NLW**
Cop index M 1754–1837 GFHS

LLANDYSILIO   *B*
The parish included the town of Porthaethwy/Menai Bridge
C 1755–94, 1803–29, 1849–97   M 1755–94, 1803–1972   B 1755–94, 1803–1959 **ACRO**
  Fac C 1755–1897   M 1755–1837   B 1755–1925 **NLW**
BT 1679, 1684, 1689–90, 1692–5, 1697, 1699–1726, 1728–31, 1733–4, 1738, 1743, 1747,
  1749–51, 1753–60, 1761–3, 1765–6, 1768–9, 1771–2, 1774, 1776–80, 1782–91,
  1793–1833, 1850, 1853, 1865–6, 1896–7 **NLW**
Cop index M 1754–1837 GFHS

LLANDDANIEL-FAB   *B*
<Llanidan
C 1746–1992   M 1746–1970 (Banns 1824–1960)   B 1746–1983 **ACRO**   Fac C 1746–1812
  M 1746–56, 1813–38   B 1748–1812 **NLW**
BT 1677–80, 1682–6, 1689–90, 1692–1714, 1716–27, 1730–1, 1733–5, 1737, 1742–3,
  1745–57, 1759–91, 1794–1802, 1804–60, 1865–6, 1877–80, 1882 **NLW**
Cop PR & BT CMB 1677–1831 & index M 1754–1837 GFHS

LLANDDEUSANT   *B*
CB 1754–74   M 1761–97 **NLW**   C 1791–1806   M 1813–1991   B 1791–1806, 1813–1991
  Parish council churchyard 1927–46 **ACRO**   Mf CB 1754–74   M1761–97 **ACRO**   Fac CB
  1791–1806 **NLW**
BT 1683, 1686, 1689, 1694–1709, 1711–13, 1715–22, 1724–31, 1733–5, 1737–66,
  1768–77, 1779–91, 1793–1843, 1845, 1849–70 **NLW**
Cop index M 1754–1837 GFHS

LLANDDONA   *B*
PR M 1754–1812 recorded in 1831 apparently lost
C 1762–1992   M 1813–1970   B 1762–1947 **ACRO**   Fac C 1813–98   M 1813–37 **NLW**
BT 1675, ?1677, 1683–5, 1690–1706, 1708–16, 1719–24, 1726–7, 1729–31, 1733–5,
  1737–46, 1748–9, 1751–66, 1768–77, 1779–82, 1785, 1787–91, 1793–4, 1796–1864 **NLW**
Cop index M 1754–1837 GFHS

LLANDDYFNAN   *B*
C 1661–1715, 1723–1992   M 1663–1714, 1723–1966   B 1668–87, 1723–1993 **ACRO**   Fac
  C 1661–1899   M 1663–1837   B 1668–1907 **NLW**

BT 1675, 1678, 1689–90, 1695–1731, 1733, 1735, 1737–66, 1768–91, 1793–1882,
1888–90, 1895 **NLW**
Cop ts PR & BT C 1665–1750 M 1663–1749 B 1663–1750 **ACRO**   index M 1754–1837
GFHS

LLANEDWEN   *B*
<Llanidan
C 1747–1994 M 1747–1969 B 1747–1966 **ACRO** Fac CB 1747–1812 M 1747–1837
NLW
BT 1672, 1677–8, 1680, 1685–6, 1689–90, 1692–6, 1698, 1701–31, 1733, 1745, 1748–66,
1768–91, 1793–1854, 1856–62, 1877–80 **NLW**
Cop index M 1754–1837 GFHS

LLANEILIAN   *B*
C 1733–1841 M 1733–53, 1758–1837 B 1733–57, 1767–78, 1781–1888 **NLW**   Mf
ACRO
BT 1675–80, 1682–6, 1689, 1692–1707, 1709–31, 1733–5, 1737–65, 1768–73, 1775–81,
1783–91, 1793–1836, 1838–41, 1844–7, 1873–1906, 1909–11 **NLW**
Cop index M 1754–1837 GFHS

LLANERCH-Y-MEDD gweler/see LLANNERCH-Y-MEDD

LLANEUGRAD   *B*
C 1725–1991 M 1725–1805, 1813–1966 B 1725–1812, 1814–1970 **ACRO** Fac CB
1725–1812 M 1725–1805, 1813–37 **NLW**
BT 1680, 1682, 1684–5, 1689–90, 1693–4, 1705–11, 1713–22, 1724–7, 1729–31, 1733–5,
1738–66, 1768–83, 1785–9, 1791, 1793–4, 1796–1823, 1825, 1827–8, 1830–5, 1852–64,
1866–70, 1885, 1889–90 **NLW**
Cop index M 1754–1837 GFHS

LLANFACHRETH/LLANFACHRAITH   *B*
C 1682–1812 M 1702–1969 B 1682–1993 **ACRO** Fac **NLW**
BT 1675–6, 1678, 1680, 1683–6, 1689–90, 1692–1731, 1733–5, 1737–45, 1747–66,
1768–91, 1793–1836, 1838–48, 1852–82, 1886–92, 1894–6, 1901 **NLW**
Cop index M 1754–1837 GFHS

LLANFAELOG   *B*
PR CMB 1689–1812 recorded in 1831 apparently lost
C 1786–96, 1813–1959 M 1754–94, 1796–1971 B 1813–1941 **NLW** Fac & MF **ACRO**
BT 1677–80, 1682–6, 1689–90, 1692–1704, 1706–8, 1710–17, 1719–25, 1727, 1730–1,
1733–5, 1737–8, 1741–5, 1747–66, 1768–80, 1782–91, 1793–1827, 1829–52, 1864–1900
NLW
Cop index M 1754–1837 GFHS

LLAN-FAES   *B*
C 1727–1975 M 1727–1970 B 1727–1962 **NLW** Mf **ACRO**

BT 1689–90, 1695–9, 1701–7, 1709–13, 1715, 1717–31, 1733–5, 1739, 1742–64, 1766, 1769, 1771–2, 1775, 1777–81, 1783–91, 1793–5, 1797–1835, 1838–40, 1844–66, 1889 **NLW**
Cop index M 1754–1837 GFHS

LLANFAETHLU   B
PR CMB 1683– recorded in 1776 apparently lost
C 1743–1974 M 1743–1970 B 1743–1952 **ACRO**   Fac CB 1743–1812 M 1743–1837 **NLW**
BT ?1672–3, 1678–9, 1684, 1689–90, 1693, 1695–1726, 1728–31, 1733–5, 1737–42, 1744–66, 1768–81, 1783–91, 1793–1866, 1868–85, 1891, 1902 **NLW**
Cop ts PR/BT CMB 1678–1840 with index **ACRO NLW & Soc Gen** index M 1754–1837 GFHS

LLANFAIR MATHAFARN EITHAF   B
C 1753–1987 M 1753–1812 B 1753–1996 **ACRO** Fac **NLW**
BT 1678, 1684, 1686, 1690, 1692, 1694–1705, 1708–11, 1713–35, 1737–49, 1751, 1753–66, 1768–91, 1793–1837, 1839–59, 1865–82, 1888–92 **NLW**
Cop index M 1754–1837 GFHS

LLANFAIR PWLLGWYNGYLL   B
C 1754–63, 1783–5, 1787–1873 M 1757–86, 1790–1, 1802–7, 1813–37 B 1754–63, 1783–5, 1787–1882 **NLW** Mf **ACRO** Fac C 1813–73 M 1813–37 B 1813–82 **ACRO**
BT 1678–9, 1682–5, 1689, 1691–9, 1702–4, 1706, 1708–31, 1733–4, 1738–9, 1741–2, 1746–66, 1768–74, 1776–80, 1782–91, 1793–1833, 1850–66, 1896–7 **NLW**
Cop ms PR C 1831–2 **NLW** Mf **ACRO** index M 1754–1837 GFHS

LLANFAIR-YNG-NGHORNWY   B
For B 1938–40 see Llanrhwydrys
C 1732–1974 M 1754–1969 (Banns 1823–1987) B 1732–1936, 1938–40 **ACRO** Fac CB 1732–1812 M 1754–1837 **NLW**
BT 1669, 1673, 1675–8, 1680, 1683, 1685–6, 1689–90, 1705, 1708, 1711, 1713, 1715–16, 1718–24, 1728–31, 1733–5, 1737–9, 1741–66, 1768–90, 1792–1836, 1838–69, 1894–8, 1900–13 **NLW**
Cop index M 1754–1837 GFHS

LLANFAIR-YN-NEUBWLL   B
<Rhoscolyn. PR going 'one hundred & fifty years back' recorded in 1776 and PR 1768–1812 recorded in 1831 apparently lost
C 1813–1975 M 1774–1812, 1837–1955 B 1813–1990 **ACRO** M 1813–37 **NLW** Mf M 1813–37 **ACRO**
BT nd, 1677, 1683–6, 1689–90, 1695–1702, 1706–9, 1711, 1713–17, 1719–31, 1733–5, 1737–58, 1760, 1763, 1765–6, 1768–71, 1773–1862, 1876, 1878–84 **NLW**
Cop ts PR/BT CB 1677–1841 (BT 1677–1812) M 1677–1837 (BT 1677–1773) with index **ACRO NLW & Soc Gen**
Cop index M 1754–1837 GFHS

LLANFAIR-YN-Y-CWMWD   *B*

An ancient chapelry of Llanidan, without registers before 1885. 'This small parish contains 150 acres of cultivated land. The church has been for years in a state of such dilapidation as to preclude the performance of divine service, but is at present being rebuilt' (Angharad Llwyd, *History of the Island of Mona* (Ruthin, 1833), p 259). Some entries for this parish are in PR for Llangeinwen

LLANFECHELL   *B*

C 1691–1801, 1806–1992 M 1691–1969 B 1691–1781, 1789–1801, 1806–89, 1891–1990 **ACRO** Fac C 1691–1769, 1806–67 M 1691–1837 B 1691–1769, 1806–89 **NLW**

BT 1680, 1682, 1689–90, 1693–5, 1697–1731, 1733–5, 1737–66, 1768–1850, 1852–4, 1858, 1864–6 **NLW**

Cop index M 1754–1837 GFHS

LLANFEIRIAN

This church was in ruins at visitation in 1776. For PR entries see Llangadwaladr

LLANFIGEL/LLANFIGAEL   *B*

Early entries are in PR for Llanfachreth

C 1682–1807, 1844–1949 M 1682–1807, 1846–1931, 1978–80 B 1682–1807, 1819–1991 **ACRO**

BT 1682, 1684–6, 1689, 1692–3, 1695–1701, 1703–31, 1733–5, 1737–44, ?1746, 1747–8, 1750–66, 1768–91, 1793–1806, 1808–14, 1844–5, 1847–50, 1852–3, 1855–7, 1859–80, 1882, 1886, 1888–91, 1893 **NLW**

Cop index M 1754–1837 GFHS

LLANFIHANGEL DINSYLWY   *B*

C 1762–1815 M 1814–37, 1841–1943 B 1762–1815 **ACRO** Fac C1815–1994 B 1814–1991 **ACRO**

BT ?1686, 1692–3, 1695–6, 1698, 1700–7, 1709–12, 1715, 1717–21, 1723–5, 1727–31, 1734–5, ?1737, 1738–43, 1745–6, 1750–2, 1754–9, 1761–6, 1771–9, 1781–4, 1786–91, 1793–5, 1797–1811, 1813–41, 1844–54, 1856, 1858, 1908, 1911–15 **NLW**

Cop index M 1754–1837 GFHS

LLANFIHANGEL TRE'R-BEIRDD   *B*

C 1695–1811, 1813–1992 M 1695–1811, 1814–1968 B 1695–1811, 1813–1992 **ACRO** Fac C 1695–1811 M 1695–1754 B 1695–1811, 1813–1920 **NLW**

BT 1678, ?1683–5, 1686, 1690, 1692–1700, 1702–31, 1733–5, 1737–66, 1768–70, 1772–90, 1793–1899 **NLW**

Cop index M 1754–1837 GFHS

LLANFIHANGEL-YN-NHYWYN   *B*

<Rhoscolyn. PR going 'one hundred & fifty years back' recorded in 1776 and PR 1788–1812 recorded in 1831 apparently lost

C 1813–1967 M 1837–1969 B 1814–1996 **ACRO**

BT ?1679, ?1683, 1685, 1689–90, 1692–7, 1700–6, 1708, 1710–11, 1713–28, 1731, 1733–5,

?1737, 1739–53, 1755–66, 1768–91, 1793–1838, 1840–9, 1851–60, 1878–83 **NLW**
Cop index M 1754–1837 GFHS ts BT 1679–1838 **NLW**

LLANFIHANGEL YSGEIFIOG   *B*
PR C includes entries for Gaerwen
C 1703–1993 M 1703–1970 B 1703–1996 **ACRO**   Fac C 1813–54 M 1813–37 B
1813–66 **NLW**
BT 1675, 1677–8, 1682–5, 1689, 1694–5, 1697–1706, 1708–26, 1729–31, 1733–5, 1737–8,
1740–66, 1768–72, 1774–82, 1784–91, 1793–1835, 1837–45, 1847–54, 1864–5 **NLW**
Cop index M 1754–1837 GFHS

* LLANFLEWYN/LLANFFLEWIN   *B*
PR CMB 1755–64 recorded in 1831 apparently lost
C 1794–1990 M 1784–1809, 1813–1966 B 1794–1987 **ACRO**   Fac M 1813–37 **NLW**
BT 1689–90, 1693, 1695, 1697–9, 1701–2, 1705, 1709–14, 1716–17, 1719, 1722–7,
1730–1, 1733–4, 1737–55, 1757–66, 1768–77, 1779–91, 1793–1872, 1888–96, 1898–1907,
1909, 1912, 1914 **NLW**
Cop index M 1754–1837 GFHS

LLANFWROG   *B*
PR CMB 1638– recorded in 1776 apparently lost
C 1760–1805, 1808–1977 M 1754–1970, 1973–92 B 1760–1805, 1808–1984 **ACRO**   Fac
CB 1760–1805 M 1754–1836 **NLW**
BT 1672–3, 1677–9, 1685–6, 1689–99, ?1701, 1702–10, 1712–31, 1733–5, 1737–47,
1749–66, 1768–77, 1779–80, 1782–91, 1793–1863, 1865–9, 1873, 1875–85, 1891–1902
NLW
Cop ts PR/BT CB 1672–1840 M 1677–1839 **ACRO NLW & Soc Gen** index M
1754–1837 GFHS

LLANFFINAN   *B*
PR CMB 1690–1807 has been damaged and is defective
C 1690–1807, 1813–1989 M 1690–1835, 1838–1967 B 1690–1807, 1814–1992 **ACRO**
Fac M 1754–1837 **NLW**
BT 1675, 1677–8, 1680, 1690, 1693–5, 1698–1708, 1710, 1712–27, 1729–31, 1733, 1735,
1737–41, 1743–6, 1748–51, 1753–66, 1768–80, 1782–91, 1793–1833, 1837–45, 1847–62
NLW
Cop index M 1754–1837 GFHS

LLANFFLEWIN/LLANFLEWYN   *B*
PR CMB 1755–64 recorded in 1831 apparently lost
C 1794–1990 M 1784–1809, 1813–1966 B 1794–1987 **ACRO**   Fac M 1813–37 **NLW**
BT 1689–90, 1693, 1695, 1697–9, 1701–2, 1705, 1709–14, 1716–17, 1719, 1722–7,
1730–1, 1733–4, 1737–55, 1757–66, 1768–77, 1779–91, 1793–1872, 1888–96, 1898–1907,
1909, 1912, 1914 **NLW**
Cop index M 1754–1837 GFHS

LLANGADWALADR (EGLWYS AIL) & LLANFEIRIAN *B*
C 1610–1999 M 1610–1970 B 1610–1999 **ACRO** Fac C 1610–1812 M 1610–1754 B 1610–1913 **NLW**
BT 1676–80, 1682–3, 1685–6, 1689, 1691–4, 1696–1708, 1710–19, 1721–31, 1733–5, 1737–66, 1768–77, 1779–80, 1782–91, 1793–9, 1801–84, 1886–95 **NLW**
Cop index M 1754–1837 GFHS

LLANGAFFO *B*
C 1659–1992 M 1660–1837, 1839–1967 B 1659–1812, 1814–1918 **ACRO** Fac M 1755–1837 B 1814–1918 **NLW**
BT 1679, 1682–6, 1690, 1692–1701, 1703–29, 1731, 1733–5, 1737–60, 1762–6, 1768–87, 1789–91, 1793–1810, 1813–83 **NLW**
Cop index M 1754–1837 GFHS

LLANGEFNI *B*
C 1709–1999 M 1709–1971 B 1709–1918 **ACRO** Fac C 1709–1871 M 1709–1837 B 1709–1918 **NLW**
BT 1669, 1676, 1678, 1680, 1683–5, 1689–90, 1693, 1695–1707, 1710–17, 1721–31, 1733–5, 1738–43, 1745–9, 1751–9, 1761–6, 1768–89, 1791, 1793–1882 **NLW**
Cop ts C 1783–1851 B 1783–1850 **ACRO** index M 1754–1837 GFHS

LLANGEINWEN *B*
C 1688–1811, 1813–1993 M 1688–1970 (Banns 1823–57) B 1688–1811, 1813–1975 **ACRO** Fac C 1688–1787, 1813–80 M 1688–1787, 1790–1837 B 1688–1812 **NLW**
BT 1675, 1678–9, 1682–6, 1689–90, 1692–1719, 1721–31, 1733–5, 1737–66, 1768–91, 1793–1883 **NLW**
Cop index M 1754–1837 GFHS

LLANGOED *B*
PR CMB going 'as far back as the reign of Edward the Sixth' recorded in 1776 apparently lost
C 1763–1905 M 1754–1970 B 1763–1908 **ACRO** Fac C 1905–94 B 1909–95 **ACRO** C 1763–1888 M 1754–1837 B 1763–1908 **NLW**
BT 1682–3, 1685–6, 1689, 1692–5, 1697, 1699–1725, 1728–31, 1733–4, 1737–40, 1742–6, 1748–58, 1760–6, 1769–91, 1793–1849, 1851–6, 1908–14, 1917 **NLW**
Cop index M 1754–1837 GFHS

LLANGRISTIOLUS *B*
Entries for CB 1757–80 and C 1916–42 are in PR for Cerrigceinwen
C 1757–1916 M 1754–1967 (Banns 1824–49) B 1757–1918 **ACRO** Fac C 1781–1916 M 1754–1837 B 1781–1918 **NLW**
BT 1675, 1678–80, 1683–4, 1689, 1693–8, 1700, 1703–5, 1709–10, 1712–13, 1716–31, 1733–5, 1737–66, 1768–77, 1779–91, 1793–1849, 1851–4, 1864–92 **NLW**
Cop index M 1754–1837 GFHS

LLANGWYFAN   B
<Trefdraeth. PR CB 1759– recorded in 1776 apparently lost.   PR CB 1775–1813 has been
   damaged
C 1775–1991 M 1754–1836, 1838–1971 B 1775–1976 **ACRO** Fac **NLW**
BT 1718–20, 1728, 1730–1, 1734–5, 1737–48, 1750–63, 1765–76, 1778–83, 1785–91,
   1793–1837, 1839–42, 1844–51, 1853–61, 1902–13, 1915–16 **NLW**
Cop index M 1754–1837 GFHS

LLANGWYLLOG   B
PR CMB 1618– recorded in 1776 apparently lost
C 1777–1811, 1813–1992 M 1793, 1800–9, 1838–1968 B 1777–1811, 1813–1996 **ACRO**
   Fac C 1777–1811 M 1800–9 B 1777–1811 **NLW**
BT 1677–9, 1683–6, 1689–90, 1692–1727, 1729–31, 1733–5, 1737–66, 1768–91,
   1793–1882, 1884–93, 1906 **NLW**
Cop index M 1754–1837 GFHS

LLANGYNFARWY gweler/see LLECHGYNFARWY

LLANIDAN   B
CMB 1666–1734 **NLW**   C 1746–85, 1787–1993 M 1746–1970 (Banns 1848–1993) B
   1746–85, 1787–1951 **ACRO** Mf CMB 1666–1734 **ACRO** Fac C 1746–85, 1787–1848
   M 1746–1837 B 1746–85, 1787–1902 **NLW**
BT 1676, 1678, 1680, ?1689, 1690, 1697–8, 1701–11, 1713–27, 1729–31, 1733–5, 1743,
   1745–6, 1748–66, 1768–91, 1794–1861, 1865–7, 1869, 1881–3, 1886, 1895–7 **NLW**
Cop index M 1754–1837 GFHS

LLANIESTYN   B
PR CMB 1755–1812 recorded in 1831 apparently lost
C 1813–1983 M 1813–34, 1837–1961 B 1813–1992 **ACRO** Fac M 1813–34 **NLW**
BT 1682–3, 1685–6, 1692–5, 1697–1719, 1721–4, ?1726, 1727–31, 1735, 1737–66,
   1768–91, 1793–1849, 1852–7, 1908–15 **NLW**
Cop index M 1754–1837 GFHS

LLANLLIBIO   B
The church for this parish was described at visitation in 1776 as 'in ruins time immemorial';
   it was formerly a chapelry of Llantrisaint. No records survive. The inhabitants attended the
   churches of Bodedern and Llantrisaint

LLANNERCH-Y-MEDD   B
<Amlwch, Gwredog, Llechgynfarwy & Rhodogeidio 1854. Formerly a chapelry of Amlwch
C 1761–1997 M 1754–1833, 1835–6, 1838–1970 (Banns 1934–97) B 1761–1998 **ACRO**
   Fac M 1970–94 **ACRO** C 1761–1878 M 1754–1833, 1835–6 B 1761–1905 **NLW**
BT 1851, 1875–85 **NLW**
Cop index M 1754–1837 GFHS

LLANRHUDDLAD *B*
PR CMB 1737–1812 recorded in 1831 apparently lost
C 1813–92 M 1785–1918 B 1813–1994 **ACRO** Fac C 1893–1994 **ACRO** C 1813–92
M 1813–1918 **NLW**
BT 1676, 1679–80, 1683, 1686, 1689–94, 1697–1700, 1702, 1704–7, 1709–11, 1713–16,
1719–25, 1727–31, 1733–4, 1737–66, 1768–91, 1793–1801, 1803–72, 1888–1914, 1916
NLW
Cop index M 1754–1837 GFHS

LLANRHWYDRYS *B*
PR CB 1792–1818 has been damaged
C 1747–1971 M 1747–1834 (Banns 1824–1976) B 1747–1974 **ACRO**
BT ?1680, 1683, 1685–6, 1690, 1692–3, 1695, 1697, 1699–1702, 1704–31, 1733–5, 1737–9,
1741–60, 1762–6, 1768–91, 1793–1855, 1857–68, 1870–3, 1894–5, 1898, 1900–1,
1906–13 **NLW**
Cop index M 1754–1837 GFHS

LLANSADWRN *B*
C 1584–1725, 1731–1968 M 1584–1725, 1731–1970 B 1584–1725, 1731–1991 **ACRO**
Fac CB 1584–1725 M 1584–1725, 1754–1837 **NLW**
BT 1692, 1694, 1696–1702, 1704–11, 1713–31, 1733–5, 1737–40, 1742–3, 1747–61,
1763–6, 1768–75, 1777, 1779–87, 1789–91, 1793–1871, 1876–82, 1884–90 **NLW**
Cop index M 1754–1837 GFHS

LLANTRISAINT/LLANTRISANT *B*
C 1745–1905 M 1745–1969 (Banns 1823–44, 1851–69) B 1745–1960 **ACRO**
BT 1683, 1685, 1689–90, 1692–7, 1699–1719, 1723, 1725, 1729, 1731, 1738–41, 1743–66,
1768–91, 1793–1846, 1848–85, 1887–96, 1900–9 **NLW**
Cop index M 1754–1837 GFHS

LLANWENLLWYFO *B*
PR CB 1792–8 recorded in 1934 apparently lost
C 1763–91, 1813–1931 M 1762–1969 B 1763–91, 1813–83 **NLW** Mf **ACRO**
BT 1690, 1693–9, 1701–3, 1706–9, 1713–31, 1733–4, ?1735, 1737–53, 1755–61, 1763–6,
1768–80, 1782–91, 1793–1915 **NLW**
Cop index M 1754–1837 GFHS

LLANYNGHENEDL *B*
C 1713–1944 Valley 1896–1990 M1713–96, 1800–1968 Valley 1888–1993 B 1713–1983
Valley 1901–94 **ACRO** Fac **NLW**
BT 1675–6, 1679–80, 1683–6, 1689–90, 1692–7, 1699–1731, 1733–5, 1737–58, 1760–6,
1768–91, 1793–1853, 1855–82, 1886–91, 1893–6, 1901 **NLW**
Cop index M 1754–1837 GFHS

LLECHGYNFARWY (LLANGYNFARWY) *B*
C 1743–1986 M 1743–92, 1794–1968 B 1743–1812 **ACRO** Fac C 1813–1986 B

1813–1994 **ACRO** C 1743–1812 M 1743–92, 1794–1837 B 1743–1812 **NLW**
BT nd, 1682–6, 1689–90, 1692–8, 1700–5, 1707–15, 1717–22, 1728, 1734, 1737–9,
1741–6, 1749–66, 1768–91, 1793–1851, 1857, 1869, 1872–4, 1877–9 **NLW**
Cop index M 1754–1837 GFHS

LLECHYLCHED   *B*
Entries for C 1896– and B 1891– are in PR for Ceirchiog
C 1803–95 M 1813–36 (Banns 1847–72) B 1803–90 **NLW** C 1895–1994 M 1837–1971
B 1891–1997 **ACRO** Mf/Fac C 1803–1895 M 1813–36 (Banns 1847–72) B 1812–90
ACRO
BT 1676–8, 1682–6, 1689–90, 1692–1701, 1703–31, 1733–5, 1737–9, 1741, 1743, 1745,
1747–63, 1765–6, 1768–75, 1777–91, 1793–1852, 1855–9, 1864–86, 1888–9, 1891–3
NLW
Cop index M 1754–1837 GFHS

MENAI BRIDGE gweler/see LLANDYSILIO

NIWBWRCH/NEWBOROUGH   *B*
'Some remains of a register as far backward as 1581 but very imperfect' recorded in 1776
C 1721–1971 M 1721–1970 (Banns 1832, 1925–7) B 1721–1934 **ACRO** Fac C
1721–1908 M 1721–54, 1813–37 B 1721–1863 **NLW**
BT 1676, 1678, 1680, 1682–5, 1690, 1692–3, 1695–1704, 1706–8, 1710–31, 1733–5,
1737–66, 1768–1837, 1839–53, 1913–14 **NLW**
Cop index M 1754–1837 GFHS

PENMON   *B*
C 1693–1995 M 1693–1812, 1814–1970 B 1693–1995 **ACRO** Fac **NLW**
BT ?1679, 1686, 1690, 1695, 1699–1707, ?1709, 1710–31, 1733–5, 1737, 1739, 1741–65,
1769, ?1771, 1772–9, 1781–91, 1793–1806, 1808–36, 1838–40, 1844–66, 1889 **NLW**
Cop index M 1754–1837 GFHS

PENMYNYDD   *B*
PR CB 1741–62 M 1741–53 recorded in 1831 apparently lost
C 1759–1994 M 1754–1970 B 1759–1925 **ACRO** Fac C 1759–1812 M 1754–1837 B
1759–1925 **NLW**
BT 1675, 1677–9, 1685–6, 1689–90, 1692–3, 1695–1706, 1708–31, 1733–4, 1738–44,
1746–66, 1768–78, 1780, 1782–3, 1785–91, 1793–1831, 1833–5, 1839–42, 1844–53,
1855–60, 1864–6, 1891 **NLW**
Cop index M 1754–1837 GFHS

PENRHOSLLUGWY   *B*
C 1578–1766, 1813–1990 M 1578–1803, 1811–1967, 1971–97 B 1578–1766, 1813–1992
ACRO Fac C 1578–1766 M 1578–1766, 1811–37 B 1578–1766, 1813–1908 **NLW**
BT 1675, 1677–8, 1680, 1682–6, 1689–90, 1692, 1696–8, 1700–1, 1703–11, 1713–21,
1723–31, 1733–5, 1737–66, 1768–91, 1793–1802, 1804–41, 1848–60, 1862–73 **NLW**
Cop PR & BT CMB 1578–1841 & index M 1754–1837 GFHS

PENTRAETH   B
C 1740–1992 M 1740–65, 1767–1970 B 1740–63, 1768–79, 1781–1981 **ACRO** Fac C
   1740–69, 1781–1915 M 1740–64, 1781–1837 B 1740–69, 1781–1859 **NLW** M
   1837–1970 **ACRO**
BT 1664–5, 1679, 1682–6, 1689, 1692–3, 1695–7, 1700–5, 1707–14, 1716–19, 1721–31,
   1733–5, 1737–66, 1768–79, 1781–91, 1793–1853, 1896 **NLW**
Cop index M 1754–1837 GFHS

PORTHAETHWY gweler/see LLANDYSILIO

RHODOGEIDIO (CEIDIO)   B
<Llantrisaint. It was claimed in 1776 that 'almost all the parish christen at Llannerchymedd
   being nearer for most of the inhabitants'. Earlier PR recorded in 1831 as 'accidentally
   destroyed by fire'
C 1783–1947 M 1754–1964 B 1783–1812 **ACRO** Fac C 1783–1812 M 1754–1836 B
   1783–1812 **NLW** Fac B 1813–1964 **ACRO**
BT 1694–6, 1698, 1700, 1702, 1704, 1706–10, 1712–30, 1737–42, 1744–6, 1748–66,
   1768–73, 1775–91, 1793–1851, 1857, 1872–82 **NLW**
Cop index M 1754–1837 GFHS

RHOSBEIRIO   B
<Llaneilian. For early PR entries see Llaneilian
C 1813–1923 M 1852–1912 B 1813–1962 **ACRO** Fac **NLW**
BT 1813, 1865, 1867–8, 1870, 1873–6, 1880–1, 1883, 1885, 1887, 1906 **NLW**
Cop index M 1754–1837 GFHS

RHOSCOLYN   B
C 1732–59, 1765, 1767, 1769–1892, 1901–2 M 1732–54, 1772–1837 B 1732–59, 1763,
   1770–1810, 1813–81 **NLW** C 1902–77 M 1754–94, 1837–1985 (Banns 1902–76) B
   1881–1990 **ACRO** Mf C 1732–1802, 1813–92, 1901–2 M 1732–54, 1772–1837 B
   1732–1810, 1813–81 **ACRO**
BT 1678, 1683–6, 1689–90, 1692, 1695–6, 1700–1, 1703, 1705–9, 1711–17, 1719–27,
   1729, 1731, 1733–5, 1737–58, 1760–6, 1768–77, 1779–91, 1793–1867, 1876, 1878–84
   NLW
Cop ts PR BT CMB 1678–1841 **ACRO & NLW** index M 1754–1837 GFHS

RHOS-Y-BOL   B
<Amlwch 1876
C 1875– M 1878– B 1877– incumbent
BT 1875–85 **NLW**

TAL-Y-LLYN   B
<Llanbeulan. In 1776 the church was said to have 'received a thorough rep[ai]r about four
   years ago, but [it] has not been served these twelve years'
C 1845–1970 **NLW** Mf & Fac **ACRO**

TREARDDUR BAY gweler/see CAERGYBI/HOLYHEAD

TREFDRAETH   B
PR CMB 1551–1707 & 1709–29 are damaged and defective
C 1551–1707, 1709–29, 1760–99, 1801–1999 M 1552–1707, 1709–29, 1756–1966 (Banns
1848–1987) B 1551–1707, 1709–29, 1760–99, 1801–1999 **ACRO** Fac C 1551–1707,
1709–29, 1760–99, 1801–67 M 1552–1707, 1709–29, 1756–76, 1813–38 B 1551–1707,
1709–29, 1760–99, 1801–70 **NLW**
BT 1682–5, 1689–90, 1692–6, 1698–1706, 1708, 1712–15, 1717–27, 1729–31, 1733–5,
1737–47, 1750, 1753–5, 1757–63, 1765–6, 1768–81, 1783–91, 1793–1861, 1902–16 **NLW**
Cop PR C 1551–1633 M 1552–1633 B 1551–1634 *Anglesey Antiquarian Society Transactions*
(1924) Cop index M 1754–1837 GFHS

TREGAEAN   B
C 1708–1992 M 1708–1968 B 1708–1992 **ACRO** Fac C 1708–1812 M 1708–1836 B
1708–1992 **NLW**
BT 1678–80, 1682–4, 1686, 1689–90, 1692–5, 1697–1718, 1721–9, 1733–5, 1739–51,
1753–9, 1761–6, 1768–9, 1771–7, 1779–91, 1793–1859, 1861–5, 1868–75 **NLW**
Cop index M 1754–1837 GFHS

TREWALCHMAI   B
C 1727–1986 M 1727–1970 (Banns 1823–1957) B 1727–1999 **ACRO** Fac C 1727–1880
M 1727–54, 1813–37 B 1727–1906 **NLW**
BT 1675–6, 1680, 1682, 1692–1731, 1733–5, 1737–9, 1741–58, 1760–6, 1768–91,
1793–1896, 1901–3, 1906 **NLW**
Cop index M 1754–1837 GFHS

VALLEY gweler/see LLANYNGHENEDL

MORGANNWG
GLAMORGAN

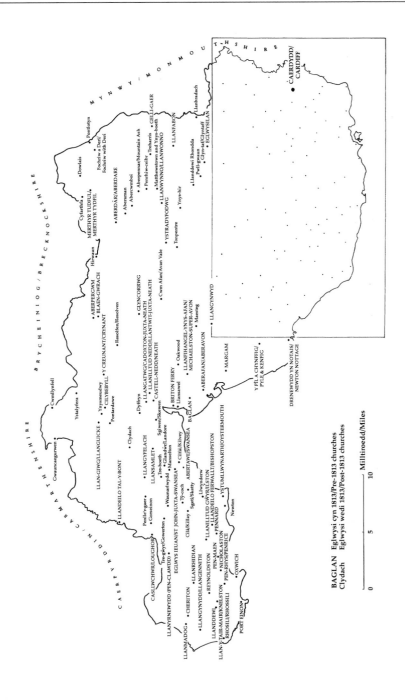

BAGLAN   Eglwysi cyn 1813/Pre-1813 churches
Clydach   Eglwysi wedi 1813/Post-1813 churches

Milltiroedd/Miles

0   5   10

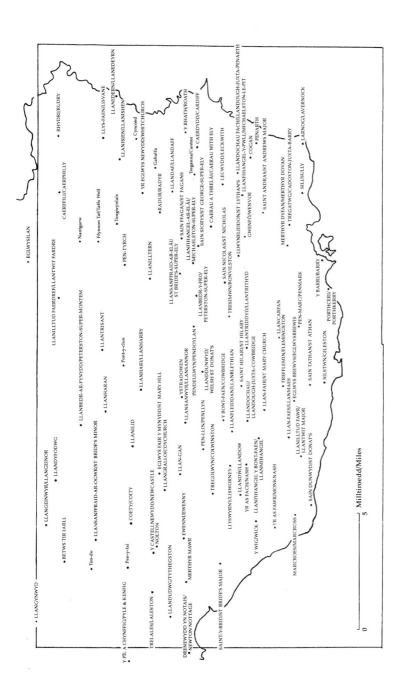

Milltiroedd/Miles

ABERAFAN/ABERAVON   *LL*
PR CB 1597–1734 recorded in 1831 but not in *A digest of the parish registers within the diocese of Llandaff...* (Cardiff, 1905) apparently lost
C 1748–1948 M 1747–1947 B 1747–1955 **Glam RO** Fac **WGAS** Fac CMB 1748–1812 **NLW**
BT 1696, 1721–1861, 1863–9 **NLW** Mf 1696–1837 **Glam RO**
Cop ts index B 1813–49 **WGAS**

ABERAMAN St Margaret   *LL*
<Aberdâr/Aberdare 1888
C 1882–1949 St Barnabas 1899–1914 Abercwmboi Mission 1899–1915 M 1887–1955 (Banns 1893–1952) **Glam RO**
BT 1900 **NLW**

ABERAVON gweler/see ABERAFAN

ABERCWMBOI St Peter   *LL*
<Aberaman
C 1920–74 M 1924–74 (Banns 1933–44) **Glam RO**

ABERDÂR/ABERDARE St Elvan   *LL*
<St John
C 1863–89 M 1855–1937 **Glam RO** Fac **WGAS**

ABERDÂR/ABERDARE St Fagan   *LL*
C 1854–1975 M 1854–1953 B 1854–1942 **Glam RO**

ABERDÂR/ABERDARE St John   *LL*
C 1734–1917 M 1734–53, 1756–7, 1769–1937 B 1734–1916, 1921, 1924, 1946 **Glam RO** Fac **WGAS**
BT 1717, 1724–1863, 1900–4 **NLW** Mf 1717–1833 **Glam RO**
Cop ms PR CB 1734–1821 M 1734–57, 1769–1836 **NLW** Mfc index PR C 1725–1900 M 1717–1837 B 1734–1924 **NLW & Soc Gen**

ABERPENNAR/MOUNTAIN ASH   *LL*
<Aberdâr/Aberdare & Llanwynno/Llanwonno 1863
C 1859– M 1865– incumbent
BT 1859–74 **NLW**

ABERPERGWM   *LL*
An ancient chapelry of Llangatwg/Cadoxton-juxta-Neath. Separate parish from 1861
C 1849–1986 M 1837–1981 (Banns 1945–87) B 1849–1987 **Glam RO** Fac (except Banns) **WGAS**
BT 1849–51 **NLW**

ABERTAWE/SWANSEA Christ Church   *SB*
<St Mary 1874
C 1872–1950 M 1872–1971 (Banns 1889–1900) **WGAS** Fac C 1872–1927 M 1872–1937
Glam RO
BT 1872–80 **NLW**

ABERTAWE/SWANSEA Eglwys Ieuan/St John   *SB*
Dedication transferred in 1880 from old church in High Street (now St Matthew) to newly-
built church at Hafod. Diocesan records suggest that *c*1790 the registers went back to 1760
C 1797–1800, 1813–1964 M 1813–1971 (Banns 1824–1974) B 1797–1800, 1813–85
WGAS Fac C 1797–1800, 1813–1923 M 1813–1918 B 1797–1800, 1813–85 **Glam RO**
BT 1785, 1787–9, 1791–8, 1800, 1802–3, 1805–73 **NLW** Mf 1785–1837 **WGAS**
Cop ts index PR C 1813–42 **WGAS**

ABERTAWE/SWANSEA Holy Trinity   *SB*
<St Mary 1843
C 1856–1939 M 1877–1941 B 1901–16 **WGAS** Fac C 1856-1939 M 1877-1941 **Glam
RO**
BT 1856–82, 1885–6 **NLW**

ABERTAWE/SWANSEA St Barnabas   *SB*
<St Mary 1928
C 1915–58 M 1929–71 (Banns 1928–40) **WGAS** Fac C 1915–58 M 1929–52 **Glam RO**

ABERTAWE/SWANSEA St Gabriel   *SB*
<St Mary 1889
C 1889–1973 St Augustine 1905-94 M 1890–1986 **WGAS** Fac C 1889–1914 M
1890–1922 **Glam RO**
BT 1889–91 **NLW**

ABERTAWE/SWANSEA St James   *SB*
<St Mary 1867
C 1867–1985 M 1867–1979 (Banns 1899–1971) **WGAS** Fac C 1867–1960 M 1867–1971
Glam RO
BT 1867–82 **NLW**

ABERTAWE/SWANSEA St Jude   *SB*
<St Mary 1920
C 1896–1965 M 1896–1988 (Banns 1896–1962) **WGAS** Fac C 1896-1921 M 1896-1928
Glam RO

ABERTAWE/SWANSEA St Luke, Cwmbwrla   *SB*
<Y Cocyd/Cockett 1911
C 1886–1957 M 1890–1989 (Banns 1905–78) **WGAS** Fac C 1886–1914 M 1890–1949
Glam RO

ABERTAWE/SWANSEA St Mark   *SB*
<St Mary 1888
C 1888–1971 M 1888–1971 (Banns 1888–1903, 1920–78) **WGAS** Fac C 1888–1918 M
  1888–1931 **Glam RO**
BT 1894–5 **NLW**

ABERTAWE/SWANSEA St Mary   *SB*
C 1631–1706, 1712–1978 M 1631–1706, 1712–1941, 1959–89 (Banns 1823–37, 1872–3,
  1894–1979) B 1631–1706, 1712–1937 & cremated remains 1957–79 **WGAS** Fac (except
  M 1924–40 and Banns) **Glam RO** Fac PR CMB 1631–1706 **NLW**
BT 1676–8, 1681, 1683–4, 1686, 1690, 1693, 1695–7, 1700–2, 1704, 1713, 1717, 1725–36,
  1738, 1740–59, 1761–86, 1788–92, 1794–1800, 1802–3, 1805–82, 1885, 1887–95,
  1898–1905 **NLW** Mf 1676–1837 **WGAS**
Cop ts index PR C 1827–56 B 1813–85 **WGAS**

ABERTAWE/SWANSEA St Matthew   *SB*
<St Mary & St John 1886
C 1886–1992 Greenhill 1918–62 M 1886–1971 Greenhill 1927–49 B 1887–1991 **WGAS**
  Fac M 1886–1927 **Glam RO**

ABERTAWE/SWANSEA St Nicholas   *SB*
<St Mary 1886. Closed 1920
C 1886–1920 M 1886–1920 (Banns 1886–1901, 1908–19) **WGAS** Fac (except Banns)
  Glam RO

ABERTAWE/SWANSEA St Nicholas-on-the-Hill   *SB*
<St Jude 1933
C 1924–63 Good Shepherd Mission 1927–46 M 1937–89 **WGAS** Fac C 1924–42 Good
  Shepherd Mission 1927-46 B 1937-50 **Glam RO**

ABERTAWE/SWANSEA St Peter, Y Cocyd/Cockett   *SB*
<St Mary 1878
C 1856–1987 M 1857–1991 (Banns 1908–39) B 1856–1990 Fforest-fach St Illtud C 1918–
  98 M 1911-85 B 1911-90 **WGAS** Fac St Peter C 1856–1943 M 1857–1919 B
  1856–1923 **Glam RO**
BT 1856–9, 1861–75 **NLW**
Cop ms PR M 1859–69 **NLW**

ABERTAWE/SWANSEA St Thomas   *SB*
<St Mary 1888
C 1888–1981 M 1888–1990 (Banns 1953–88) Port Tennant 1903–59 (Banns 1936–58)
  WGAS Fac C 1888–1924 M 1888–1927 **Glam RO**
BT 1888–9 **NLW**

★ AFAN VALE /CWM AFAN (ABERGWYNFI)   *LL*
  <Glyncorrwg & Llangynwyd 1906

C 1907–42 Y Cymer/Cymmer 1939–88 M 1907–85 (Banns 1907–62) Y Cymer/Cymmer 1927–81 (Banns 1952–88) **Glam RO** Fac C 1907–16 M 1907–14 **WGAS**

AS FACH, YR/NASH *LL*
Extra-parochial. A private chapel at one time. The manor was the only house in the parish, which comprises only 200 acres. Population since 1800 averaged about 10, until recent housing developments

AS FAWR, YR/MONKNASH *LL*
At visitation in 1781 there was 'an old register book of paper here, but sadly abused before I had care of it; and but few leaves remain of it; it goes, in some part of it, as far back as 1677'. PR CMB 1746–1812 recorded in 1831 apparently partly lost by 1940
C 1813–1987 M 1754–1969 B 1813–1987 **Glam RO** Fac **WGAS**
BT 1721, 1723–7, 1730–7, 1739–40, 1743, 1745, 1747–8, 1750–1820, 1822–45, 1848–62, 1865, 1869–74 **NLW** Mf 1721–1837 **Glam RO**
Cop Mfc index PR/BT CB 1721–1987 M 1721–1837 **NLW & WGAS**

BAGLAN *LL*
PR CMB 1626–1768 recorded in 1831 but not in *A digest* ... (Cardiff, 1905) apparently lost
C 1769–1874 M 1769–1923 (Banns 1824–1930) B 1769–1904 **Glam RO** Fac (except Banns) **WGAS**
BT 1721, 1723–1817, 1819, 1821–67 **NLW** Mf 1721–1837 **Glam RO**

BARRI, Y/BARRY *LL*
C 1724–6, 1733, 1741–1921 M 1724/5–25, 1733, 1741–1808, 1816–1925 B 1724–5, 1730/1–1811, 1813–1958 **Glam RO** Fac **WGAS**
BT 1724–45, 1747–50, 1752–70, 1772–1813, 1815–89, 1891-4 **NLW** Mf 1724–1837 **Glam RO**
Cop ts PR C 1724–1812 M 1724–1808 B 1724–1811 **Glam RO** Mfc index PR CB 1724–1900 M 1724–1837 **NLW & Soc Gen**

BARRI, Y/BARRY St Paul *LL*
<Merthyr Dyfan/Merthyr Dovan
M 1901–27 (Banns 1947–63, 1969–77) **NLW** C 1928–43 M 1927–91 Fac/Mf M 1901–27 (Banns 1947–63, 1969–77) **Glam RO**

BARRY DOCK gweler/see TREGATWG/CADOXTON-JUXTA-BARRY

BETWS TIR IARLL *LL*
C 1725–45, 1760–1817 M 1722–5 B 1723–46, 1760–1819 **NLW** C 1813–1939 M 1754–1963 (Banns 1823–1908) B 1813–1950 Fac C 1725–45, 1760–1817 M 1722–5 B 1723–46, 1760–1819 **Glam RO** Fac C 1725–45, 1760–1939 M 1722-5, 1754–1963 B 1723–46, 1760–1950 **WGAS**
BT 1721, 1723–45, 1747–1821, 1823–66, 1868, 1870–6 **NLW** Mf 1721–1837 **Glam RO**

BIRCHGROVE gweler/see LLANSAMLET

★ BISHOPSTON/LLANDEILO FERWALLT   *SB*
   C 1716–1807, 1810–1965 M 1716–1952 (Banns 1899–1959) B 1716–1807, 1810–1979
   NLW Mf (except Banns) **WGAS**
   BT 1671, 1675, 1677–8, 1681–2, 1686–7, 1690, 1693, 1696–8, 1700–2, 1704, 1707–8,
   1710, 1712–13, 1716, 1727–31, 1733–76, 1778–1800, 1802–3, 1805, 1807–82, 1885,
   1887–90 **NLW** Mf 1671–1838 **WGAS**
   Cop ms PR CMB 1716–1812 Mfc index PR/BT C 1677–1891 M 1678–1838 B
   1677–1890 **NLW**

BLAEN-GWRACH   *LL*
An ancient chapelry with pre-1812 entries of CMB included in PR Glyncorrwg (1831
survey). CB 1813–94 and M 1813–36 also included in PR Glyncorrwg
C 1895–1970 M 1837–1970 (Banns 1896–1950) B 1895–1988 **Glam RO** Fac (except
Banns) **WGAS**
BT 1846–60 **NLW**

BONT-FAEN, Y/COWBRIDGE   *LL*
C 1718–24, 1735–7, 1744–5, 1750–1, 1753–1972 M 1753–1983 (Banns 1823–1993) B
1735–7, 1750–1, 1753–1928 **Glam RO** Fac C 1718–24, 1735–7, 1744–5, 1750–1,
1753–1972 M 1753–1971 B 1735–7, 1750–1, 1753–1928 **WGAS**
BT 1721, 1724–31, 1733–7, 1739–46, 1748–1881 **NLW** Mf 1721–1837 **Glam RO**
Cop Mfc index PR/BT C 1718–1887 M 1721–1837 B 1735–1873 **NLW & Soc Gen**

★ BONVILSTON (BOULSTON)/TRESIMWN   *LL*
   PR M 1813–37 apparently lost. Hearsay evidence recorded in 1940 reply to NLW
   questionnaire that 'some old registers were seen burning at Bonvilston House after the
   death of a Mr Bassett'
   C 1761–1983 M 1758–1812, 1837–1970, 1972–91 (Banns 1824–1977) B 1761–1982
   Glam RO Fac C 1761–1983 M 1758–1812, 1837–1970 B 1761–1982 **WGAS**
   BT 1696, 1724–1817, 1819–24, 1826–42, 1845–55, 1857–81 **NLW** Mf 1696–1837 **Glam
   RO**
   Cop Mfc index PR/BT C 1696–1900 M 1696–1837 B 1696–1901 **NLW & Soc Gen**

BÔN-Y-MAEN gweler/see GLANTAWE

BRITON FERRY St Clement   *LL*
Built 1866, and replaced St Mary as the parish church. For St Mary see Llansawel
C 1668–1731, 1739–1969 St Thomas 1936–65 M 1668–1731, 1739–1944 (Banns
1867–1954) B 1686–1731, 1744–1924 **Glam RO** Fac (except Banns) **WGAS**
BT 1696, 1721, 1723–1818, 1820–67 **NLW** Mf 1696–1837 **Glam RO**

★ CADOXTON-JUXTA-BARRY/TREGATWG   *LL*
   Earlier PR possibly mutilated: some entries C 1644–5, 1662–3 on dorse of BT 1735 & 1738
   C 1753–72, 1781–90, 1806–9, 1813–89, 1925–51 M 1754–83, 1813–37 Barry Dock, St

Mary (Banns 1956–63) B 1752–73, 1781–95, 1803–8, 1814–1982 **Glam RO** Fac (except Banns) **WGAS**
BT 1724–43, 1745–1867, 1869 **NLW** Mf 1724–1837 **Glam RO**
Cop Mfc index PR/BT C 1724–1889 M 1724–1837 B 1724–1901 **NLW & Soc Gen**

* CADOXTON-JUXTA-NEATH/LLANGATWG   *LL*
There was a tradition here that some of the church registers were thrown 'gleefully' into the vicarage fire by 'the demented wife of a former incumbent', D Rhys Phillips, *The History of the Vale of Neath* (Swansea, 1925), 74
Lay register CMB 1638–47, 1653–79 **Glam RO** Fac **WGAS**
C 1738–1965 M 1738–1935 (Banns 1823–44) B 1738–1919 **Glam RO** Fac (except Banns) **WGAS**
BT 1721, 1723–33, 1735–6, 1738–1842, 1848, 1850–6, 1858–65, 1867–8, 1870–2 **NLW** Mf 1721–1837 **Glam RO**
Cop Mfc index PR/BT CB 1721–1899 M 1721–1837 **NLW & Soc Gen**

CAERAU A THRELÁI/CAERAU WITH ELY   *LL*
PR M 1754–1812 supposed in 1831 to be with the executors of the Rev William Davies now apparently lost
C 1742–56, 1761–1952, 1961–73 M 1741–55, 1813–36, 1843–1972 B 1742–56, 1761–72, 1774–1812, 1815–1974 **Glam RO** Mf C 1742–56, 1761–74 M 1741–55 B 1742–56, 1761–72 **NLW**
BT 1724–40, 1742–3, 1745–7, 1751–2, 1754–1824, 1826–67, 1869–70, 1878–82 **NLW** Mf 1724–1837 **Glam RO**
Cop Mfc index PR/BT C 1725–1903 M 1727–1836 B 1724–1903 **NLW**

CAERDYDD/CARDIFF All Saints   *LL*
<St Mary 1867. B at various cemeteries and churchyards — no burial ground at All Saints
C 1867–93 M 1867–99, 1928–64 B 1867–1944 **Glam RO**
BT 1867–8 **NLW**

CAERDYDD/CARDIFF St Andrew   *LL*
<St John 1884. Rededicated as Eglwys Dewi Sant 1956
C 1863–1954 M 1863–1954 B 1863–4, 1884–1911 **Glam RO** Fac **WGAS**
BT 1863–4, 1869–73, 1875–84 **NLW**

CAERDYDD/CARDIFF St Dyfrig   *LL*
<St Mary 1895
C 1885–94 M (Banns 1930–43) B 1895–1927 **Glam RO** Fac C 1885–94 **WGAS**

CAERDYDD/CARDIFF St Illtud   *LL*
<St Andrew
C 1890–1937 **Glam RO**

CAERDYDD/CARDIFF St John   *LL*
C 1669–1921 M 1669–1871, 1887–1903 B 1669–1911 **Glam RO** Fac C 1735–1921 M

1735–1871, 1895–1903 B 1735–1911 **WGAS** Mf CMB 1669–96 **NLW**
BT 1717, 1724–1914, 1916 **NLW** Mf 1717–1837 **Glam RO**
Cop ts PR CM 1813–40 (Adult C 1841–68) B 1813–41 with index **Soc Gen** ts PR C
index 1813–40 **Glam RO & WGAS** Mfc index PR C 1669–1840 M 1669–1837 B
1669–1841 **NLW & Soc Gen**

CAERDYDD/CARDIFF St Mary *LL*
Attached to St John 1607–1842. PR B records burials of parishioners at Cardiff 'Old
Cemetery' (Adamsdown) — St Mary had no churchyard
C 1843–1932 M 1847–1923 (Banns 1902–10) B 1848–1918 **Glam RO** Fac C 1843–1907
WGAS
BT 1843–77 **NLW**

CAERDYDD/CARDIFF St Samson *LL*
<St Mary & Grangetown, St Paul 1924
C 1904–18 (Banns 1930–40) **Glam RO**

CAERDYDD/CARDIFF St Stephen *LL*
<St Mary 1887
C 1878–1927 M 1912–25 (Banns 1912–48) **Glam RO** Fac M 1912–25 **WGAS**

CAERDYDD/CARDIFF St Teilo *LL*
<St Andrew. Parish church of St Andrew and St Teilo since 1956
C 1884–1959 M 1898–1951 (Banns 1898–1923, 1954–88) **Glam RO** Fac C 1884–1921
WGAS

CAERFFILI/CAERPHILLY St Martin *LL*
<Bedwas & Eglwysilan 1850. PR M 1754–1812 recorded in 1831 as being in a separate
volume at Eglwysilan now apparently lost. B 1813–22 entered in PR Eglwysilan
C 1834–1924 Pwll-y-pant 1899–1902 M 1813–20, 1850–1925 (Banns 1868–1915) B
1813–1923 **Glam RO** Fac C 1834–1904 B 1822–89 **NLW**
BT 1816–24, 1826–41, 1846–8, 1850–5, 1857–76 **NLW** Mf 1816–37 **Glam RO**

⋆ CANTON/TREGANNA St John *LL*
<Llandaf/Llandaff 1858
C 1858–1924 M 1858–1927 (Banns 1914–55, 1961–8) **Glam RO** Fac C 1858–68 **WGAS**
BT 1858–69, 1880–90 **NLW**

⋆ CARDIFF/CAERDYDD All Saints *LL*
<St Mary 1867. B at various cemeteries and churchyards — no burial ground at All Saints
C 1867–93 M 1867–99, 1928–64 B 1867–1944 **Glam RO**
BT 1867–8 **NLW**

⋆ CARDIFF/CAERDYDD St Andrew *LL*
<St John 1884. Rededicated as Eglwys Dewi Sant 1956

C 1863–1954 M 1863–1954 B 1863–4, 1884–1911 **Glam RO** Fac **WGAS**
BT 1863–4, 1869–73, 1875–84 **NLW**

★ CARDIFF/CAERDYDD St Dyfrig   *LL*
<St Mary 1895
C 1885–94 M (Banns 1930–43) B 1895–1927 **Glam RO** Fac C 1885–94 **WGAS**

★ CARDIFF/CAERDYDD St Illtud   *LL*
<St Andrew
C 1890–1937 **Glam RO**

★ CARDIFF/CAERDYDD St John   *LL*
C 1669–1921 M 1669–1871, 1887–1903 B 1669–1911 **Glam RO** Fac C 1735–1921 M
1735–1871, 1895–1903 B 1735–1911 **WGAS** Mf CMB 1669–96 **NLW**
BT 1717, 1724–1914, 1916 **NLW** Mf 1717–1837 **Glam RO**
Cop ts PR CM 1813–40 (Adult C 1841–68) B 1813–41 with index **Soc Gen** ts PR C
index 1813–40 **Glam RO & WGAS** Mfc index PR C 1669–1840 M 1669–1837 B
1669–1841 **NLW & Soc Gen**

★ CARDIFF/CAERDYDD St Mary   *LL*
Attached to St John 1607-1842. PR B records burials of parishioners at Cardiff 'Old
Cemetery' (Adamsdown) — St Mary had no churchyard
C 1843–1932 M 1847–1923 (Banns 1902–10) B 1848–1918 **Glam RO** Fac C 1843–1907
WGAS
BT 1843–77 **NLW**

★ CARDIFF/CAERDYDD St Samson   *LL*
<St Mary & Grangetown, St Paul 1924
C 1904–18 (Banns 1930–40) **Glam RO**

★ CARDIFF/CAERDYDD St Stephen   *LL*
<St Mary 1877
C 1878–1927 M 1912–25 (Banns 1912–48) **Glam RO** Fac M 1912–25 **WGAS**

★ CARDIFF/CAERDYDD St Teilo   *LL*
<St Andrew. Parish church of St Andrew and St Teilo since 1956
C 1884–1959 M 1898–1951 (Banns 1898–1923, 1954–88) **Glam RO** Fac C 1884–1921
WGAS

CASLLWCHWR/LOUGHOR   *SB*
C 1717–1969 M 1717–1971 St David 1950–82 St Paul, Garden Village 1950–71 B
1717–1994 **WGAS** Fac C 1717–1921 M 1717–1924 B 1717–1912 **Glam RO** Mf C
1813–50 M 1754–1812 **NLW**
BT 1678–9, 1681–2, 1684, 1686–7, 1694–6, 1700–2, 1704, 1707–8, 1713, 1718, 1725–7,
1730–4, 1736–7, 1740–2, 1745–7, 1750–1, 1753–7, 1759–96, 1798–1800, 1802–3,

1805–83, 1885, 1887–92 **NLW** Mf 1678–1837 **Glam RO**
Cop ts PR M 1754–1837 with index **NLW & Soc Gen**

CASTELL-NEDD/NEATH   *LL*
Lay register CMB 1638–47, 1653–79 **Glam RO** Fac **WGAS**
C 1692–1785, 1787–1900 St David 1867–1902 M 1694–1896 B 1692–1784, 1786–1898
Glam RO Fac **WGAS**
BT 1721, 1723–1861, 1866–8 **NLW** Mf 1721–1837 **Glam RO & WGAS**

CASTELLNEWYDD, Y/NEWCASTLE   *LL*
C 1739–1943 M 1755–1900 (Banns 1823–81) B 1762–1897 **NLW** Fac C 1739–1943 M
1755–1900 B 1762–1897 **Glam RO** C 1739–1943 M 1755–1900 B 1762–1812 **WGAS**
BT 1721, 1723–63, 1765–1824, 1826–62, 1865–76 **NLW** Mf 1721–1837 **Glam RO**
Cop ts PR M 1813–37 with index **Glam RO**

CHERITON   *SB*
PR CB 1783–1812 recorded in 1831 apparently lost (Glam RO survey 1951). Terrier &
inventory 1900 states that an old register was 'supposed to have perished from damp, having
been kept in a wooden box in the church'
C 1813–1992 M 1757–1810, 1813–1969 (Banns 1824–1992) B 1813–1991 **NLW** Mf
(except Banns) **WGAS**
BT 1671–2, 1684, 1700–1, 1704, 1708, 1712–13, 1725, 1727, 1729–39, 1741, 1743–50,
1752–7, 1759–61, 1764–7, 1770–1, 1774, 1778–9, 1781–3, 1785–1800, 1802–3, 1805,
1807–22, 1824–40, 1843–4, 1848–82, 1885, 1887–96, 1898–1905, 1907 **NLW** Mf
1671–1837 **WGAS**
Cop ms PR & BT CMB 1672–1841 **WGAS**

CILÂ/KILLAY   *SB*
<Sgeti/Sketty. The original mission church in Dynfant/Dunvant was replaced by
Cilâ/Killay, St Hilary in 1926. A new church in Dynfant/Dunvant was opened in 1949
C 1897–1981 M 1898–1923, 1926–43, 1953–97 Dynfant/Dunvant 1952, 1957 B 1923–80
WGAS

CILFÁI/KILVEY   *SB*
<Llansamlet & Abertawe/Swansea St Mary 1881
C 1845–1932 M 1857–1971 (Banns 1857–1927) **WGAS** Fac C 1845–1932 M 1857–1936
Glam RO

CILYBEBYLL   *LL*
PR CMB 1736–67 M 1755–1812 recorded in *A digest* ... (Cardiff, 1905) apparently lost
(Glam RO survey 1951). At visitation in 1781 the PR were said to go 'as far down as
1704'
Lay register CMB 1638–47, 1653–79 **Glam RO** Fac **WGAS**
C 1773–1931 M 1813–1929 B 1768, 1774–1812 **Glam RO** Fac **WGAS**
BT 1721, 1723–92, 1794–1821, 1824–68 **NLW** Mf 1721–1837 **Glam RO & WGAS**

CLUN, Y gweler/see LLWYNDERW

CLYDACH St John   SB
<Llangyfelach & Llangatwg/Cadoxton-juxta-Neath 1847
C 1847–1987 St Mary 1905–82 M 1847–1971 (Banns 1905–39) St Mary 1905–82 (Banns
  1939–96) Trebannws/Trebanos 1912–70 B 1847–1981 WGAS Fac C 1847–94 St Mary
  1905–22 M 1847–87 St Mary 1905–31 Trebannws/Trebanos 1912–35 B 1847–1927
  Glam RO
BT 1847–53, 1855–7, 1859–67 NLW

CLYNE gweler/see LLWYNDERW

COCYD, Y/COCKETT gweler/see ABERTAWE/SWANSEA St Peter

COETY/COITY   LL
C 1694, 1713, 1720–1918 M 1738–57, 1759–1950 B 1720–1916 Glam RO Mf 1694,
  1702, 1713, 1720–1844 NLW
BT 1721, 1723–30, 1732–56, 1758–1857, 1873–5 NLW Mf 1721–1837 Glam RO

COGAN   LL
C 1784–1830, 1857, 1932–48 M 1935–45 B 1784–1812 NLW M 1786–1808, 1813–21 B
  1818, 1823, 1948–79 Mf C 1784–1830, 1857, 1932–48 M 1935–45 B 1784–1812 Glam
  RO Fac M 1786–1808, 1813–21 B 1818, 1823, 1948–79 WGAS
BT 1724–52, 1754, 1756–1826, 1828–30 NLW Mf 1724–1837 Glam RO & WGAS
Cop ts PR C 1830–80 NLW & Glam RO Mfc index PR/BT C 1724–1857 M
  1728–1821 B 1724–1823 NLW & Soc Gen

COITY gweler/see COETY

* COLWINSTON/TREGOLWYN   LL
At visitation in 1781 PR was said to go 'so far back as February 1694/5'
C 1766–1951 M 1771–1806, 1813–1949 B 1766–1812 NLW M 1949–83 B 1813–1992
  Mf C 1766–1951 M 1771–1806, 1813–1949 B 1766–1812 Glam RO Fac M 1949–83
  WGAS
BT 1696, 1721, 1723–51, 1753–1862 NLW Mf 1696–1837 Glam RO
Cop Mfc index PR/BT C 1696–1951 M 1725–1836 B 1696–1992 NLW

* COWBRIDGE/Y BONT-FAEN   LL
C 1718–24, 1735–7, 1744–5, 1750–1, 1753–1972 M 1753–1983 (Banns 1823–1993) B
  1735–7, 1750–1, 1753–1928 Glam RO Fac C 1718–24, 1735–7, 1744–5, 1750–1,
  1753–1972 M 1753–1971 B 1735–7, 1750–1, 1753–1928 WGAS
BT 1721, 1724–31, 1733–7, 1739–46, 1748–1881 NLW Mf 1721–1837 Glam RO
Cop Mfc index PR/BT C 1718–1887 M 1721–1837 B 1735–1873 NLW & Soc Gen

* COYCHURCH/LLANGRALLO   LL
C 1736–94, 1797–1959 M 1736–1808, 1813–1953 (Banns 1755–1808, 1824, 1899–1969)

B 1736–1867, 1882–1935 **Glam RO** Fac (except Banns) **WGAS**
BT 1721, 1723–4, 1726–87, 1789–90, 1792–4, 1797–1862 **NLW** Mf 1721–1837 **Glam RO**
Cop ts PR C 1760–1850 Mfc index PR/BT C 1733–1900 M 1723–1837 B 1736–1900 **NLW & Soc Gen**

CREUNANT, Y/CRYNANT *LL*
An ancient chapelry of Llangatwg/Cadoxton-juxta-Neath with earlier CMB entered in the registers of the mother church
M 1838–1942 B 1879–1938 **Glam RO** Fac **WGAS** C 1878– incumbent

CWM AFAN (ABERGWYNFI)/AFAN VALE *LL*
<Glyncorrwg & Llangynwyd 1906
C 1907–42 Y Cymer/Cymmer 1939–88 M 1907–85 (Banns 1907–62) Y Cymer/Cymmer 1927–81 (Banns 1952–88) **Glam RO** Fac C 1907–16 M 1907–14 **WGAS**

CWMAFAN/CWMAVON gweler/see LLANFIHANGEL-YNYS-AFAN/MICHAELSTON-SUPER-AVON

CWMBWRLA gweler/see ABERTAWE/SWANSEA St Luke

CWMLLYNFELL *SD*
<Brynaman
M 1905–76 (Banns 1924–74) **Carm RO**

CYFARTHFA *LL*
<Merthyr Tudful/Merthyr Tydfil 1857
C 1857–1916 M 1857–1928, 1944–89 (Banns 1857–1976) **NLW** Mf **Glam RO**

CYMER, Y gweler/see CWM AFAN/AFAN VALE

CYMMER gweler/see CWM AFAN/AFAN VALE

CYNCOED All Saints *LL*
Opened as daughter church to Llanedern/Llanedeyrn 1923. Parish church since 1979
C 1926–78 M 1930–79 (Banns 1972–7) **Gwent RO** Fac (except Banns) **Glam RO & WGAS**

CYNFFIG gweler/see PÎL A CHYNFFIG, Y/PYLE & KENFIG

DOWLAIS *LL*
<Merthyr Tudful/Merthyr Tydfil 1837
C 1839–1946 Eglwys Gymraeg 1927–8 M 1838–1982 (Banns 1895–1907, 1910–47, 1949–67) B 1839–55, 1881–1920 **Glam RO** Fac B 1839–55 **WGAS**
BT 1839–53, 1862–3 **NLW**

DRENEWYDD YN NOTAIS/NEWTON NOTTAGE   *LL*
At visitation in 1781 the earliest PR was said to include entries of CMB 1687–8, 1691–1703, 1708–14 but these had apparently been lost by 1831. PR CB 1782–1812 has had leaves cut out
C 1715–1941 M 1715–1957 (Banns 1875–1911) B 1715–1952 **NLW** Mf **Glam RO**
BT 1722–1805, 1807–23, 1825–38, 1847–61 **NLW** Mf 1722–1837 **Glam RO**
Cop Mfc index PR C 1715–1900 M 1716–1837 B 1715–1898 **NLW WGAS & Soc Gen**

DUNVANT gweler/see CILÂ/KILLAY

DYFFRYN   *LL*
<Llangatwg/Cadoxton-juxta-Neath & Sgiwen/Skewen 1873
C 1871–1965 M 1874–1970 (Banns 1875–1983) B 1872–1960 **Glam RO** Fac (except Banns) **WGAS**
BT 1909–10 **NLW**

DYNFANT gweler/see CILÂ/KILLAY

EGLWYS BREWYS/EGLWYSBREWIS   *LL*
PR CB 1813– post 1951 M 1781–1808 recorded in 1951 apparently lost (Glam RO survey)
C 1750–1811 M 1752, 1820–1923, 1935–70 B 1752–1807 **Glam RO** Fac **WGAS**
BT 1721, 1724–6, 1728, 1731, 1743, 1745, 1747–98, 1800–17, 1834–5 **NLW** Mf 1721–1837 **Glam RO**
Cop Mfc index PR/BT C 1722–1939 M 1724–1860 B 1721–1935 **NLW**

EGLWYS FAIR Y MYNYDD/ST MARY HILL   *LL*
C 1738–45, 1747, 1751–1985 M 1741, 1747, 1751–79, 1837–1970 B 1741–3, 1747, 1751–1811, 1813–1985 **Glam RO** M 1755–1838 **NLW** Fac C 1738–1985 M 1741–1970 B 1741–1985 **WGAS**
BT 1696, 1721, 1723–7, 1729–46, 1748–9, 1751–1860 **NLW** Mf 1696–1837 **Glam RO**
Cop Mfc index PR/BT CB 1696–1985 M 1696–1837 **NLW**

EGLWYSILAN   *LL*
C 1679–1930 Senghennydd, St Peter 1898–1917 Senghennydd, St Cennydd 1909–47 M 1695–1847, 1853–1922 (Banns 1823–34, 1844–1901) B 1694–1929 **Glam RO** Mf C 1679–1748, 1769–1812 M 1695–1748 B 1694–1748, 1769–1812 **NLW** Fac C Senghennydd, St Peter 1898–1917 Senghennydd, St Cennydd 1909–47 **WGAS**
BT 1696–7, 1717, 1724–1875, 1877, 1880, 1890–1 **NLW** Mf 1696–1837 **Glam RO**
Cop ts PR C 1679–1747 Mfc index PR C 1679–1900 M 1695–1837 B 1694–1891 **NLW**

EGLWYS NEWYDD, YR/WHITCHURCH   *LL*
PR CB 1766–76 M 1754–1812 recorded in 1831 but not in *A digest* ... (Cardiff, 1905) apparently lost
C 1732–66, 1778–1938 M 1732–58, 1813–1929 B 1732–66, 1777–1932 **Glam RO** Fac C 1732–66, 1778–1812, 1870, 1913–44 M 1732–58, 1813–37 B 1732–66 **WGAS**
BT 1717, 1724, 1732, 1734–48, 1750–1, 1754–1875 **NLW** Mf 1717–1837 **Glam RO**

Cop Mfc index PR/BT C 1718–1853 M 1732–1837 B 1717–1838 **NLW**

ELY gweler/see CAERAU A THRELÁI/CAERAU WITH ELY

EWENNI/EWENNY   *LL*
C 1738, 1754, 1757, 1767–1992 M 1755–1967 B 1714–61, 1769–1942 **Glam RO**
BT 1721, 1723–1817, 1819–67, 1870–98 **NLW** Mf 1721–1837 **Glam RO**

* FLEMINGSTON (FLIMSTON)/TREFFLEMIN   *LL*
  C 1576–1725 M 1578–1725 B 157[0?]–1725 **NLW** C 1726–1991 M 1726–48,
  1757–1968 B 1726–1992 Fac C 1576–1725 M 1578–1725 B 157[0?]–1725 **Glam RO**
  Fac C 1726–1812 M 1726–48, 1757–1968 B 1726–1812 **WGAS** Mf CMB 1576–1725
  Soc Gen
  BT 1721, 1724–39, 1741–51, 1753–9, 1761–1814, 1816–17, 1819–29, 1831–54, 1856,
  1858–63, 1865–70 **NLW** Mf 1721–1837 **Glam RO**
  Cop Mfc index PR CB 1576–1900 M 1578–1839 **NLW WGAS & Soc Gen**

FOCHRIW A DERI/FOCHRIW WITH DERI   *LL*
<Pontlotyn & Bargod/Bargoed 1921
M (Banns 1911–49) **Glam RO** C 1917– M 1911– B 1924– incumbent

FFOREST-FACH gweler/see ABERTAWE/SWANSEA St Peter

FFYNNON TAF [TRELYWY]/TAFFS WELL St James   *LL*
Formerly a chapel of ease to Eglwysilan. Transferred to Tongwynlais 1954
C 1897–1933 M 1925–71 (Banns 1942–79) **Glam RO**

GABALFA   *LL*
<Llandaf/Llandaff 1876
C 1876–1927 M 1877–1926 **Glam RO**
BT 1876–85, 1887–1913 **NLW**

GARDEN VILLAGE gweler/see CASLLWCHWR/LOUGHOR

GELLI-GAER   *LL*
PR CB 1707–1800 M 1707–53 recorded in 1940 apparently lost
C 1813–1933 Gilfach, St Margaret 1907–23 M 1754–1929 (partly indexed) B 1812–1922
(partly indexed) **Glam RO** Fac **WGAS** Mf C 1707–1800, 1813–36 M 1707–53,
1802–37 B 1707–1800 **NLW** CB 1707–1800 M 1707–53 **Glam RO**
BT 1696, 1717–18, 1724–1800, 1802–9, 1811–12, 1814–15, 1817–70 **NLW** Mf 1696–1837
Glam RO
Cop ts PR (extracts) C 1759–1800 B 1708–93 **Glam RO**

* GILESTON/SILSTWN   *LL*
  PR M 1783–1810 recorded in 1951 apparently lost (Glam RO survey)
  C 1701–1812 M 1701–79 B 1702–1811 Fac C 1813–1991 M 1820–1970 B 1814–1992

Glam RO Fac C 1701–1812 M 1701–79 B 1702–1811 **WGAS**
BT 1721–2, 1724–32, 1734–8, 1740–2, 1744–9, 1751–5, 1757–8, 1760–8, 1771–1818,
1820–80 **NLW** Mf 1721–1837 **Glam RO**
Cop Mfc index PR/BT C 1701–1940 M 1701–1836 B 1702–1946 **NLW**

GILFACH gweler/see GELLI-GAER

GLAIS, Y gweler/see LLANSAMLET

GLANDŴR/LANDORE   SB
<Llangyfelach 1906
C 1906–33 M 1891–1926 (Banns 1891–1931) **WGAS** Fac (except Banns) **Glam RO**

GLANTAWE   SB
<Cilfái/Kilvey & Llansamlet 1972
C Bôn-y-maen 1931–98 M Bôn-y-maen 1966–71 (Banns 1966–83) Pentre-chwyth
1967–79 **WGAS**

GLYNCORRWG   LL
For entries 1750–3 see Ystradyfodwg PR
CMB 1702–1813 **NLW** C 1750–3, 1813–1988 M 1750–3, 1813–1971 (Banns 1824–1923)
B 1750–3, 1813–1940 Mf CMB 1702–1813 **Glam RO** Fac C 1750–3, 1813–1988 M
1750–3, 1813–1971 B 1750–3, 1813–1908 **WGAS**
BT 1721, 1723–8, 1730–61, 1763–1813, 1815–19, 1821–2, 1824–36, 1839–60 **NLW** Mf
1721–1837 **Glam RO & WGAS**
Cop ts PR CMB 1750–3 Mfc index PR C 1702–1905 M 1724–1837 B 1702–1908 **NLW**

GLYN-TAF/GLYNTAFF   LL
<Eglwysilan, Llanilltud Faerdref/Llantwit Fardre, Llanwynno/Llanwonno 1848
C 1848–1952 M 1848–1981 (Banns 1904–20, 1932–48) Rhydyfelin, St Luke (Banns
1964–76) B 1848–84 **Glam RO** Fac C 1848–87 **WGAS**
BT 1848–77 **NLW**

GODRE'R-GRAIG gweler/see YSTALYFERA

GORSEINON   SB
<Llandeilo Tal-y-bont 1913
C Holy Trinity 1892–1926 St Catherine 1913–79 M Holy Trinity 1883–1978 (Banns
1884–1971) St Catherine 1914–92 (Banns 1980–6) **WGAS**

GOWERTON/TRE-GŴYR   SB
<Casllwchwr/Loughor 1920. PR C 1881– recorded in 1935 apparently lost
C 1906–56 M 1883–1970 (Banns 1882–1959) **WGAS** Fac C 1906–56 **Glam RO**

GREENHILL gweler/see ABERTAWE/SWANSEA St Matthew

GWAUNCAEGURWEN (LLANFAIR CWM-GORS)   *SD*
<Llan-giwg/Llanguicke
C 1936–76   M 1892–1970 (Banns 1925–74) **Carm RO**   Fac (except Banns) **WGAS &**
Glam RO

GWENFÔ/WENVOE   *LL*
C 158[5]–1971   M 158[5]–1970 (Banns 1824–1973)   B 158[5]–1983 **Glam RO**   Fac C
1740–1971   M 1741–53, 1755–1970   B 1740–1983 **WGAS**   Fac/Mf CMB 158[5]–1739
NLW
BT 1724–1866 **NLW**   Mf 1724–1837 **Glam RO**
Cop ts C 1740–1971   M 1741–1971   B 1740–1973 **Glam RO**   Mfc index PR C 1585–1891
M 1586–1837   B 1585–1900 **NLW & Soc Gen**

HIRWAUN   *LL*
<Aberdâr/Aberdare, co Glamorgan & Penderyn, co Brecknock 1886
C 1858–1944   M 1884–1941 (Banns 1899–1960) **Glam RO**

* ILSTON/LLANILLTUD GŴYR   *SB*
C 1653–99, 1730–1985   M 1653–99, 1730–1970 (Banns 1857–1900, 1936–59)   B 1653–99,
1730–1992 **NLW**   Mf (except Banns) **WGAS**
BT 1672, 1678–9, 1681–3, 1686–7, 1693, 1697, 1700–2, 1704, 1711–13, 1716, 1727–56,
1758–98, 1800, 1802–3, 1805–41, 1843–4, 1846–82, 1885, 1887–8, 1890 **NLW**   Mf
1672–1838 **WGAS**
Cop ts BT 1672–1837 **Glam RO**

KENFIG gweler/see PÎL A CHYNFFIG, Y/PYLE & KENFIG

* KILLAY/CILÂ   *SB*
<Sgeti/Sketty. The original mission church in Dynfant/Dunvant was replaced by
Cilâ/Killay, St Hilary in 1926. A new church in Dynfant/Dunvant was opened in 1949
C 1897–1981   M 1898–1923, 1926–43, 1953–97 Dynfant/Dunvant 1952, 1957   B 1923–80
WGAS

* KILVEY/CILFÁI   *SB*
<Llansamlet & Abertawe/Swansea St Mary 1881
C 1845–1932   M 1857–1971 (Banns 1857–1927) **WGAS**   Fac C 1845–1932   M 1857–1936
Glam RO

* KNELSTON/LLAN-Y-TAIR-MAIR   *SB*
Ancient ruined church without records. See Llanddewi
BT 1784, 1790–4, 1872–4, 1876–83 **NLW**   Mf 1784–94 **WGAS**

* LALESTON/TRELALES   *LL*
C 1742–1937   M 1742–1839   B 1742–1936 **NLW**   M 1837–1971 (Banns 1886–1953)   Fac
C 1742–1937   M 1742–1839   B 1742–1936 **Glam RO**   Fac C 1742–1937   M 1754–1971
B 1742–1936 **WGAS**

BT 1721, 1723–1869, 1871–5 **NLW** Mf 1721–1837 **Glam RO**
Cop Mfc index PR/BT C 1721–1899 M 1721–1837 B 1721–1900 **NLW & Soc Gen**

LANDORE/GLANDŴR   *SB*
<Llangyfelach 1906
C 1906–33 M 1891–1926 (Banns 1891–1931) **WGAS** Fac (except Banns) **Glam RO**

LARNOG/LAVERNOCK   *LL*
PR CMB 1733–1812 recorded in 1831 as being in one volume apparently lost in part
C 1769–1956 M 1769–1812, 1815–36, 1842–1902 (Banns 1883–1943) B 1778–1812,
1821–1964 **Glam RO**
BT 1724–7, 1729–1830, 1832–73, 1875–6, 1878–9, 1881, 1883 **NLW** Mf 1724–1837
Glam RO
Cop Mfc index PR/BT C 1724–1904 M 1725–1836 B 1724–1902 **NLW WGAS & Soc
Gen**

LECWYDD/LECKWITH   *LL*
C 1781–1966 M 1781–1810, 1813–1963 (Banns 1823–1959) B 1781–1986 **NLW** Mf
Glam RO
BT 1724–52, 1754–69, 1771–1876, 1878 **NLW** Mf 1724–1837 **Glam RO**
Cop ts PR CB 1830–80 M 1828–82 **NLW** & **Glam RO** Mfc index PR/BT CB
1724–1880 M 1725–1838 **NLW WGAS & Soc Gen**

LISVANE/LLYS-FAEN   *LL*
C 1760–1810, 1813–22, 1862–1980 M 1755–1861 B 1760–1992 **Glam RO** Fac C
1813–1980 M 1755–1811 B 1760–1812 **WGAS**
BT 1724–75, 1777–1821, 1823–7, 1829–30, 1832–80, 1883–4, 1886 **NLW** Mf 1724–1837
Glam RO
Cop Mfc index PR/BT CB 1724–1902 M 1724–1838 **NLW & WGAS**

LISWORNEY see LLYSWYRNY/LLYSWORNEY

LOUGHOR/CASLLWCHWR   *SB*
C 1717–1969 M 1717–1971 St David 1950–82 St Paul, Garden Village 1950–71 B
1717–1994 **WGAS** Fac C 1717–1921 M 1717–1924 B 1717–1912 **Glam RO** Mf C
1813–50 M 1754–1812 **NLW**
BT 1678–9, 1681–2, 1684, 1686–7, 1694–6, 1700–2, 1704, 1707–8, 1713, 1718, 1725–7,
1730–4, 1736–7, 1740–2, 1745–7, 1750–1, 1753–7, 1759–96, 1798–1800, 1802–3,
1805–83, 1885, 1887–92 **NLW** Mf 1678–1837 **Glam RO**
Cop ts PR M 1754–1837 with index **NLW & Soc Gen**

LLANBEDR-AR-FYNYDD/PETERSTON-SUPER-MONTEM   *LL*
C 1745–1811, 1813–1970 M 1745–53, 1755–1812, 1814–1970 (Banns 1755–1834) B
1745–1992 **Glam RO**
BT 1721, 1732–5, 1737–48, 1750–3, 1755–95, 1797–1848, 1850–60 **NLW** Mf 1721–1837
Glam RO

Cop Mfc index PR/BT CB 1745–1900 M 1721–1837 **NLW WGAS & Soc Gen**

LLANBEDR-Y-FRO/PETERSTON-SUPER-ELY　　　　*LL*
C 1749–78, 1780–1966 M 1754–1989 B 1749–78, 1780–7, 1790–1932 **Glam RO** Fac
WGAS
BT 1724–59, 1761–1815, 1817–21, 1824–31, 1833–67 **NLW** Mf 1724–1837 **Glam RO**
Cop printed PR CB 1749–1812 M 1754–1812 (ed A F C Chichester-Langley, 1888)
Cop Mfc index PR/BT C 1724–1900 M 1724–1839 B 1724–1900 **NLW WGAS & Soc
Gen**

* LLANBLETHIAN/LLANFLEIDDAN　　　　*LL*
C 1661–94, 1734–7, 1748–50, 1757–61, 1766–1992 M 1664–89, 1734–7, 1748, 1754–5,
1767–70, 1776–1986 (Banns 1823–1919, 1921–90) B 1661–5, 1674–9, 1685–96, 1734–7,
1748–50, 1758–94, 1813–93 **Glam RO** Fac C 1734–7, 1748–50, 1757–61, 1766–95 M
1734–7, 1748, 1754–5, 1767–70, 1776–1971 B 1734–7, 1748–50, 1758–94 **WGAS** Fac
CMB 1661–96 **NLW**
BT 1696, 1721, 1723–31, 1733–45, 1747–1879, 1881 **NLW** Mf 1696–1837 **Glam RO**
Cop ts PR CMB 1661–96 Mfc index PR/BT CB 1661–1893 M 1664–1837 **NLW**

LLANBRADACH　　　　*LL*
<Caerffili/Caerphilly & Ystradmynach 1904
(Banns 1935–84) **NLW** C 1899– M 1904– incumbent
BT 1909–14 **NLW**

LLANCARFAN　　　　*LL*
C 1618–40, 1724–63, 1775–1810, 1813–1901 M 1618–40, 1724–63, 1788–1970 (Banns
1828–1920) B 1618–40, 1724–63, 1775–1810, 1813–1976 **Glam RO**
BT 1696, 1724–6, 1728–35, 1737–1867, 1870–2 **NLW** Mf 1696–1837 **Glam RO**
Cop Mfc index PR/BT C 1696–1900 M 1618–1838 B 1696–1899 **NLW WGAS & Soc
Gen**

LLANDAF/LLANDAFF　　　　*LL*
C 1724–1933 M 1724–1939 B 1724–1968 **Glam RO** M (Banns 1867–1905) **NLW** Fac
B 1874–1968 **WGAS**
BT 1717, 1725–51, 1753–1890, 1894–6, 1899–1910 **NLW** Mf 1717–1837 **Glam RO**
Cop Mfc index PR/BT C 1724–1844 M 1717–1838 B 1724–1845 **NLW WGAS & Soc
Gen**

LLANDEILO FERWALLT/BISHOPSTON　　　　*SB*
C 1716–1807, 1810–1965 M 1716–1952 (Banns 1899–1959) B 1716–1807, 1810–1979
NLW Mf (except Banns) **WGAS**
BT 1671, 1675, 1677–8, 1681–2, 1686–7, 1690, 1693, 1696–8, 1700–2, 1704, 1707–8,
1710, 1712–13, 1716, 1727–31, 1733–76, 1778–1800, 1802–3, 1805, 1807–82, 1885,
1887–90 **NLW** Mf 1671–1838 **WGAS**
Cop ms PR CMB 1716–1812 Mfc index PR/BT C 1677–1891 M 1678–1838 B
1677–1890 **NLW**

LLANDEILO TAL-Y-BONT *SB*
C 1662–1757, 1782–1980 M 1662–1990 (Banns 1883–1973) St Michael 1934–70 (Banns 1934–75) B 1662–1757, 1782–1960 **NLW** Mf (except Banns) **WGAS** Mf C 1662–1757, 1782–1950 M 1662–1928 (Banns 1883–1918) B 1662–1757, 1782–1960 **Soc Gen**
BT 1672, 1679, 1681–2, 1684, 1693, 1696–8, 1700–1, 1703–4, 1710, 1712–13, 1718, 1725, 1727, 1729, 1731–4, 1736–46, 1749–1800, 1802–3, 1805–59, 1861–5, 1868, 1872–3 **NLW** Mf 1672–1837 **WGAS**

LLANDOCHAU/LLANDOUGH-JUXTA-COWBRIDGE *LL*
C 1583–1984 M 1585–1744, 1756–1812, 1814–1970 B 1583–1812, 1814–1986 **Glam RO**
Fac C 1583–1984 M 1585–1744, 1756–1812, 1814–39 B 1583–1812, 1814–1986 **WGAS**
Fac CB 1583–1812 M 1583–1744 **NLW**
BT 1721, 1724–90, 1792–1863 **NLW** Mf 1721–1837 **Glam RO**
Cop Mfc index PR/BT C 1583–1943 M 1585–1839 B 1583–1986 **NLW & WGAS**

LLANDOCHAU FACH/LLANDOUGH-JUXTA-PENARTH *LL*
At visitation in 1781 PR CB was said 'to go back as far as the year 1754'
C 1784–1938 M 1755–1991 (Banns 1929–88) B 1784–1928 **NLW** Mf C 1784–1938 M 1755–1973 (Banns 1929–88) B 1784–1928 **Glam RO**
BT 1724–52, 1754–64, 1766–1876, 1878 **NLW** Mf 1724–1837 **Glam RO**
Cop ts PR CB 1813–80 M 1830–84 **NLW & Glam RO** Mfc index PR/BT C 1724–1880 M 1725–1839 B 1725–1883 **NLW & WGAS**

LLANDOW gweler/see LLANDŴ

LLANDUDWG/TYTHEGSTON *LL*
Earliest register includes C 1795–1813 by dissenting ministers
C 1758–1813, 1830–1 M 1757–1837 B 1766–1812 **NLW** C 1813–1987 M 1837–1965 (Banns 1824–31) B 1813–1987 Fac C 1758–1813, 1830–1 B 1766–1812 **Glam RO** Fac C 1758–1987 M 1837–1965 B 1766–1987 **WGAS**
BT 1721, 1723–1835, 1837–60, 1862–9, 1871–5 **NLW** Mf 1721–1837 **Glam RO**
Cop Mfc index PR/BT CB 1721–1901 M 1723–1837 **NLW & Soc Gen**

LLANDŴ/LLANDOW *LL*
C 1688–1812 M 1745–1836 B 1688–1812 **NLW** C 1813–1991 M 1839–1969 (Banns 1897–1985) B 1813–1992 Mf CB 1688–1812 M 1745–1836 **Glam RO** Fac M 1839–1969 **WGAS**
BT 1723–4, 1727–1860, 1865 **NLW** Mf 1723–1837 **Glam RO**
Cop ts PR M 1813–37 with index **Glam RO**

LLANDYFODWG *LL*
PR earliest date given as 1748 in 1831 survey
C 1770–1897 M 1755–1812 B 1770–1905 **NLW** Mf **Glam RO**
BT 1696, 1721, 1723–79, 1781–1864 **NLW** Mf 1696–1837 **Glam RO**

LLANDDEWI   *SB*
C 1718–1978 M 1718–1811, 1813–1970 B 1718–1976 **WGAS**   Fac C 1813-1978   M
  1813-1970 B 1813-1976 **Glam RO**
BT 1678, 1684, 1686, 1697, 1702, 1704, 1707, 1710, 1712, 1717, 1725, 1727–31, 1733–6,
  1738–9, 1741–1800, 1802–3, 1805–6, 1808–31, 1833–48, 1850–62, 1864–83 **NLW**   Mf
  1678–1837 **WGAS**
Cop ms PR CMB 1718–1812 **NLW**

LLANDDEWI RHONDDA   *LL*
<Llanwynno/Llanwonno 1914. Church erected 1851
C 1897–1916 M 1854–1924 **Glam RO** B 1894– incumbent Fac C 1897–1916 **WGAS**

LLANDDUNWYD/WELSH ST DONAT'S   *LL*
C 1726–36, 1758–1981 M 1726–47, 1757–1970 (Banns 1824–1979) B 1726–1982 **Glam
  RO** Fac (except Banns) **WGAS**
BT 1724–51, 1753, 1755–69, 1771–89, 1791–1802, 1804–68, 1870–3, 1875–6, 1878, 1881
  NLW Mf 1724–1837 **Glam RO**

LLANEDERN/LLANEDEYRN   *M*
Ancient parish church until 1979. Daughter church to Cyncoed, All Saints 1979–
C 1701–9, 1713–1978 M 1701–9, 1715–1811, 1813–1982 (Banns 1824–1971) B 1701–9,
  1714–1929 **Gwent RO** Fac (except Banns) **Glam RO & WGAS**
BT 1717, 1724–1811, 1813–43, 1845–9, 1853–8, 1864–9 **NLW** Mf 1717–1837 **Glam RO**
Cop ts PR CMB 1700–1837 with index **NLW & Soc Gen** Mfc index PR/BT CB
  1701–1900 M 1701–1837 **NLW & Soc Gen**

LLANENEWYR gweler/see LLANYRNEWYDD

LLANFABON   *LL*
PR CB 1694–1768 M 1694–1753 recorded in 1831 but not in *A digest* ... (Cardiff, 1905)
  apparently lost
C 1769–1916 M 1754–1916 (Banns 1857–1929) Nelson 1904–16 B 1769–1922 **NLW** Mf
  Glam RO
BT 1717, 1724–1870 **NLW** Mf 1717–1832 **Glam RO**

LLAN-FAES/LLANMAES   *LL*
C 1583–1988 M 1583–1968 (Banns 1872–1987) B 1583–1988 **NLW** Mf **Glam RO** Fac
  CMB 1583–1812 **Glam RO & WGAS**
BT 1721, 1723–30, 1732–52, 1754–76, 1778–1869, 1871 **NLW** Mf 1721–1837 **Glam RO**

LLAN-FAIR/ST MARY CHURCH   *LL*
C 1584–1985 M 1577–1759, 1761–1970 B 1602–1985 **Glam RO** Fac C 1584–1985 M
  1577–1759, 1761–1839 B 1602–1985 **WGAS** Fac C 1584–1812 M 1577–1818 B
  1602–1812 **NLW**
BT 1721, 1724–7, 1729–1854, 1856–63 **NLW** Mf 1721–1837 **Glam RO**
Cop Mfc index PR/BT C 1584–1912 M 1577–1839 B 1605–1985 **NLW**

LLANFIHANGEL-AR-ELÁI/MICHAELSTON-SUPER-ELY   *LL*
C 1761–1992 M 1754–1835, 1841–1965 (Banns 1906–72) B 1761–1993 **NLW** Mf **Glam RO**
BT 1721, 1724–6, 1728–79, 1781–1820, 1823–6, 1828–38, 1840–69 **NLW** Mf 1721–1837 **Glam RO**
Cop Mfc index PR/BT C 1721–1905 M 1724–1835 B 1724–1909 **NLW & WGAS**

LLANFIHANGEL Y BONT-FAEN/LLANMIHANGEL   *LL*
C 1755–94, 1796 M 1759–1804, 1816–37, 1841–1969 (Banns 1892–1958) B 1731, 1756, 1763–1811 **NLW** Mf C 1755–94, 1796, 1813–1993 M 1759–1804, 1816–37, 1841–1969 (Banns 1892–1958) B 1731, 1756, 1763–1811, 1813–1991 **Glam RO**
BT 1813–16, 1820–1, 1836–50, 1852–81 **NLW** Mf 1813–37 **Glam RO**

LLANFIHANGEL-YNYS-AFAN/MICHAELSTON-SUPER-AVON   *LL*
Diocesan records suggest that in 1805 this parish had PR going back to 1769
C 1785–1890 M 1786–1930 (Banns 1827–30, 1835–43) B 1785–1862, 1868–90 **Glam RO**
Fac (except Banns) **WGAS**
BT 1696, 1723–8, 1730–1819, 1821–70 **NLW** Mf 1696–1837 **Glam RO & WGAS**

LLANFIHANGEL-Y-PWLL/MICHAELSTON-LE-PIT   *LL*
At visitation in 1771 the rector admitted that 'the last curate's register book I could never find it'
C 1783–1980 M 1783, 1786–7, 1813–1968 B 1784–1980 **Glam RO**
BT 1724–5, 1729–36, 1738–53, 1755–62, 1764–1876, 1878, 1882–1913 **NLW** Mf 1724–1837 **Glam RO**
Cop Mfc index PR/BT CB 1724–1900 M 1725–1838 **NLW & Soc Gen**

LLANFLEIDDAN/LLANBLETHIAN   *LL*
C 1661–94, 1734–7, 1748–50, 1757–61, 1766–1992 M 1664–89, 1734–7, 1748, 1754–5, 1767–70, 1776–1986 (Banns 1823–1919, 1921–90) B 1661–5, 1674–9, 1685–96, 1734–7, 1748–50, 1758–94, 1813–93 **Glam RO** Fac C 1734–7, 1748–50, 1757–61, 1766–95 M 1734–7, 1748, 1754–5, 1767–70, 1776–1971 B 1734–7, 1748–50, 1758–94 **WGAS** Fac CMB 1661–96 **NLW**
BT 1696, 1721, 1723–31, 1733–45, 1747–1879, 1881 **NLW** Mf 1696–1837 **Glam RO**
Cop ts PR CMB 1661–96 Mfc index PR/BT CB 1661–1893 M 1664–1837 **NLW**

LLANFRYNACH gweler/see PEN-LLIN/PENLLYN

LLAN-GAN   *LL*
At visitation in 1781 this parish had no PR for recording marriages
C 1688–1978 M 1725–47, 1763, 1792–1970 (Banns 1824–1977) B 1708, 1716, 1724–1984 **Glam RO** Fac M 1792–1838 B 1813–1984 **WGAS** Mf C 1688–1812 M 1725–47, 1763 B 1708, 1716, 1724–1812 **NLW**
BT 1721, 1723–45, 1747–1810, 1812–50, 1855–60 **NLW** Mf 1721–1837 **Glam RO**
Cop Mfc index PR/BT C 1689–1978 M 1724–1838 B 1705–1984 **NLW & WGAS**

LLANGATWG/CADOXTON-JUXTA-NEATH　　　　*LL*

There was a tradition here that some of the church registers were thrown 'gleefully' into the vicarage fire by 'the demented wife of a former incumbent', D Rhys Phillips, *The History of the Vale of Neath* (Swansea, 1925), 74

Lay register CMB 1638–47, 1653–79 **Glam RO** Fac **WGAS**

C 1738–1965 M 1738–1935 (Banns 1823–44) B 1738–1919 **Glam RO** Fac (except Banns) **WGAS**

BT 1721, 1723–33, 1735–6, 1738–1842, 1848, 1850–6, 1858–65, 1867–8, 1870–2 **NLW** Mf 1721–1837 **Glam RO**

Cop Mfc index PR/BT CB 1721–1899 M 1721–1837 **NLW & Soc Gen**

LLANGEINWYR/LLANGEINOR　　　　*LL*

At visitation in 1771 this parish was said to have a PR going 'about thirty years back'

C 1782–1892 M 1755–1898 B 1782–1882 **NLW** Mf **Glam RO**

BT 1723–1865 **NLW** Mf 1723–1837 **Glam RO**

* LLANGENNITH/LLANGYNYDD　　　　*SB*

C 1726–1993 M 1754–1807, 1813–1971 B 1742–1971 **WGAS** Fac C 1726–98 M 1754–1807, 1813–1971 B 1742–1971 **Glam RO**

BT 1671, 1673, 1677–9, 1682–3, 1686–9, 1691, 1693–4, 1696–7, 1700–1, 1704, 1707–8, 1710–11, 1713, 1725, 1727–37, 1739, 1741, 1743–95, 1797–1800, 1802–3, 1809–31, 1833–46, 1848–51, 1853, 1855–82, 1885, 1887–96, 1898–9 **NLW** Mf 1671–1836 **WGAS**

LLAN-GIWG/LLANGUICKE　　　　*SB*

PR CB 1767–1812 recorded in 1831 apparently lost

C 1703–67, 1813–92 M 1704–1979 (Banns 1823–61) B 1703–67, 1813–81 **WGAS** Fac C 1703–67, 1813–92 M 1704–1859 B 1703–67, 1813–81 **Glam RO**

BT 1672, 1677, 1682–3, 1685–6, 1690, 1693, 1696–7, 1701–2, 1704, 1707–8, 1711–13, 1725, 1727–8, 1730–4, 1736–52, 1754–79, 1782–95, 1797–1800, 1802–3, 1805–35, 1839–42, 1844, 1846–7, 1851–6, 1858, 1863, 1866 **NLW** Mf 1672–1837 **WGAS**

LLANGRALLO/COYCHURCH　　　　*LL*

C 1736–94, 1797–1959 M 1736–1808, 1813–1953 (Banns 1755–1808, 1824, 1899–1969) B 1736–1867, 1882–1935 **Glam RO** Fac (except Banns) **WGAS**

BT 1721, 1723–4, 1726–87, 1789–90, 1792–4, 1797–1862 **NLW** Mf 1721–1837 **Glam RO**

Cop ts PR C 1760–1850 Mfc index PR/BT C 1733–1900 M 1723–1837 B 1736–1900 **NLW & Soc Gen**

LLANGUICKE gweler/see LLAN-GIWG

LLANGYFELACH　　　　*SB*

PR B 1813–1915 recorded in 1966 apparently lost

C 1693–1798, 1802–1958 M 1693–1975 (Banns 1847–1941) Treforys/Morriston 1891–1971 (Banns 1955–90) B 1693–1797, 1802–12 **WGAS** Fac C 1693–1798, 1802–1905 M 1693–1931 B 1693–1797, 1802–12 **Glam RO** Fac CMB 1693–1750

NLW
BT 1682–3, 1686–7, 1693, 1697, 1700–1, 1707, 1710, 1712–13, 1716, 1727–80, 1782–90, 1792–1800, 1802–3, 1805–7, 1809–53 **NLW** Mf 1682–1837 **WGAS** Mf 1682–1794 **Soc Gen**
Cop Mfc index PR/BT C 1686–1905 M 1693–1837 B 1686–1863 **NLW & WGAS**

LLANGYNWYD   *LL*
C 1662–1769, 1849–1901 M 1662–1753, 1851–1909 B 1662–1769, 1856–1902 **Glam RO** C 1769–1849 M 1754–1851 (Banns 1847–63) B 1769–1856 Mf CB 1662–1769 M 1662–1753 **NLW** Fac C 1662–1769 M 1662–1753 B 1662–1769 **WGAS** BT 1721, 1723–1882 **NLW** Mf 1721–1837 **Glam RO**

LLANGYNYDD/LLANGENNITH   *SB*
C 1726–1993 M 1754–1807, 1813–1971 B 1742–1971 **WGAS** Fac C 1726–98 M 1754–1807, 1813–1971 B 1742–1971 **Glam RO**
BT 1671, 1673, 1677–9, 1682–3, 1686–9, 1691, 1693–4, 1696–7, 1700–1, 1704, 1707–8, 1710–11, 1713, 1725, 1727–37, 1739, 1741, 1743–95, 1797–1800, 1802–3, 1809–31, 1833–46, 1848–51, 1853, 1855–82, 1885, 1887–96, 1898–9 **NLW** Mf 1671–1836 **WGAS**

LLANHARAN   *LL*
C 1615–58, 1720–1984 M 1754–1967 B 1641–69, 1719–1812, 1814–1943 **Glam RO** Fac C 1932–84 M 1837–1967 **WGAS**
BT 1721, 1723–39, 1741, 1743–1820, 1822–4, 1826–33, 1846–9, 1851–64, 1868, 1876 **NLW** 1821, 1877–8 **Glam RO** Mf 1721–1837 **Glam RO**
Cop Mfc index PR/BT C 1615–1901 M 1721–1838 B 1641–1900 **NLW & WGAS**

LLANHARI/LLANHARRY   *LL*
PR 1750–1812 recorded in 1831 but not in *A digest ... (Cardiff,* 1905) apparently lost
C 1813–1983 M 1814–1983 B 1813–1982 **Glam RO** Fac C 1951–83 M 1971–83 B 1813–1982 **WGAS**
BT 1725–44, 1747, 1751–1820, 1823–36, 1838–91 **NLW** Mf 1725–1836 **Glam RO**
Cop Mfc index PR/BT CB 1725–1901 M 1725–1837 **NLW & WGAS**

LLANILID   *LL*
C 1706–1809 M 1729–52, 1754–1834 B 1729–31, 1734–44, 1747–1812 **NLW** C 1815–1987 M 1839–1970 B 1813–1978 Fac CB 1706–1812 M 1754–1834 **Glam RO** Fac C 1706–1812, 1815–1987 M 1754–1834, 1839–1970 B 1706–1987 **WGAS**
BT 1696, 1721, 1723–1820, 1822–3, 1826–33, 1846, 1848–63, 1868, 1875–6 **NLW** Mf 1696–1833 **Glam RO**
Cop ms BT 1696, 1721, 1723–8 ts PR M 1813–34 with index **Glam RO** Cop Mfc index PR/BT C 1696–1922 M 1730–1834 B 1696–1924 **NLW**

LLANILLTERN   *LL*
PR 1726–1812 recorded in 1831 but not in *A digest ...* (Cardiff, 1905) apparently lost.
Formerly a chapelry of Sain Ffagan/St Fagans. At visitation in 1781 the earliest PR was 'very good from the year 1695'

M 1756–67 **NLW** CMB 1813– incumbent
BT 1717, 1724–40, 1742–4, 1747–9, 1752, 1755, 1758–63, 1765–90, 1792–1814, 1816–68
NLW Mf 1717–44 **Glam RO**

LLANILLTUD FACH gweler/see LLANILLTUD NEDD

LLANILLTUD FAERDREF/LLANTWIT FARDRE   *LL*
C 16[?26]–7, 16[?30]–49, 1659–1835, 1837–40, 1846–1934 M 16[?26], 1630–48,
1663–1739, 1754–1972 (Banns 1947–59) B 16[?26], 1630–49, 1662–1739, 1757–1832,
1834, 1837–43, 1846–1949 **Glam RO** Fac C 1776–1934 M 1754–1972 B 1776–1949
WGAS
BT 1717, 1724–39, 1741–74, 1776–1828, 1831–2, 1837–9, 1846–61, 1864–5, 1868–9,
1873–4 **NLW** Mf 1717–1837 **Glam RO**
Cop Mfc index PR/BT C 1632–1850 M 1625–1837 B 1632–1857 **NLW & WGAS**

LLANILLTUD FAWR/LLANTWIT MAJOR   *LL*
At a visitation in 1771 this parish had PR going back to 1598
C 1721–1948 M 1721–1990 B 1721–1991 **NLW** Mf **Glam RO**
BT 1721, 1723–1868, 1870 **NLW** Mf 1721–1837 **Glam RO**
Cop ts PR CB 1721–1812 M 1724–1812 **Glam RO** Mfc index PR CB 1721–1900 M
1696–1837 **NLW WGAS & Soc Gen**

LLANILLTUD GŴYR/ILSTON   *SB*
C 1653–99, 1730–1985 M 1653–99, 1730–1970 (Banns 1857–1900, 1936–59) B 1653–99,
1730–1992 **NLW** Mf (except Banns) **WGAS**
BT 1672, 1678–9, 1681–3, 1686–7, 1693, 1697, 1700–2, 1704, 1711–13, 1716, 1727–56,
1758–98, 1800, 1802–3, 1805–41, 1843–4, 1846–82, 1885, 1887–8, 1890 **NLW** Mf
1672–1838 **WGAS**
Cop ts BT 1672–1837 **Glam RO**

LLANILLTUD NEDD/LLANTWIT-JUXTA-NEATH   *LL*
Lay register CMB 1638–47, 1653–79 **Glam RO** Fac **WGAS**
C 1695–1780, 1787–1896 M 1696–1919 B 1696–1780, 1787–1891 **Glam RO** Fac
WGAS
BT 1698–9, 1721, 1723–94, 1796–1861 **NLW** Mf 1698–1837 **Glam RO**

LLANISIEN/LLANISHEN   *LL*
C 1752–1914 M 1754–1939 (Banns 1873–1926) B 1752–1914 **Glam RO** Fac B
1813–1914 **WGAS** Mf CB 1752–1812 **NLW**
BT 1717, 1724–57, 1759–99, 1801–27, 1829–30, 1832, 1834–43, 1845–62, 1864–85 **NLW**
Mf 1717–1837 **Glam RO**
Cop Mfc index PR/BT C 1717–1901 M 1725–1837 B 1717–1900 **NLW & WGAS**

LLANMADOG   *SB*
PR M 1757–1812 recorded in terrier & inventory 1900 apparently lost (Glam RO survey
1952)

C 1724–1992 M 1724–57, 1813–1967 (Banns 1824–1981) B 1724–1991 **NLW** Mf (except Banns) **WGAS**
BT 1672, 1683, 1690, 1700–1, 1704, 1707–8, 1710, 1712–13, 1725, 1727–43, 1745–76, 1778–97, 1799–1800, 1802–3, 1805–6, 1808–17, 1819–20, 1822–35, 1839–82, 1885, 1887–96, 1898–1905, 1908–10 **NLW** Mf 1672–1835 **WGAS**
Cop ms PR/BT C 1673–1840 MB 1672–1840 **Glam RO**

* LLANMAES/LLAN-FAES *LL*
C 1583–1988 M 1583–1968 (Banns 1872–1987) B 1583–1988 **NLW** Mf **Glam RO** Fac
CMB 1583–1812 **Glam RO & WGAS**
BT 1721, 1723–30, 1732–52, 1754–76, 1778–1869, 1871 **NLW** Mf 1721–1837 **Glam RO**

* LLANMIHANGEL/LLANFIHANGEL Y BONT-FAEN *LL*
C 1755–94, 1796 M 1759–1804, 1816–37, 1841–1969 (Banns 1892–1958) B 1731, 1756, 1763–1811 **NLW** Mf C 1755–94, 1796, 1813–1993 M 1759–1804, 1816–37, 1841–1969 (Banns 1892–1958) B 1731, 1756, 1763–1811, 1813–1991 **Glam RO**
BT 1813–16, 1820–1, 1836–50, 1852–81 **NLW** Mf 1813–37 **Glam RO**

LLANRHIDIAN *SB*
C 1730–1885 M 1730–1969 (Banns 1754–1930) B 1730–1908 **NLW** Mf **WGAS**
BT 1671, 1678, 1686–7, 1691, 1697, 1700–2, 1704, 1707–8, 1710, 1718, 1725, 1727–8, 1730–41, 1743–57, 1759–61, 1764–7, 1770–1, 1774–5, 1778–9, 1781–1800, 1802–3, 1805–38, 1840–8, 1850–8, 1860–75, 1878–82 **NLW** Mf 1671–1837 **WGAS**
Cop Mfc index PR/BT C 1671–1885 M 1671–1928 B 1671–1908 **NLW & WGAS**

LLANSAMLET *SB*
C 1704–1981 Birchgrove 1931–73 M 1704–88, 1792–1992 (Banns 1899–1992) Y Glais/Glais 1884–1977 Birchgrove 1954–86 B 1704–1983 **WGAS** Fac C 1704–1920 M 1704–88, 1792–1959 Y Glais/Glais 1884–1970 B 1704–1935 **Glam RO**
BT 1672, 1677–8, 1680–1, 1683–7, 1690, 1693, 1695–7, 1701–2, 1707–8, 1710, 1712–13, 1716–17, 1725, 1727–1800, 1802–3, 1805–17, 1819–72, 1876–8 **NLW** Mf 1672–1837 **WGAS**
Cop ts index PR C 1813–34 B 1861–73 **WGAS & Glam RO** ts PR CB 1807–12 **Soc Gen**

LLANSANFFRAID-AR-ELÁI/ST BRIDE'S-SUPER-ELY *LL*
At visitation in 1781 the PR was said to go back sixty years
C 1747–1991 M 1754–1970 B 1747–1991 **Glam RO** Fac C 1747–1814 M 1754–1970 B 1747–1814 **WGAS**
BT 1717, 1724–51, 1753–60, 1762–1800, 1802, 1804–21, 1823–48, 1851–70 **NLW** Mf 1717–1837 **Glam RO**
Cop Mfc index PR/BT C 1717–1901 M 1724–1837 B 1717–1902 **NLW & WGAS**

LLANSANFFRAID-AR-OGWR/ST BRIDE'S MINOR *LL*
C 1723–1802, 1813–1949 M 1725–30, 1734–1947 B 1723–1807, 1813–1942 **Glam RO**
Fac C 1813–1949 M 1813–1947 B 1813–1942 **WGAS**

BT 1696, 1721, 1723–1816, 1819, 1821–62, 1869–73 **NLW** Mf 1696–1837 **Glam RO**
Cop Mfc index PR/BT C 1723–1899 M 1696–1837 B 1723–1901 **NLW WGAS & Soc Gen**

LLANSANWYR/LLANSANNOR   *LL*
C 1727–1992 M 1727–1984 (Banns 1823–1975) B 1727–1992 **NLW** Mf **Glam RO**
BT 1724–49, 1751–1854, 1856–68, 1880 **NLW** Mf 1724–1837 **Glam RO**
Cop ts PR M 1813–45 with index **Glam RO** Mfc index PR/BT C 1723–1901 M 1724–1845 B 1723–1900 **NLW WGAS & Soc Gen**

LLANSAWEL   *LL*
Ancient parish church until 1866. Chapel-of-ease to Briton Ferry, St Clement 1866-1913. Rebuilt 1891-2 and made a separate ecclesiastical parish 1913
C 1913–51 M 1913–40 B 1913–65 **Glam RO** Fac **WGAS**

LLANTRIDDYD/LLANTRITHYD   *LL*
C 1597–1979 M 1571–1653, 1663–1752, 1756–1811, 1816–1970 B 1571–1978 **Glam RO**
BT 1724–1874, 1876, 1878 **NLW** Mf 1724–1837 **Glam RO**
Cop printed PR C 1597–1810 M 1571–1751 B 1571–1810 (ed H S Hughes, 1888)

LLANTRISANT   *LL*
C 1728–1921 M 1728–1920 (Banns 1857–1927) B 1728–1908 **NLW** C 1921–62 M 1920–39 Fac C 1728–1921 M 1728–1920 B 1728–1908 **Glam RO** Fac C 1855–1962 M 1837–1865 B 1858–1908 **WGAS**
BT 1717–18, 1724–1882 **NLW** Mf 1717–1837 **Glam RO**
Cop Mfc index PR/BT C 1717–1871 M 1717–1837 B 1728–1870 **NLW WGAS & Soc Gen**

LLANTRITHYD gweler/see LLANTRIDDYD

* LLANTWIT FARDRE/LLANILLTUD FAERDREF   *LL*
C 16[?26]–7, 16[?30]–49, 1659–1835, 1837–40, 1846–1934 M 16[?26], 1630–48, 1663–1739, 1754–1972 (Banns 1947–59) B 16[?26], 1630–49, 1662–1739, 1757–1832, 1834, 1837–43, 1846–1949 **Glam RO** Fac C 1776–1934 M 1754–1972 B 1776–1949 **WGAS**
BT 1717, 1724–39, 1741–74, 1776–1828, 1831–2, 1837–9, 1846–61, 1864–5, 1868–9, 1873–4 **NLW** Mf 1717–1837 **Glam RO**
Cop Mfc index PR/BT C 1632–1850 M 1625–1837 B 1632–1857 **NLW & WGAS**

* LLANTWIT-JUXTA-NEATH/LLANILLTUD NEDD   *LL*
Lay register CMB 1638–47, 1653–79 **Glam RO** Fac **WGAS**
C 1695–1780, 1787–1896 M 1696–1919 B 1696–1780, 1787–1891 **Glam RO** Fac **WGAS**
BT 1698–9, 1721, 1723–94, 1796–1861 **NLW** Mf 1698–1837 **Glam RO**

LLANTWIT MAJOR/LLANILLTUD FAWR   *LL*
At a visitation in 1771 this parish had PR going back to 1598
C 1721–1948 M 1721–1990 B 1721–1991 **NLW** Mf **Glam RO**
BT 1721, 1723–1868, 1870 **NLW** Mf 1721–1837 **Glam RO**
Cop ts PR CB 1721–1812 M 1724–1812 **Glam RO** Mfc index PR CB 1721–1900 M
1696–1837 **NLW WGAS & Soc Gen**

LLANWYNNO/LLANWONNO   *LL*
C 1717–1897 M 1717–1910 B 1717–1894 **NLW** Mf **Glam RO**
BT 1717, 1724–1860, 1907–8 **NLW** Mf 1717–1837 **Glam RO**

LLANYRNEWYDD (PEN-CLAWDD)   *SB*
<Llanrhidian 1925
C 1841–84, 1907–88 M 1835–1971 (Banns 1854–1959) B 1841–90, 1907–92 **WGAS** Fac
  C 1841–84, 1948–88 M 1835–1971 B 1841–90, 1907–92 **Glam RO**
BT 1853–4 **NLW**

LLAN-Y-TAIR-MAIR/KNELSTON   *SB*
Ancient ruined church without records. See Llanddewi
BT 1784, 1790–4, 1872–4, 1876–83 **NLW** Mf 1784–94 **WGAS**

LLWYNDERW (Y CLUN/CLYNE CHAPEL)   *SB*
<Ystumllwynarth/Oystermouth 1956
C 1908–87 M 1908–88 (Banns 1908–75) Holy Cross 1961–70 (Banns 1961–86) **WGAS**
  Fac M 1908–25 **Glam RO**

LLWYNELIDDON/ST LYTHAN'S   *LL*
C 1750–1985 M 1748–1812, 1820–1970 B 1749–1983 **Glam RO** Fac **WGAS**
BT 1724–31, 1733–5, 1737–47, 1751–7, 1759–66, 1768–1863 **NLW** Mf 1724–1837 **Glam**
  RO Mf 1724–1800 **Soc Gen**
Cop Mfc index PR/BT CB 1724–1901 M 1724–1838 **NLW**

LLYS-FAEN/LISVANE   *LL*
C 1760–1810, 1813–22, 1862–1980 M 1755–1861 B 1760–1992 **Glam RO** Fac C
  1813–1980 M 1755–1811 B 1760–1812 **WGAS**
BT 1724–75, 1777–1821, 1823–7, 1829–30, 1832–80, 1883–4, 1886 **NLW** Mf 1724–1837
  Glam RO
Cop Mfc index PR/BT CB 1724–1902 M 1724–1838 **NLW & WGAS**

LLYSWYRNY/LLYSWORNEY   *LL*
C 1684–1735, 1737–9, 1747–1812 M 1588–1634, 1687, 1696–1737, 1753 B 1602–38,
  1657–9, 1663–1715, 1719–34, 1747–84 **NLW** C 1813–1992 M 1754–1811, 1813–34,
  1837–1970 (Banns 1823–1981) B 1785–1991 Mf C 1684–1735, 1737–9, 1747–1812 M
  1588–1634, 1687, 1696–1737 B 1602–38, 1657–9, 1663–1715, 1719–34, 1747–84 **Glam**
  RO Fac M 1754–1970 B 1785–1812 **WGAS**
BT 1721, 1723–72, 1774–1867 **NLW** Mf 1721–1837 **Glam RO**

MAESTEG   *LL*
<Llangynwyd
C 1845–98 **Glam RO**
BT 1845–82 **NLW**

MANSELTON   *SB*
<Abertawe/Swansea St John *c*1919
C 1911–60 M 1906–93 (Banns 1908–28) **WGAS** Fac C 1911–42 M 1906–28 **Glam RO**

MARCROES/MARCROSS   *LL*
PR CB 1731–1812, described at visitation in 1781 as 'a small register book of parchment carefully kept,' and recorded in 1940 apparently lost
C 1813–1986 M 1756–1811, 1814–36, 1840–1968, 1972–97 (Banns 1972–83) B 1813–1986 **Glam RO** Fac C 1813–1986 M 1814–1968 B 1813–1986 **WGAS**
BT 1696, 1722–39, 1741–1870 **NLW** Mf 1696–1837 **Glam RO**
Cop Mfc index PR/BT CB 1696–1986 M 1728–1836 **NLW & WGAS**

MARGAM   *LL*
C 1672–1731/2, 1734–1951 Port Talbot 1850–95 M 1675–1731/2, 1735–1837 B 1672–1731/2, 1735–1953 Port Talbot 1850–95 **Glam RO** Fac C 1672–1951 Port Talbot 1850–95 M 1675–1837 B 1672–1953 **WGAS** Fac C 1672–1763 M 1672–1755 B 1675–1754 **NLW**
BT 1721, 1723–1883 **NLW** Mf 1721–1837 **Glam RO**
Cop ts PR with index C 1672–1894 M 1672–1862 B 1672–1953 **WGAS** ts PR C 1672–1894 M 1672–1887 B 1672–1953 partly indexed **Soc Gen** ts index PR C 1859–94 **Glam RO**
Cop Mfc index PR/BT C 1672–1901 M 1675–1837 B 1672–1900 **NLW & WGAS**

MATTHEWSTOWN AND YNYS-BOETH   *LL*
<Penrhiw-ceibr 1903. Formerly known as Tyntetown and Ynys-boeth
C 1903–48 M 1923–71 (Banns 1949–76) **Glam RO** Fac (except Banns) **WGAS**

MERTHYR DYFAN/MERTHYR DOVAN   *LL*
At visitation in 1781 this parish had PR CB beginning 1753. Pre-1812 records were said to be missing in 1831
C 1813–1928 M 1754–1812, 1814–36, 1839–1925 (Banns 1901–53) **NLW** C 1928–65 M 1925–80 B 1813–1990 Fac C 1813–1928 M 1754–1812, 1814–36, 1839–1925 Mf M 1839–1925 **Glam RO**
BT 1724–43, 1745–65, 1767–1853, 1855–64, 1867–82, 1884–7 **NLW** Mf 1724–1837 **Glam RO**
Cop Mfc index PR/BT C 1724–1886 M 1728–1836 B 1724–1900 **NLW WGAS & Soc Gen**

MERTHYR MAWR   *LL*
C 1749–1981 M 1756–1970 (Banns 1823–1988) B 1749–1988 **Glam RO** Fac C 1749–1981 M 1756–1970 B 1749–1812 **WGAS**

BT 1696, 1721, 1723–1874 **NLW** Mf 1696–1837 **Glam RO**
Cop Mfc index PR/BT CB 1696–1899 M 1737–1836 **NLW & WGAS**

MERTHYR TUDFUL/MERTHYR TYDFIL St David *LL*
Built 1847 as chapel of ease to St Tudful/St Tydfil. Succeeded St Tudful/St Tydfil as parish
church in 1968. PR C recorded separately from 1944 and include entries for St Tydfil's
Well
C 1944–60 M 1861–1992 (Banns 1911–80) **NLW** Mf C 1944–60 M 1861–1992 (Banns
1911–80) **Glam RO**

MERTHYR TUDFUL/MERTHYR TYDFIL St Tudful/St Tydfil *LL*
Closed in 1968
C 1704–1968 M 1704–1843, 1846–1968 (Banns 1792–1832, 1889–94, 1957–64) B
1704–1888 **NLW** Fac C 1704–1836 M 1704–1820 B 1704–1833 Mf C 1813–1968 M
1763–1843, 1846–89, 1921–68 (Banns 1792–1832, 1889–94, 1957–64) B 1833–88 **Glam
RO** Fac B 1813–35 **WGAS**
BT 1717, 1724–38, 1740–1851, 1855–8 **NLW** Mf 1717–1837 **Glam RO**
Cop Mfc index PR/BT C 1703–1837 M 1717–1837 B 1704–1838 **NLW WGAS & Soc
Gen**

⁕ MICHAELSTON-LE-PIT/LLANFIHANGEL-Y-PWLL *LL*
At visitation in 1771 the rector admitted that 'the last curate's register book I could never
find it'
C 1783–1980 M 1783, 1786–7, 1813–1968 B 1784–1980 **Glam RO**
BT 1724–5, 1729–36, 1738–53, 1755–62, 1764–1876, 1878, 1882–1913 **NLW** Mf
1724–1837 **Glam RO**
Cop Mfc index PR/BT CB 1724–1900 M 1725–1838 **NLW & Soc Gen**

⁕ MICHAELSTON-SUPER-AVON/LLANFIHANGEL-YNYS-AFAN *LL*
Diocesan records suggest that in 1805 this parish had PR going back to 1769
C 1785–1890 M 1786–1930 (Banns 1827–30, 1835–43) B 1785–1862, 1868–90 **Glam RO**
Fac (except Banns) **WGAS**
BT 1696, 1723–8, 1730–1819, 1821–70 **NLW** Mf 1696–1837 **Glam RO & WGAS**

⁕ MICHAELSTON-SUPER-ELY/LLANFIHANGEL-AR-ELÁI *LL*
C 1761–1992 M 1754–1835, 1841–1965 (Banns 1906–72) B 1761–1993 **NLW** Mf **Glam
RO**
BT 1721, 1724–6, 1728–79, 1781–1820, 1823–6, 1828–38, 1840–69 **NLW** Mf 1721–1837
Glam RO
Cop Mfc index PR/BT C 1721–1905 M 1724–1835 B 1724–1909 **NLW & WGAS**

⁕ MONKNASH/YR AS FAWR *LL*
At visitation in 1781 there was 'an old register book of paper here, but sadly abused before I
had care of it; and but few leaves remain of it; it goes, in some part of it, as far back as
1677'. PR CMB 1746–1812 recorded in 1831 apparently partly lost by 1940
C 1813–1987 M 1754–1969 B 1813–1987 **Glam RO** Fac **WGAS**

BT 1721, 1723–7, 1730–7, 1739–40, 1743, 1745, 1747–8, 1750–1820, 1822–45, 1848–62,
1865, 1869–74 **NLW** Mf 1721–1837 **Glam RO**
Cop Mfc index PR/BT CB 1721–1987 M 1721–1837 **NLW & WGAS**

MORRISTON gweler/see LLANGYFELACH

* MOUNTAIN ASH/ABERPENNAR   *LL*
<Aberdâr/Aberdare & Llanwynno/Llanwonno 1863
C 1859– M 1865– incumbent
BT 1859–74 **NLW**

NANTGARW St Mary   *LL*
Formerly a chapel of ease to Eglwysilan. Transferred to Tongwynlais 1954
C 1897–1933 M 1952–76 (Banns 1952–85) **Glam RO**

* NASH/YR AS FACH   *LL*
Extra-parochial. A private chapel at one time. The manor was the only house in the parish,
which comprises only 200 acres. Population since 1800 averaged about 10, until recent
housing developments

* NEATH/CASTELL-NEDD   *LL*
Lay register CMB 1638–47, 1653–79 **Glam RO** Fac **WGAS**
C 1692–1785, 1787–1900 St David 1867–1902 M 1694–1896 B 1692–1784, 1786–1898
Glam RO Fac **WGAS**
BT 1721, 1723–1861, 1866–8 **NLW** Mf 1721–1837 **Glam RO & WGAS**

NELSON gweler/see LLANFABON

* NEWCASTLE/Y CASTELLNEWYDD   *LL*
C 1739–1943 M 1755–1900 (Banns 1823–81) B 1762–1897 **NLW** Fac C 1739–1943 M
1755–1900 B 1762–1897 **Glam RO** C 1739–1943 M 1755–1900 B 1762–1812 **WGAS**
BT 1721, 1723–63, 1765–1824, 1826–62, 1865–76 **NLW** Mf 1721–1837 **Glam RO**
Cop ts PR M 1813–37 with index **Glam RO**

NEWTON   *SB*
<Ystumllwynarth/Oystermouth 1933
C 1903–78 M 1903–90 (Banns 1903–93) **WGAS**

* NEWTON NOTTAGE/DRENEWYDD YN NOTAIS   *LL*
At visitation in 1781 the earliest PR was said to include entries of CMB 1687–8, 1691–1703,
1708–14 but these had apparently been lost by 1831. PR CB 1782–1812 has had leaves cut
out
C 1715–1941 M 1715–1957 (Banns 1875–1911) B 1715–1952 **NLW** Mf **Glam RO**
BT 1722–1805, 1807–23, 1825–38, 1847–61 **NLW** Mf 1722–1837 **Glam RO**
Cop Mfc index PR C 1715–1900 M 1716–1837 B 1715–1898 **NLW WGAS & Soc Gen**

NICHOLASTON   *SB*
PR 1766–87 recorded in 1831 but not listed in terrier & inventory 1900 apparently lost (Glam RO survey 1952)
C 1787–1811, 1813–1985 M 1797–1969 B 1788–1811, 1815–1984 **WGAS** Fac **Glam RO**
BT 1671–2, 1677–9, 1681–4, 1686–7, 1690–1, 1696–7, 1701, 1707–8, 1710, 1713, 1716, 1725, 1727–54, 1756–8, 1760–75, 1777–89, 1791–1800, 1802–3, 1805–46, 1849–70, 1873, 1875–9, 1882, 1885, 1887–93, 1895–6, 1898 **NLW** Mf 1671–1837 **WGAS**
Cop ts BT 1671–1837 **Glam RO**

NOLTON   *LL*
An ancient chapelry with earlier entries of CMB included in PR Coety/Coity
C 1840–1946 M 1837–1940 **Glam RO** B 1841– incumbent
BT 1844, 1847–57, 1873–5 **NLW**

OAKWOOD   *SB*
<Port Talbot, St Theodore 1920
M 1920–96 **Glam RO**

OXWICH   *SB*
PR 1655–1771 recorded in 1831 and 1728–68 recorded in 1940 apparently lost (Glam RO survey 1952). The latter was listed in terrier & inventory 1900 as being 'leaves of parchment simply sewn together' containing entries of C 1728–72 M 1724–61 B 1724–72
C 1772–1983 M 1777–1970 (Banns 1824–1970) B 1772–1984 **WGAS** Fac (except Banns) **Glam RO**
BT 1671–2, 1677–9, 1681–4, 1686–7, 1690–1, 1696, 1701, 1704, 1707–8, 1710, 1713–16, 1723, 1725, 1727–31, 1733, 1735–67, 1769–71, 1773–93, 1795–6, 1798–1800, 1802–3, 1805–41, 1843–4, 1847–79, 1881–2, 1885, 1887–96, 1898–9 **NLW** Mf 1671–1837 **WGAS**
Cop ms PR & BT CB 1672–1837 M 1673–1837 **WGAS**

OYSTERMOUTH/YSTUMLLWYNARTH   *SB*
C 1719–1961 M 1719–1984 (Banns 1824–47, 1970–89) B 1719–1954 **NLW** Mf (except Banns 1970–89) **WGAS** Mf C 1719–1929 M 1719–1922 (Banns 1824–47) B 1719–1954 **Soc Gen**
BT 1671–2, 1690, 1693, 1695–7, 1700–1, 1716, 1727–61, 1763–5, 1768–86, 1788–93, 1795, 1797–1800, 1802–3, 1805, 1808–71 **NLW** Mf 1672–1837 **WGAS**
Cop ts PR C 1715–1840 M 1714–1840 B 1719–1840 with index **NLW WGAS Glam RO & Soc Gen**

PENARTH All Saints   *LL*
<St Augustine 1895
C 1891–1923 M 1895–1926 (Banns 1915–29) **Glam RO**

PENARTH St Augustine   *LL*
PR 1768–1812 recorded in 1831 but not in *A digest* ... (Cardiff, 1905) apparently lost. At
visitation in 1781 it was recorded that a new PR had been bought 'not above two months
ago' for registering M as well as CB: 'The same doth for all uses in our little parish'. Pre-
1769 register was reported lost as early as 1771 visitation
C 1813–1938 M 1813–1922 (Banns 1824–90, 1899–1905, 1913–46) B 1813–1940 **Glam**
RO
BT 1724–47, 1749, 1751–1813, 1815–16, 1818–30, 1832–51, 1853–88 **NLW** Mf
1724–1837 **Glam RO**
Cop ts PR C 1835–63 M 1831–79 B 1832–86 **NLW Glam RO & Soc Gen** Mfc index
PR/BT CB 1724–1900 M 1725–1837 **NLW WGAS & Soc Gen**

PEN-CLAWDD gweler/see LLANYRNEWYDD

PENDEULWYN/PENDOYLAN   *LL*
C 1569–1632, 1634, 1645 M 1569–1629 B 1569–1633, 1669–72 **NLW** C 1727–1955 **M**
1727–1975 (Banns 1823–1961) B 1727–68, 1787–1968 Fac C 1569–1632, 1634, 1645 M
1569–1629 B 1569–1633, 1669–72 **Glam RO** Mf CM 1569–1632 B 1569–1633 **Glam**
RO & Soc Gen
BT 1717, 1724–33, 1735–9, 1741–3, 1745–52, 1754–80, 1782–1868 **NLW** Mf 1717–1837
Glam RO
Cop Mfc index PR/BT C 1569–1901 M 1569–1840 B 1569–1902 **NLW & WGAS**

PENLLE'R-GAER   *SB*
<Llangyfelach 1937
C 1865–1970 M 1851–1998 B 1866–1961 **WGAS** Fac C 1865–1932 M 1851–1960 **B**
1866–1915 **Glam RO**

PEN-LLIN/PENLLYN (LLANFRYNACH)   *LL*
PR 1733–1812 recorded in 1831 apparently lost
C 1813–1992 M 1813–1970 (Banns 1824–1976) B 1813–1990 **NLW** Mf **Glam RO**
BT 1721, 1723–1851, 1854–6 **NLW** Mf 1721–1837 **Glam RO**
Cop Mfc index CB 1721–1902 M 1731–1845 **NLW**

PEN-MAEN   *SB*
Diocesan records suggest that *c*1790 the registers went 'but 50 years back'
C 1765–1985 M 1765–1970 B 1768–1810, 1815–1985 **WGAS** Fac **Glam RO**
BT 1686–7, 1690, 1696–7, 1700–1, 1704, 1707–8, 1710, 1712–13, 1716, 1730–3, 1735
1737–56, 1758–9, 1761–1800, 1802, 1804–70, 1873–5, 1880, 1885, 1887, 1891–1902
NLW Mf 1686–1837 **WGAS**
Cop ms PR & BT C 1687–1837 M 1686–1836 B 1686–1837 **WGAS**

PEN-MARC/PENMARK   *LL*
At visitation in 1781 PR said to go back with 'considerable omissions' to 1726
C 1751, 1764–1972 M 1751, 1755–1970 (Banns 1939–80) B 1751, 1764–1985 **Glam RO**
Fac C 1751, 1764–1893 M 1751, 1755–1842 B 1751, 1764–1985 **WGAS** Fac C 1751,

1764–1893 M 1751, 1755–1841 B 1751, 1764–1897 **NLW**
BT 1696, 1724–46, 1748–56, 1758–70, 1772–1861, 1863–6, 1868, 1873–87, 1890 **NLW**
Mf 1696–1837 **Glam RO**
Cop Mfc index PR/BT CB 1696–1893 M 1696–1837 **NLW WGAS & Soc Gen**

PENNARD   *SB*
Diocesan records suggest that *c*1790 the registers went back to 1720
C 1743–1965 M 1743–1992 (Banns 1899–1970) B 1743–1944 **NLW** Mf (except Banns)
WGAS Mf C 1743–1965 M 1743–1971 B 1743–1944 **Soc Gen**
BT 1677–9, 1681–4, 1686, 1690, 1693, 1696–7, 1699–1702, 1704, 1707, 1710, 1713, 1716,
1718, 1725, 1727, 1729–40, 1742–71, 1773–6, 1778–80, 1782–95, 1797–1800, 1802–3,
1805–6, 1808–82, 1885, 1887–91 **NLW** Mf 1677–1837 **WGAS**
Cop ms PR CB 1743–67 M 1743–54 **NLW**

PENRHIW-CEIBR   *LL*
<Aberpennar/Mountain Ash 1897
C 1883–1979 M 1884–1986 (Banns 1884–97, 1904–85) B 1904–85 **Glam RO** Fac C
1929–79 M 1919–86 **WGAS**

PEN-RHYS/PENRICE   *SB*
PR M 1776–1811 recorded in 1831 apparently lost (Glam RO survey 1952)
C 1638–52, 1677, 1682–1716, 1728–1993 M [1631]–75, 1681, 1724–73, 1837–1970 B
1637–57, 1681–4, 1707–16, 1724–1987 **WGAS** Fac C 1638–52, 1677, 1682–1716,
1728–1812 M [1631]–75, 1681, 1724–73, 1837–1970 B 1637–57, 1681–4, 1707–16,
1724–1987 **Glam RO**
BT 1672, 1677–9, 1683, 1686–7, 1690, 1701, 1708, 1710, 1713, 1716, 1718, 1725,
1727–33, 1735–45, 1747–67, 1769–71, 1774–1800, 1802–3, 1805–7, 1809–36, 1838,
1840–1, 1843–4, 1846–82 **NLW** Mf 1677–1837 **WGAS**
Cop ts PR C 1638–1715 M 1631–74 B 1643–1715 & ms PR & BT C 1638–1837 M
1631–1837 B 1640–1837 **WGAS**

PENTRE gweler/see YSTRADYFODWG

PENTRE-CHWYTH gweler/see GLANTAWE

PEN-TYRCH   *LL*
At visitation in 1771 the PR were said to begin in 1664 and to be 'carefully kept and in good
preservation'. M 1754–1812 apparently lost
C 1678–9, 1723–1842, 1846–53, 1858–61, 1864–6, 1868 M 1695–1703, 1724–53,
1813–78, 1882–1946 (Banns 1813–34, 1887–95) B 1695–1700, 1723–1841, 1846–53
Glam RO Fac M 1837–78, 1882–1946 **WGAS**
BT 1717, 1724–1821, 1823–33, 1837–40, 1846–53, 1859–61, 1864–6, 1868–9, 1871–4
NLW Mf 1717–1837 **Glam RO**
Cop Mfc index PR/BT C 1678–1868 M 1695–1845 B 1695–1868 **NLW & WGAS**

PEN-Y-FAI   *LL*
<Y Castellnewydd/Newcastle 1903
M 1904–58 (Banns 1904–62) **Glam RO**

PETERSTON-SUPER-ELY/LLANBEDR-Y-FRO   *LL*
C 1749–78, 1780–1966 M 1754–1989 B 1749–78, 1780–7, 1790–1932 **Glam RO** Fac
WGAS
BT 1724–59, 1761–1815, 1817–21, 1824–31, 1833–67 **NLW** Mf 1724–1837 **Glam RO**
Cop printed PR CB 1749–1812 M 1754–1812 (ed A F C Chichester-Langley, 1888)
Cop Mfc index PR/BT C 1724–1900 M 1724–1839 B 1724–1900 **NLW WGAS & Soc**
Gen

* PETERSTON-SUPER-MONTEM/LLANBEDR-AR-FYNYDD   *LL*
C 1745–1811, 1813–1970 M 1745–53, 1755–1812, 1814–1970 (Banns 1755–1834) B
1745–1992 **Glam RO**
BT 1721, 1732–5, 1737–48, 1750–3, 1755–95, 1797–1848, 1850–60 **NLW** Mf 1721–1837
Glam RO
Cop Mfc index PR/BT CB 1745–1900 M 1721–1837 **NLW WGAS & Soc Gen**

* PÎL A CHYNFFIG, Y/PYLE & KENFIG   *LL*
C 1695–1920 M 1695–1837 (Banns 1824–60, 1904–49) B 1695–1925 **Glam RO** Fac
(except Banns) **WGAS**
BT 1696, 1721, 1723–4, 1726–47, 1749–1872 **NLW** Mf 1696–1837 **Glam RO**
Cop Mfc index PR C 1695–1836 M 1688–1837 B 1695–1898 **NLW WGAS & Soc Gen**

PONTARDAWE St Peter   *SB*
<Llan-giwg/Llanguicke
C 1862–1977 All Saints 1887–1949 M 1863–1985 All Saints 1887–1979 B 1862–1948
WGAS Fac C 1862–1915 M 1863–1934 **Glam RO**

PONTLOTYN   *LL*
<Gelli-gaer 1870
C 1870– M 1864– B 1871– incumbent Fac C 1870–1918 M 1864–1928 B 1871–1924
Glam RO

PONT-Y-CLUN A THAL-Y-GARN/PONTYCLUN WITH TALYGARN   *LL*
<Llantrisant 1924
C 1903–57 M 1908–71 Tal-y-garn 1963–77, 1986–7 (Banns 1908–88) B 1903–84 **Glam**
RO Fac B 1903–53 **WGAS**

PORT EINON/PORT EYNON   *SB*
PR M 1807–12 recorded in 1831 apparently lost (Glam RO survey 1952)
C 1740–81, 1786–1921 M 1741–1806, 1813–1970 (Banns 1807–1912) B 1741–82
1787–1939 **WGAS** Fac (except Banns) **Glam RO**
BT 1672, 1681–2, 1684, 1693, 1696–8, 1708, 1710, 1713, 1716, 1725, 1727–33, 1735–9
1741–89, 1792–1800, 1805–83 **NLW** Mf 1672–1837 **WGAS**
Cop ms PR & BT CB 1672–1837 M 1673–1837 with index **WGAS** Mfc index PR/BT C

1672–1921 M 1681–1837 B 1672–1939 **NLW WGAS & Soc Gen**

PORT TALBOT gweler/see MARGAM

PORT TENNANT gweler/see ABERTAWE/SWANSEA St Thomas

PORTHCERI/PORTHKERRY *LL*
C 1776–1969 M 1754–1811, 1815–36, 1841–1983 (Banns 1824–1908) B 1776–1985
Glam RO Fac C 1776–1812 M 1754–1811, 1815–36, 1841–1970 B 1776–1985 **WGAS**
Fac M 1754–1811, 1815–36 **NLW**
BT 1724–49, 1751, 1753–5, 1757–8, 1760–77, 1779–1895 **NLW** Mf 1724–1837 **Glam RO**
Cop ms PR CB 1776–1900 M 1754–1811, 1815–36, 1841–1900 (Banns 1754–1809, 1824–1908) **Glam RO** Mfc index PR/BT C 1724–1899 M 1724–1837 B 1724–1902 **NLW & Soc Gen**

PWLL-GWAUN *LL*
<Llantrisant
M 1920–56 **NLW** Mf **Glam RO** C 1920– B 1931– incumbent

PWLL-Y-PANT gweler/see CAERFFILI/CAERPHILLY

➤ PYLE & KENFIG/Y PÎL A CHYNFFIG *LL*
C 1695–1920 M 1695–1837 (Banns 1824–60, 1904–49) B 1695–1925 **Glam RO** Fac (except Banns) **WGAS**
BT 1696, 1721, 1723–4, 1726–47, 1749–1872 **NLW** Mf 1696–1837 **Glam RO**
Cop Mfc index PR C 1695–1836 M 1688–1837 B 1695–1898 **NLW WGAS & Soc Gen**

RADUR/RADYR *LL*
C 1725–1994 M 1725–1971 (Banns 1824–65) Christ Church 1906–57 B 1725–1926 **Glam RO** Fac C 1916–63 **WGAS**
BT 1717, 1724–45, 1747–1829, 1832–76 **NLW** Mf 1717–1837 **Glam RO**
Cop Mfc index PR/BT C 1725–1900 M 1717–1836 B 1717–1900 **NLW WGAS & Soc Gen**

RESOLFEN/RESOLVEN *LL*
<Llanilltud Nedd/Llantwit-juxta-Neath 1850. The ancient chapel here was in ruins at visitation in 1763 and none of its records survives
C 1850–1953 M 1850–1919 (Banns 1852–61) B 1850–1993 **Glam RO** Fac C 1850–1953 M 1850–1919 B 1850–1969 **WGAS**
BT 1850–61 **NLW**

REYNOLDSTON *SB*
PR M 1787–1812 recorded in terrier & inventory 1900 apparently lost (Glam RO survey 1952)
C 1713–1971 M 1713–86, 1813–1970 B 1713–1993 **WGAS** Fac C 1713–1971 M 1713–86, 1813–1970 B 1713–1812 **Glam RO**

BT 1682–4, 1686, 1690, 1700, 1707–8, 1710, 1712–13, 1716, 1727–31, 1733–6, 1738–42, 1744–7, 1749–58, 1760–76, 1778–91, 1793–1800, 1802–3, 1805–73 **NLW**   Mf 1682–1837 **WGAS**

★ ROATH/Y RHATH St German   *LL*
  <St Margaret 1887
  C 1884–1927 M 1887–1918 **Glam RO** Fac **WGAS**

★ ROATH/Y RHATH St Margaret   *LL*
  C 1731–1923 M 1732–1926 (Banns 1872–1926) B 1740–1876 **Glam RO** Fac C 1897–1904 M 1837–78 **WGAS**
  BT 1717, 1724, 1726–7, 1731–52, 1754–1807, 1809–15, 1817–38, 1840–55 **NLW**   Mf 1717–1837 **Glam RO**
  Cop Mfc index PR/BT C 1724–1879 M 1724–1837 B 1724–1876 **NLW WGAS & Soc Gen**

★ ROATH/Y RHATH St Saviour   *LL*
  <St German 1893
  C 1886–1952 St Francis 1913–67 M 1893–1972 **NLW**   Mf C 1886–1952 M 1893–1972 **Glam RO**

★ RUDRY/RHYDRI   *M*
  C 1626–33, 1639–1758, 1767–1937 M 1640–65, 1696–1753, 1755–1811, 1813–35, 1837–1970 (Banns 1824–1976) B 1637?–66, 1695–1757, 1767–1935 **Gwent RO** Fac (except Banns) **Glam RO** Fac C 1767–1812 M 1755–1835 B 1767–1935 **WGAS**
  BT 1717, 1724–90, 1792–1887 **NLW**   Mf 1717–1837 **Glam RO**
  Cop ts PR C 1626–1757 M 1640–1757 B 1637–1757 **Glam RO**   Mfc index PR/BT C 1625–1900 M 1640–1835 B 1637–1900 **NLW & WGAS**

  RHATH, Y/ROATH St German   *LL*
  <St Margaret 1887
  C 1884–1927 M 1887–1918 **Glam RO** Fac **WGAS**

  RHATH, Y/ROATH St Margaret   *LL*
  C 1731–1923 M 1732–1926 (Banns 1872–1926) B 1740–1876 **Glam RO** Fac C 1897–1904 M 1837–78 **WGAS**
  BT 1717, 1724, 1726–7, 1731–52, 1754–1807, 1809–15, 1817–38, 1840–55 **NLW**   Mf 1717–1837 **Glam RO**
  Cop Mfc index PR/BT C 1724–1879 M 1724–1837 B 1724–1876 **NLW WGAS & Soc Gen**

  RHATH, Y/ROATH St Saviour   *LL*
  <St German 1893
  C 1886–1952 St Francis 1913–67 M 1893–1972 **NLW**   Mf C 1886–1952 M 1893–1972 **Glam RO**

RHOSILI/RHOSSILI *SB*
C 1641–2, 1665–1807, 1813–1978 M 1665–6, 1671–1970 (Banns 1823–1937) B 1642,
1644–5, 1665–1807, 1813–1911 **WGAS** Fac (except Banns) **Glam RO**
BT 1671–2, 1677–9, 1682–3, 1685–8, 1694, 1696–7, 1700–1, 1704, 1707–8, 1710,
1712–13, 1725, 1727, 1729–31, 1733–6, 1738–90, 1794–1800, 1802–3, 1805–69, 1871–82,
1885, 1887–94, 1896, 1898 **NLW** Mf 1671–1837 **WGAS**
Cop ts PR C 1642, 1665–1807, 1813–36 M 1665, 1671–1836 B 1644–5, 1665–1807,
1813–36 **WGAS**

RHYDRI/RUDRY *M*
C 1626–33, 1639–1758, 1767–1937 M 1640–65, 1696–1753, 1755–1811, 1813–35,
1837–1970 (Banns 1824–1976) B 1637?–66, 1695–1757, 1767–1935 **Gwent RO** Fac
(except Banns) **Glam RO** Fac C 1767–1812 M 1755–1835 B 1767–1935 **WGAS**
BT 1717, 1724–90, 1792–1887 **NLW** Mf 1717–1837 **Glam RO**
Cop ts PR C 1626–1757 M 1640–1757 B 1637–1757 **Glam RO** Mfc index PR/BT C
1625–1900 M 1640–1835 B 1637–1900 **NLW & WGAS**

RHYDYFELIN gweler/see GLYN-TAF/GLYNTAFF

SAIN DUNWYD/ST DONAT'S *LL*
C 1572–1658, 1663–1987 M 1570–1655, 1664–1729, 1743, 1747, 1755–1970 B
1571–1658, 1663–1987 **NLW** Mf **Glam RO**
BT 1696, 1721, 1723–42, 1745–1830, 1832–4, 1836–69, 1871 **NLW** Mf 1696–1837 **Glam
RO**
Cop ts PR M 1813–37 with index **Glam RO** Mfc index PR/BT C 1572–1900 M
1570–1837 B 1571–1900 **NLW WGAS & Soc Gen**

SAIN FFAGAN/ST FAGANS *LL*
C 1689–1882 M 1689–1837 B 1689–1966 **NLW** Mf **Glam RO**
BT 1717, 1724–1872 **NLW** Mf 1717–1837 **Glam RO**
Cop Mfc index PR C 1689–1882 M 1689–1837 B 1689–1884 **NLW & Soc Gen**

SAIN NICOLAS/ST NICHOLAS *LL*
C 1762–1915 M 1755–1930 (Banns 1824–1973) B 1762–1966 **Glam RO** Fac C 1762–85,
1813–1914 M 1837–1930 B 1762–85 **WGAS**
BT 1724–54, 1756–1881, 1883 **NLW** Mf 1724–1837 **Glam RO**
Cop Mfc index PR/BT C 1724–1900 M 1724–1837 B 1724–1902 **NLW**

SAIN SIORYS/ST GEORGE-SUPER-ELY *LL*
C 1693–1717, 1722, 1725–33, 1737, 1739, 1753, 1757–1983 M 1697–1715, 1725–33,
1758–1811, 1813–1970 B 1695–1717, 1725–32, 1757–86, 1791–6, 1799, 1802–12,
1814–1984 **Glam RO** Fac **WGAS** Mf 1695–1814 **NLW**
BT 1724–1820, 1822–31, 1833–68 **NLW** Mf 1724–1837 **Glam RO**
Cop Mfc index PR/BT C 1693–1900 M 1697–1837 B 1695–1902 **NLW WGAS & Soc
Gen**

SAINT ANDRAS/ST ANDREWS MAJOR   *LL*
C 1744–57, 1771–1931 M 1749–1940 (Banns 1824–1920) B 1745–56, 1772–1940 **Glam
RO**
BT 1696, 1724–1863, 1865–6, 1869–70, 1872–3 **NLW** Mf 1696–1837 **Glam RO**
Cop Mfc index PR/BT C 1696–1905 M 1696–1837 B 1696–1901 **NLW**

SAIN TATHAN/ST ATHAN   *LL*
PR C 1891– *c*1973 recorded in 1979 apparently lost
C 1677–95, 1750–1891 M 1683–95, 1720–1964 B 1663–95, 1719–50, 1760–7, 1771–1939
Glam RO Fac C 1677–95, 1750–1812 M 1683–95, 1720–1964 B 1663–95, 1719–50,
1760–7, 1771–1812 **WGAS** Mf C 1679–95, 1750–1812 M 1683–95, 1720–1812 B
1663–95, 1719–50, 1760–7, 1771–1812 **Soc Gen**
BT 1721, 1724–87, 1789–1820, 1822–76 **NLW** Mf 1721–1837 **Glam RO** Mf 1721–80
Soc Gen
Cop ms PR C 1675–95, 1750–1812 M 1683–95, 1720–54 B 1663–95, 1719–1812 **NLW**
Mfc index PR/BT C 1677–1891 M 1683–1838 B 1663–1899 **NLW & Soc Gen**

★ ST BRIDE'S MAJOR/SAINT-Y-BRID   *LL*
C 1723–1992 M 1723–1807, 1813–1962 (Banns 1847–1961) B 1723–1955 **Glam RO** Fac
C 1723–1805 M 1723–53 B 1723–1831 **WGAS**
BT 1721, 1723–1864 **NLW** Mf 1721–1837 **Glam RO**
Cop Mfc index PR/BT CB 1721–1901 M 1721–1837 **NLW & WGAS**

★ ST BRIDE'S MINOR/LLANSANFFRAID-AR-OGWR   *LL*
C 1723–1802, 1813–1949 M 1725–30, 1734–1947 B 1723–1807, 1813–1942 **Glam RO**
Fac C 1813–1949 M 1813–1947 B 1813–1942 **WGAS**
BT 1696, 1721, 1723–1816, 1819, 1821–62, 1869–73 **NLW** Mf 1696–1837 **Glam RO**
Cop Mfc index PR/BT C 1723–1899 M 1696–1837 B 1723–1901 **NLW WGAS & Soc
Gen**

★ ST BRIDE'S-SUPER-ELY/LLANSANFFRAID-AR-ELÁI   *LL*
At visitation in 1781 the PR was said to go back sixty years
C 1747–1991 M 1754–1970 B 1747–1991 **Glam RO** Fac C 1747–1814 M 1754–1970
B 1747–1814 **WGAS**
BT 1717, 1724–51, 1753–60, 1762–1800, 1802, 1804–21, 1823–48, 1851–70 **NLW** Mf
1717–1837 **Glam RO**
Cop Mfc index PR/BT C 1717–1901 M 1724–1837 B 1717–1902 **NLW & WGAS**

★ ST DONAT'S/SAIN DUNWYD   *LL*
C 1572–1658, 1663–1987 M 1570–1655, 1664–1729, 1743, 1747, 1755–1970 B
1571–1658, 1663–1987 **NLW** Mf **Glam RO**
BT 1696, 1721, 1723–42, 1745–1830, 1832–4, 1836–69, 1871 **NLW** Mf 1696–1837 **Glam
RO**
Cop ts PR M 1813–37 with index **Glam RO** Mfc index PR/BT C 1572–1900 M
1570–1837 B 1571–1900 **NLW WGAS & Soc Gen**

* ST FAGANS/SAIN FFAGAN   *LL*
  C 1689–1882 M 1689–1837 B 1689–1966 **NLW** Mf **Glam RO**
  BT 1717, 1724–1872 **NLW** Mf 1717–1837 **Glam RO**
  Cop Mfc index PR C 1689–1882 M 1689–1837 B 1689–1884 **NLW & Soc Gen**

* ST GEORGE-SUPER-ELY/SAIN SIORYS   *LL*
  C 1693–1717, 1722, 1725–33, 1737, 1739, 1753, 1757–1983 M 1697–1715, 1725–33,
  1758–1811, 1813–1970 B 1695–1717, 1725–32, 1757–86, 1791–6, 1799, 1802–12,
  1814–1984 **Glam RO** Fac **WGAS** Mf 1695–1814 **NLW**
  BT 1724–1820, 1822–31, 1833–68 **NLW** Mf 1724–1837 **Glam RO**
  Cop Mfc index PR/BT C 1693–1900 M 1697–1837 B 1695–1902 **NLW WGAS & Soc Gen**

SAINT HILARI/ST HILARY   *LL*
  C 1690–1984 M 1690–1994 (Banns 1913–63) B 1690–1985 **Glam RO** Fac C 1690–1984
  M 1690–1970 B 1690–1985 **WGAS**
  BT 1721, 1724–52, 1754–1852, 1854–5, 1857–61, 1864, 1866 **NLW** Mf 1721–1837 **Glam RO**

ST JOHN-JUXTA-SWANSEA gweler/see ABERTAWE/SWANSEA Eglwys Ieuan/St John

* ST LYTHAN'S/LLWYNELIDDON   *LL*
  C 1750–1985 M 1748–1812, 1820–1970 B 1749–1983 **Glam RO** Fac **WGAS**
  BT 1724–31, 1733–5, 1737–47, 1751–7, 1759–66, 1768–1863 **NLW** Mf 1724–1837 **Glam RO** Mf 1724–1800 **Soc Gen**
  Cop Mfc index PR/BT CB 1724–1901 M 1724–1838 **NLW**

* ST MARY CHURCH/LLAN-FAIR   *LL*
  C 1584–1985 M 1577–1759, 1761–1970 B 1602–1985 **Glam RO** Fac C 1584–1985 M 1577–1759, 1761–1839 B 1602–1985 **WGAS** Fac C 1584–1812 M 1577–1818 B 1602–1812 **NLW**
  BT 1721, 1724–7, 1729–1854, 1856–63 **NLW** Mf 1721–1837 **Glam RO**
  Cop Mfc index PR/BT C 1584–1912 M 1577–1839 B 1605–1985 **NLW**

* ST MARY HILL/EGLWYS FAIR Y MYNYDD   *LL*
  C 1738–45, 1747, 1751–1985 M 1741, 1747, 1751–79, 1837–1970 B 1741–3, 1747, 1751–1811, 1813–1985 **Glam RO** M 1755–1838 **NLW** Fac C 1738–1985 M 1741–1970 B 1741–1985 **WGAS**
  BT 1696, 1721, 1723–7, 1729–46, 1748–9, 1751–1860 **NLW** Mf 1696–1837 **Glam RO**
  Cop Mfc index PR/BT CB 1696–1985 M 1696–1837 **NLW**

* ST NICHOLAS/SAIN NICOLAS   *LL*
  C 1762–1915 M 1755–1930 (Banns 1824–1973) B 1762–1966 **Glam RO** Fac C 1762–85, 1813–1914 M 1837–1930 B 1762–85 **WGAS**

BT 1724–54, 1756–1881, 1883 **NLW** Mf 1724–1837 **Glam RO**
Cop Mfc index PR/BT C 1724–1900 M 1724–1837 B 1724–1902 **NLW**

SAINT-Y-BRID/ST BRIDE'S MAJOR   *LL*
C 1723–1992 M 1723–1807, 1813–1962 (Banns 1847–1961) B 1723–1955 **Glam RO** Fac
   C 1723–1805 M 1723–53 B 1723–1831 **WGAS**
BT 1721, 1723–1864 **NLW** Mf 1721–1837 **Glam RO**
Cop Mfc index PR/BT CB 1721–1901 M 1721–1837 **NLW & WGAS**

SENGHENNYDD gweler/see EGLWYSILAN

SGETI/SKETTY   *SB*
<Abertawe/Swansea St Mary 1851
C 1850–1961 M 1851–1984 (Banns 1850–88, 1909–19) B 1851–1993 **WGAS** Fac C
   1850–1913 M 1851–1918 B 1851–1920 **Glam RO**
BT 1851–63, 1865–9, 1871–8 **NLW**

SGIWEN/SKEWEN   *LL*
<Llangatwg/Cadoxton-juxta-Neath 1845
C 1850–1986 M 1850–1993 (Banns 1866–1951) B 1851–1992 **Glam RO** Fac (except
   Banns) **WGAS**
BT 1850–61, 1864–7, 1873–81 **NLW**

SILI/SULLY   *LL*
C 1759–1928 M 1754–1964 (Banns 1823–1931) B 1759–1953 **Glam RO** Fac M
   1754–1812 **WGAS**
BT 1724–33, 1735–46, 1748–1827, 1830–4, 1838–61, 1864–6, 1870, 1872, 1874–80, 1884,
   1898–1907 **NLW** Mf 1724–1837 **Glam RO**
Cop Mfc index PR/BT C 1725–1901 M 1727–1836 B 1725–1900 **NLW & Soc Gen**

SILSTWN/GILESTON   *LL*
PR M 1783–1810 recorded in 1951 apparently lost (Glam RO survey)
C 1701–1812 M 1701–79 B 1702–1811 Fac C 1813–1991 M 1820–1970 B 1814–1992
   Glam RO Fac C 1701–1812 M 1701–79 B 1702–1811 **WGAS**
BT 1721–2, 1724–32, 1734–8, 1740–2, 1744–9, 1751–5, 1757–8, 1760–8, 1771–1818,
   1820–80 **NLW** Mf 1721–1837 **Glam RO**
Cop Mfc index PR/BT C 1701–1940 M 1701–1836 B 1702–1946 **NLW**

★ SKETTY/SGETI   *SB*
<Abertawe/Swansea St Mary 1851
C 1850–1961 M 1851–1984 (Banns 1850–88, 1909–19) B 1851–1993 **WGAS** Fac C
   1850–1913 M 1851–1918 B 1851–1920 **Glam RO**
BT 1851–63, 1865–9, 1871–8 **NLW**

★ SKEWEN/SGIWEN   *LL*
<Llangatwg/Cadoxton-juxta-Neath 1845

C 1850–1986 M 1850–1993 (Banns 1866–1951) B 1851–1992 **Glam RO** Fac (except Banns) **WGAS**
BT 1850–61, 1864–7, 1873–81 **NLW**

SULLY/SILI   *LL*
C 1759–1928 M 1754–1964 (Banns 1823–1931) B 1759–1953 **Glam RO** Fac M 1754–1812 **WGAS**
BT 1724–33, 1735–46, 1748–1827, 1830–4, 1838–61, 1864–6, 1870, 1872, 1874–80, 1884, 1898–1907 **NLW** Mf 1724–1837 **Glam RO**
Cop Mfc index PR/BT C 1725–1901 M 1727–1836 B 1725–1900 **NLW & Soc Gen**

SWANSEA/ABERTAWE Christ Church   *SB*
<St Mary 1874
C 1872–1950 M 1872–1971 (Banns 1889–1900) **WGAS** Fac C 1872–1927 M 1872–1937 **Glam RO**
BT 1872–80 **NLW**

SWANSEA/ABERTAWE Holy Trinity   *SB*
<St Mary 1843
C 1856–1939 M 1877–1941 B 1901–16 **WGAS** Fac C 1856-1939 M 1877-1941 **Glam RO**
BT 1856–82, 1885–6 **NLW**

SWANSEA/ABERTAWE St Barnabas   *SB*
<St Mary 1928
C 1915–58 M 1929–71 (Banns 1928–40) **WGAS** Fac C 1915–58 M 1929–52 **Glam RO**

SWANSEA/ABERTAWE St Gabriel   *SB*
<St Mary 1889
C 1889–1973 St Augustine 1905-94 M 1890–1986 **WGAS** Fac C 1889–1914 M 1890–1922 **Glam RO**
BT 1889–91 **NLW**

SWANSEA/ABERTAWE St James   *SB*
<St Mary 1867
C 1867–1985 M 1867–1979 (Banns 1899–1971) **WGAS** Fac C 1867–1960 M 1867–1971 **Glam RO**
BT 1867–82 **NLW**

SWANSEA/ABERTAWE St John/Eglwys Ieuan   *SB*
Dedication transferred in 1880 from old church in High Street (now St Matthew) to newly-built church at Hafod. Diocesan records suggest that c1790 the registers went back to 1760
C 1797–1800, 1813–1964 M 1813–1971 (Banns 1824–1974) B 1797–1800, 1813–85 **WGAS** Fac C 1797–1800, 1813–1923 M 1813–1918 B 1797–1800, 1813–85 **Glam RO**
BT 1785, 1787–9, 1791–8, 1800, 1802–3, 1805–73 **NLW** Mf 1785–1837 **WGAS**
Cop ts index PR C 1813–42 **WGAS**

* SWANSEA/ABERTAWE St Jude *SB*
  <St Mary 1920
  C 1896–1965 M 1896–1988 (Banns 1896–1962) **WGAS** Fac C 1896-1921 M 1896-1928
  Glam RO

* SWANSEA/ABERTAWE St Luke, Cwmbwrla *SB*
  <St Peter 1911
  C 1886–1957 M 1890–1989 (Banns 1905–78) **WGAS** Fac C 1886–1914 M 1890–1949
  Glam RO

* SWANSEA/ABERTAWE St Mark *SB*
  <St Mary 1888
  C 1888–1971 M 1888–1971 (Banns 1888–1903, 1920–78) **WGAS** Fac C 1888–1918 M
  1888–1931 **Glam RO**
  BT 1894–5 **NLW**

* SWANSEA/ABERTAWE St Mary *SB*
  C 1631–1706, 1712–1978 M 1631–1706, 1712–1941, 1959–89 (Banns 1823–37, 1872–3,
  1894–1979) B 1631–1706, 1712–1937 & cremated remains 1957–79 **WGAS** Fac (except
  M 1924–40 and Banns) **Glam RO** Fac PR CMB 1631–1706 **NLW**
  BT 1676–8, 1681, 1683–4, 1686, 1690, 1693, 1695–7, 1700–2, 1704, 1713, 1717, 1725–36,
  1738, 1740–59, 1761–86, 1788–92, 1794–1800, 1802–3, 1805–82, 1885, 1887–95,
  1898–1905 **NLW** Mf 1676–1837 **WGAS**
  Cop ts index PR C 1827–56 B 1813–85 **WGAS**

* SWANSEA/ABERTAWE St Matthew *SB*
  <St Mary & St John 1886
  C 1886–1992 Greenhill 1918–62 M 1886–1971 Greenhill 1927–49 B 1887–1991 **WGAS**
  Fac M 1886–1927 **Glam RO**

* SWANSEA/ABERTAWE St Nicholas *SB*
  <St Mary 1886. Closed 1920
  C 1886–1920 M 1886–1920 (Banns 1886–1901, 1908–19) **WGAS** Fac (except Banns)
  Glam RO

* SWANSEA/ABERTAWE St Nicholas-on-the-Hill *SB*
  <St Jude 1933
  C 1924–63 Good Shepherd Mission 1927–46 M 1937–89 **WGAS** Fac C 1924-42 Good
  Shepherd Mission 1927-46 B 1937-50 **Glam RO**

* SWANSEA/ABERTAWE St Peter, Y Cocyd/Cockett *SB*
  <St Mary 1878
  C 1856–1987 M 1857–1991 (Banns 1908–39) B 1856–1990 Fforest-fach St Illtud C 1918–
  98 M 1911-85 B 1911-90 **WGAS** Fac St Peter C 1856–1943 M 1857–1919 B
  1856–1923 **Glam RO**

BT 1856–9, 1861–75 **NLW**
Cop ms PR M 1859–69 **NLW**

★ SWANSEA/ABERTAWE St Thomas   *SB*
<St Mary 1888
C 1888–1981 M 1888–1990 (Banns 1953–88) Port Tennant 1903–59 (Banns 1936–58)
  WGAS Fac C 1888–1924 M 1888–1927 **Glam RO**
BT 1888–9 **NLW**

★ TAFFS WELL/FFYNNON TAF [TRELYWY] St James   *LL*
Formerly a chapel of ease to Eglwysilan. Transferred to Tongwynlais 1954
C 1897–1933 M 1925–71 (Banns 1942–79) **Glam RO**

TON-DU   *LL*
<Y Castellnewydd/Newcastle 1923
C 1868–1915 M 1869–1971 B 1868–1933 **Glam RO**
BT see Y Castellnewydd/Newcastle

TONGWYNLAIS St Michael   *LL*
<Yr Eglwys Newydd/Whitchurch 1921. Earliest PR C includes baptisms 1873–8 to be
  entered at Whitchurch
C 1879–1968 M 1922–71 (Banns 1926–82) **Glam RO** Fac **WGAS**

TONPENTRE St David   *LL*
<Ystradyfodwg 1920. Erected 1881, consecrated as a parish 1920
C 1920–85 M 1920–86 (Banns 1920–86) B 1952–73 **Glam RO** Fac C 1920–85 M
  1959–86 **WGAS**

TREBANNWS/TREBANOS gweler/see CLYDACH

TRE-BOETH   *SB*
<Glandŵr/Landore 1965?
C 1928–57 M 1929–89 (Banns 1932–79) **WGAS**

TREFORYS gweler/see LLANGYFELACH

TREFFLEMIN/FLEMINGSTON [FLIMSTON]   *LL*
C 1576–1725 M 1578–1725 B 157[0?]–1725 **NLW** C 1726–1991 M 1726–48,
  1757–1968 B 1726–1992 Fac C 1576–1725 M 1578–1725 B 157[0?]–1725 **Glam RO**
  Fac C 1726–1812 M 1726–48, 1757–1968 B 1726–1812 **WGAS** Mf CMB 1576–1725
  Soc Gen
BT 1721, 1724–39, 1741–51, 1753–9, 1761–1814, 1816–17, 1819–29, 1831–54, 1856,
  1858–63, 1865–70 **NLW** Mf 1721–1837 **Glam RO**
Cop Mfc index PR CB 1576–1900 M 1578–1839 **NLW WGAS & Soc Gen**

TREGANNA/CANTON St John   *LL*
<Llandaf/Llandaff 1858
C 1858–1924 M 1858–1927 (Banns 1914–55, 1961–8) **Glam RO** Fac C 1858–68 **WGAS**
BT 1858–69, 1880–90 **NLW**

TREGATWG/CADOXTON-JUXTA-BARRY   *LL*
Earlier PR possibly mutilated: some entries C 1644–5, 1662–3 on dorse of BT 1735 & 1738
C 1753–72, 1781–90, 1806–9, 1813–89, 1925–51 M 1754–83, 1813–37 Barry Dock, St
  Mary (Banns 1956–63) B 1752–73, 1781–95, 1803–8, 1814–1982 **Glam RO** Fac (except
  Banns) **WGAS**
BT 1724–43, 1745–1867, 1869 **NLW** Mf 1724–1837 **Glam RO**
Cop Mfc index PR/BT C 1724–1889 M 1724–1837 B 1724–1901 **NLW & Soc Gen**

TREGOLWYN/COLWINSTON   *LL*
At visitation in 1781 PR was said to go 'so far back as February 1694/5'
C 1766–1951 M 1771–1806, 1813–1949 B 1766–1812 **NLW** M 1949–83 B 1813–1992
  Mf C 1766–1951 M 1771–1806, 1813–1949 B 1766–1812 **Glam RO** Fac M 1949–83
  WGAS
BT 1696, 1721, 1723–51, 1753–1862 **NLW** Mf 1696–1837 **Glam RO**
Cop Mfc index PR/BT C 1696–1951 M 1725–1836 B 1696–1992 **NLW**

TRE-GŴYR/GOWERTON   *SB*
<Casllwchwr/Loughor *c*1920. PR C 1881– recorded in 1935 apparently lost
C 1906–56 M 1883–1970 (Banns 1882–1959) **WGAS** Fac C 1906–56 **Glam RO**

TREHARRIS St Cynon   *LL*
Formerly chapel of ease to Llanfabon. Joined Treharris St Matthias 1951
M 1863–1971 (Banns 1967–74) B 1907–51 **Glam RO** Fac M 1863–1971 **WGAS**
Cop ts index PR C *c*.1907–*c*.1970 **Glam RO**

TREHARRIS St Matthias   *LL*
<Merthyr Tudful/Merthyr Tydfil, Gelli-gaer 1900
C 1896–1944 M 1900–45 (Banns 1912–60) **Glam RO** Fac M 1900–45 **WGAS**

TREHERBERT St Albans   *LL*
<Ystradyfodwg 1891
C 1893–1959 M 1891–1996 Ynysfaio All Saints 1898–1964 St Mary the Virgin 1940–67
  Glam RO

TRELÁI gweler/see CAERAU A THRELÁI/CAERAU WITH ELY

TRELALES/LALESTON   *LL*
C 1742–1937 M 1742–1839 B 1742–1936 **NLW** M 1837–1971 (Banns 1886–1953) Fac
  C 1742–1937 M 1742–1839 B 1742–1936 **Glam RO** Fac C 1742–1937 M 1754–1971
  B 1742–1936 **WGAS**

BT 1721, 1723–1869, 1871–5 **NLW** Mf 1721–1837 **Glam RO**
Cop Mfc index PR/BT C 1721–1899 M 1721–1837 B 1721–1900 **NLW & Soc Gen**

TRESIMWN/BONVILSTON (BOULSTON) *LL*
PR M 1813–37 apparently lost. Hearsay evidence recorded in 1940 reply to NLW
questionnaire that 'some old registers were seen burning at Bonvilston House after the
death of a Mr Bassett'
C 1761–1983 M 1758–1812, 1837–1970, 1972–91 (Banns 1824–1977) B 1761–1982
Glam RO Fac C 1761–1983 M 1758–1812, 1837–1970 B 1761–1982 **WGAS**
BT 1696, 1724–1817, 1819–24, 1826–42, 1845–55, 1857–81 **NLW** Mf 1696–1837 **Glam
RO**
Cop Mfc index PR/BT C 1696–1900 M 1696–1837 B 1696–1901 **NLW & Soc Gen**

TŶ-COCH *SB*
<Sgeti/Sketty 1957
M 1966–91 **WGAS**

TYTHEGSTON/LLANDUDWG *LL*
Earliest register includes C 1795–1813 by dissenting ministers
C 1758–1813, 1830–1 M 1757–1837 B 1766–1812 **NLW** C 1813–1987 M 1837–1965
(Banns 1824–31) B 1813–1987 Fac C 1758–1813, 1830–1 B 1766–1812 **Glam RO** Fac
C 1758–1987 M 1837–1965 B 1766–1987 **WGAS**
BT 1721, 1723–1835, 1837–60, 1862–9, 1871–5 **NLW** Mf 1721–1837 **Glam RO**
Cop Mfc index PR/BT CB 1721–1901 M 1723–1837 **NLW & Soc Gen**

WAUNARLWYDD *SB*
<Tre-gŵyr/Gowerton 1980. Until 1920 in Swansea St Peter, Y Cocyd/Cockett
C 1888–1951 M 1892–1986 (Banns 1969–84) B 1895–1992 **WGAS**

WELSH ST DONAT'S/LLANDDUNWYD *LL*
C 1726–36, 1758–1981 M 1726–47, 1757–1970 (Banns 1824–1979) B 1726–1982 **Glam
RO** Fac (except Banns) **WGAS**
BT 1724–51, 1753, 1755–69, 1771–89, 1791–1802, 1804–68, 1870–3, 1875–6, 1878, 1881
NLW Mf 1724–1837 **Glam RO**

WENVOE/GWENFÔ *LL*
C 158[5]–1971 M 158[5]–1970 (Banns 1824–1973) B 158[5]–1983 **Glam RO** Fac C
1740–1971 M 1741–53, 1755–1970 B 1740–1983 **WGAS** Fac/Mf CMB 158[5]–1739
NLW
BT 1724–1866 **NLW** Mf 1724–1837 **Glam RO**
Cop ts C 1740–1971 M 1741–1971 B 1740–1973 **Glam RO** Mfc index PR C 1585–1891
M 1586–1837 B 1585–1900 **NLW & Soc Gen**

WHITCHURCH/YR EGLWYS NEWYDD *LL*
PR CB 1766–76 M 1754–1812 recorded in 1831 but not in *A digest* ... (Cardiff, 1905)
apparently lost

C 1732–66, 1778–1938 M 1732–58, 1813–1929 B 1732–66, 1777–1932 **Glam RO** Fac (
1732–66, 1778–1812, 1870, 1913–44 M 1732–58, 1813–37 B 1732–66 **WGAS**
BT 1717, 1724, 1732, 1734–48, 1750–1, 1754–1875 **NLW** Mf 1717–1837 **Glam RO**
Cop Mfc index PR/BT C 1718–1853 M 1732–1837 B 1717–1838 **NLW**

WIG, Y/WICK   *LL*
PR CB pre-1802 recorded in 1831 as being lost. At visitation in 1781 the earliest PR wa
said to go back 'as far as the year 1570'
C 1802–1986 M 1754–1993 (Banns 1825–1923) B 1802–1987 **Glam RO** Fac M
1754–1812 **WGAS**
BT 1721, 1723–91, 1793–1864 **NLW** Mf 1721–1837 **Glam RO**
Cop Mfc index PR/BT C 1721–1915 M 1721–1837 B 1721–1987 **NLW**

YNYS-HIR   *LL*
<Llwynypia & Llanwynno/Llanwonno 1887
C 1888–1940 M 1888–1990 (Banns 1927–79) **Glam RO**

YNYSMEUDWY, St Mary   *SB*
<Llan-giwg/Llanguicke
C 1913–79 M 1927–88 B 1917–83 **WGAS**

YSTALYFERA   *SB*
<Llan-giwg/Llanguicke. The newer church of St David was made parish church o
formation of separate parish 1903
C 1890–1981 M 1903–71 B 1934–91 Godre'r-graig, Holy Trinity C 1874–1917 M
1859–1979 (Banns 1893–1934) B 1868–1933 **WGAS** Fac C 1890–1948 M 1903–2
Godre'r-graig, Holy Trinity C 1874–1917 B 1868–1934 **Glam RO**

YSTRADOWEN   *LL*
C 1761–1973 M 1754–1971 B 17[?80]–1974 **NLW** Mf **Glam RO**
BT 1696, 1725–41, 1743, 1745–1886 **NLW** Mf 1696–1837 **Glam RO**
Cop Mfc index PR/BT C 1696–1904 M 1697–1837 B 1696–1927 **NLW & Soc Gen**

YSTRADYFODWG   *LL*
C 1719–1944 M 1719–61, 1779–1973 (Banns 1779–1826, 1864–1977) Pentre, St Pete
1891–1971 (Banns 1891–1973) B 1719–1968 **Glam RO** Mf CB 1719–34 M 1719–174
NLW Mf CB 1719–1812 M 1719–61 **Soc Gen**
BT 1717, 1724–34, 1736–1819, 1821–39, 1841–3, 1850, 1858, 1861–7 **NLW** M
1717–1837 **Glam RO**
Cop ts PR CB 1719–1812 M 1719–61 **NLW** Mfc index PR/BT C 1717–1883 M
1717–1837 B 1629–1987 **NLW & Soc Gen**

YSTUMLLWYNARTH/OYSTERMOUTH   *SB*
C 1719–1961 M 1719–1984 (Banns 1824–47, 1970–89) B 1719–1954 **NLW** Mf (excep
Banns 1970–89) **WGAS** Mf C 1719–1929 M 1719–1922 (Banns 1824–47) B 1719–195
Soc Gen

BT 1671–2, 1690, 1693, 1695–7, 1700–1, 1716, 1727–61, 1763–5, 1768–86, 1788–93, 1795, 1797–1800, 1802–3, 1805, 1808–71 **NLW** Mf 1672–1837 **WGAS** Cop ts PR C 1715–1840 M 1714–1840 B 1719–1840 with index **NLW WGAS Glam RO & Soc Gen**

MYNWY
MONMOUTHSHIRE

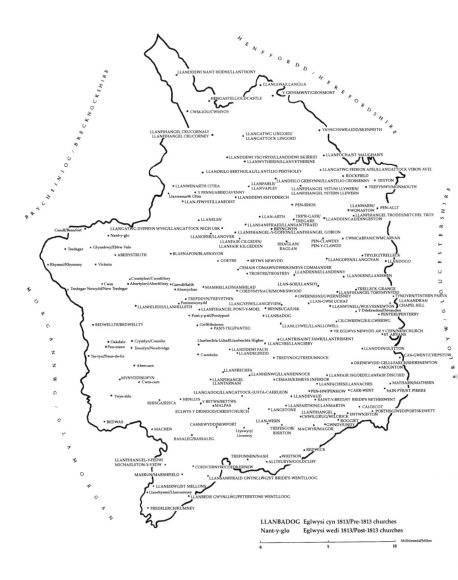

LLANDDEWI NANT HODNI/LLANTHONY

H E N F F O R D D / H E R E F O R D S H I R E

B R Y C H E I N I O G / B R E C K N O C K S H I R E

LLANGIWA/LLANGUA

Y GRYSMWNT/GROSMONT

HENGASTELL/OLDCASTLE

CWM-IOU/CWMYOY

LLANFIHANGEL CRUCORNAU/ LLANFIHANGEL CRUCORNEY

LLANGATWG LINGOED/ LLANGATTOCK LINGOED

YNYSGYNWRAIDD/SKENFRITH

LLANDDEWI YSGYRYD/LLANDDEWI SKIRRID LLANWYTHERIN/LLANVETHERINE

LLANFOCHA/ST MAUGHAN'S

LLANDEILO BERTHOLAU/LLANTILIO PERTHOLEY

LLANGATWG FEIBION AFEL/LLANGATTOCK VIBON AVEL

ROCKFIELD

LLANWENARTH CITRA

LLANFABLE/ LLANVAPLEY

LLANDEILO GRESYNNI/LLANTILIO CROSSENNY

DIXTON

Y FENNI/ABERGAVENNY

LLANFIHANGEL YSTUM LLYWERN/ LLANFIHANGEL YSTERN LLEWERN

TREFYNWY/MONMOUTH

Llanwenarth Ultra

LLANDDEWI RHYDDERCH

LLAN-FFWYST/LLANFOIST

PEN-RHOS

LLANWARW/ WONASTOW

PEN-ALLT

LLANELEN

LLAN-ARTH

TRE'R-GAER/ TREGARE

LLANFIHANGEL TRODDI/MITCHEL TROY

LLANDDINGAD/DINGESTOW

Cendl/Beaufort

LLANGATWG DYFFRYN WYSG/LLANGATTOCK NIGH USK

LLANSANFFRAID/LLANSANTFFRAED

BRYNGWYN

LLANFIHANGEL-Y-GOFION/LLANFIHANGEL GOBION

Nant-y-glo

LLANOFER/LLANOVER

CWMCARFAN/CWMCARVAN

Tredegar

Glynebwy/Ebbw Vale

LLANFAIR CILGEDIN/ LLANFAIR KILGEDDIN

RHAGLAN/ RAGLAN

PEN-CLAWDD/ PEN-Y-CLAWDD

ABERYSTRUTH

BLAENAFON/BLAENAVON

COETRE

BETWS NEWYDD

LLANGOFEN/LLANGOVAN

TRYLEG/TRELLECK

LLANDOGO

Rhymni/Rhymney

Victoria

CEMAIS COMAWNDWR/KEMEYS COMMANDER

TROSTRE/TROSTREY

LLANDENNI/LLANDENNY

LLANISIEN/LLANISHEN

Cwmtyleri/Cwmtillery

Abertyleri/Abertillery

Garndiffaith

LLAN-SOE/LLANSOY

Tredegar Newydd/New Tredegar

Cwm

Abersychan

MAMHEILAD/MAMHILAD

COEDYMYNACH/MONKSWOOD

TRELLECK GRANGE

LLANFIHANGEL TORYMYNYDD

GWERNESNI/GWERNESNEY

LYNDYRN/TINTERN PARVA

TREFDDYN/TREVETHIN

Pontnewynydd

LLANGYFIW/LLANGEVIEW

LLAN-GWM UCHAF

LLANANDRAS/ CHAPEL HILL

LLANHILEDD/LLANHILLETH

LLANFIHANGEL PONT-Y-MOEL

BRYNBUGA/USK

LLANWYNELL/WOLVESNEWTON

Y Ddefawdon/Devauden

PENTERI/PENTERRY

Pont-y-pŵl/Pontypool

LLANBADOG

BEDWELLTE/BEDWELLTY

Griffithstown

PANT-TEG/PANTEG

LLANLLYWEL/LLANLLOWELL

CILGWRRWG/KILGWRRWG

YR EGLWYS NEWYDD AR Y CEFN/NEWCHURCH

ST ARVANS

Oakdale

Crymlyn/Crumlin

Llanfrechfa Uchaf/Llanfrechfa Higher

LLANTRISAINT FAWR/LLANTRISSENT

Pen-maen

Trecelyn/Newbridge

LLANGYBI/LLANGIBBY

LLANDDINOL/ITTON

Tre-lyn/Fleur-de-lis

Aber-carn

LLANDDEWI FACH

LLANDEGFEDD

CAS-GWENT/CHEPSTOW

Cwmbrân

TREDYNOG/TREDUNNOCK

DRENEWYDD GELLI-FARCH/SHIRENEWTON

MOUNTON

LLANFRECHFA

LLANHENWG/LLANHENNOCK

LLANFAIR ISGOED/LLANFAIR DISCOED

MYNYDDISLWYN

Cwm-carn

LLANFIHANGEL LLANTARNAM

CEMAIS/KEMEYS INFERIOR

LLANFACHES/LLANVACHES

MATHARN/MATHERN

Ynys-ddu

LLANGADOG/LLANGATTOCK-JUXTA-CAERLEON

PEN-HW/PENHOW

CAER-WENT

SAIN PŶR/ST. PIERRE

RHISCA/RISCA

HENLLYS

Y BETWS/BETTWS

LLANDEVAUD

SAINT-Y-BRID/ST BRIDE'S NETHERWENT

MALPAS

LLANFARTHIN/LLANMARTIN

CALDICOT

EGLWYS Y DRINDOD/CHRISTCHURCH

LANGSTONE

LLANFIHANGEL

CHWILGRUG/WILCRICK

PORTHSGIWED/PORTSKEWETT

IFFTWN/IFTON

BEDWAS

CASNEWYDD/NEWPORT

LLAN-WERN

TREFESGOB/ BISHTON

GWNDY/UNDY

ROGGIET

MACHEN

Llyswyry/ Liswerry

MAGWYR/MAGOR

BASALEG/BASSALEG

REDWICK

LLANFIHANGEL-Y-FEDW/ MICHAELSTON-Y-VEDW

TREFONNEN/NASH

WHITSON

ALLTEURYN/GOLDCLIFF

COEDCERNYW/COEDKERNEW

MAERUN/MARSHFIELD

LLANSANFFRAID GWYNLLŴG/ST BRIDE'S WENTLLOOG

LLANEIRWG/ST MELLONS

Llanrhymni/Llanrumney

LLANBEDR GWYNLLŴG/PETERSTONE WENTLLOOG

TREDELERCH/RUMNEY

M O R G A N N W G / G L A M O R G A N

B R O G W Y / G L O U C E S T E R S H I R E

LLANBADOG Eglwysi cyn 1813/Pre-1813 churches
Nant-y-glo   Eglwysi wedi 1813/Post-1813 churches

Milltiroedd/Miles

0   5   10

ABERBARGOD/ABERBARGOED gweler/see BEDWELLTE/BEDWELLTY

ABER-BIG/ABERBEEG gweler/see LLANHILEDD/LLANHILLETH

ABER-CARN   M
<Mynyddislwyn 1921
C 1904–24 M 1917–71 (Banns 1917–68) **Gwent RO**

ABERGAVENNY/Y FENNI Holy Trinity   M
<St Mary 1895
C 1888–1976 M 1895–1971 (Banns 1923–50, 1972–88) B 1895–1958 **Gwent RO**

ABERGAVENNY/Y FENNI St Mary   M
C 1653–89, 1692–1707, 1719–1968 M 1653–8, 1663–88, 1695–1706, 1719–1990 (Banns
1905–26, 1941–72) B 1653–89, 1691–1707, 1710–1957 **Gwent RO**
BT 1696, 1725–1835, 1863–86 **NLW**
Cop ts PR C 1652–1707, 1719–1900 M 1653–8, 1663–78, 1719–1900 (Banns 1754–1855)
B 1653–1900 **Soc Gen**

ABERSYCHAN   M
<Trefddyn/Trevethin 1844
C 1835–1947 M 1844–1971 (Banns 1889–1902, 1920–31) B 1835–95 **Gwent RO**
BT see Trefddyn/Trevethin
Cop ts index PR B 1835–95 **Gwent RO**

ABERTYLERI/ABERTILLERY   M
<Aberystruth 1854
C 1855–1934 M 1854–1970 (Banns 1854–1967) **Gwent RO**

ABERYSTRUTH (BLAINA)   M
At visitation in 1771 the register was said to go back 'about ninety six years'
C 1736–1838 M 1736–1837 B 1736–1829 **NLW** C 1838–1946 M 1837–1969 (Banns
1889–1981) B 1829–1974 **Gwent RO** Mf C 1736–1838 M 1736–1837 B 1736–1829
Gwent RO & Soc Gen
BT 1696, 1725–99, 1801–59 (see also Cendl/Beaufort & Nant-y-glo) **NLW**
Cop ms PR/BT (extracts) CMB 1736–1847 **NLW** ts index PR B 1829–1944 **Gwent RO**

ALLTEURYN/GOLDCLIFF   M
C 1728–1924 M 1728–1900, 1903–55 B 1728–1981 **Gwent RO**
BT 1725–50, 1753–6, 1758–98, 1800–19, 1824–48, 1850, 1852–7, 1859–68, 1870,
1872–80, 1882–92 **NLW**
Cop ts PR B 1813–1981 with index **Gwent RO & Soc Gen**

BASALEG/BASSALEG   M
C 1742–62, 1768–1908 M 1743–1922 (Banns 1933–50) B 1742–62, 1768–1922 **Gwent
RO**

BT 1725–31, 1735–75, 1777–1876 **NLW**
Cop ts (index only in part) PR C 1768–1908 M 1813–37 B 1813–1921 with index **Gwent RO**

⋆ BEAUFORT/CENDL *M*
<Llangatwg/Llangattock & Llangynidr, co Brecknock, Aberystruth & Bedwellte/Bedwellty 1846. New church of St David replaced St John as parish church 1890
C 1843–1958 M 1891–1975 St John 1873–1946 (Banns 1891–1971) B 1896–1961 St John 1843–1915 **Gwent RO**

BEDWAS *M*
C 1635–1767, 1769–1936 M 1653–1811, 1813–1971 (Banns 1930–54, 1956–61) B 1653–1753, 1769–1942 **Gwent RO** Fac CMB 1653–98 **NLW**
BT 1717, 1725–64, 1766–75, 1777–1811, 1813–88 **NLW**
Cop ms PR C 1641–1767 M 1653–1754 B 1653–1753 with index **Gwent RO** C 1635–1715 M 1715–39 B 1656–1730 **Gwent RO & Soc Gen**

BEDWELLTE/BEDWELLTY *M*
C 1624–1954 Aberbargod/Aberbargoed 1905–58 St John, Markham 1957–79 St Mary, Hollybush 1957–75 M 1634–1974 (Banns 1829–62, 1960–82) B 1627–1921 **Gwent RO** Fac C 1624–1812 M 1634–1754 B 1627–1812 **NLW**
BT 1696, 1717, 1724–75, 1777–97, 1799–1811, 1813–79 (see also Tredegar) **NLW**
Cop ms PR CMB 1624–1812 **NLW** ts PR C 1624–1814 M 1634–1754 B 1627–1815 with index ts PR C 1624–1731 M 1634–1732 B 1627–1733 **Gwent RO** M 1815–17 **Soc Gen**

BETWS, Y/BETTWS *M*
C 1696–1757, 1785–1810, 1813–1969 M 1696–1752, 1756–1837, 1839–1971 (Banns 1826–1977) B 1696–1759, 1784–1810, 1823–1977 **Gwent RO**
BT 1725–75, 1777–1834, 1836, 1838–40, 1844, 1847, 1849–50, 1852, 1856–7, 1860–4, 1867–9, 1871–2 **NLW**

BETWS NEWYDD *M*
C 1734–1974 M 1734–73, 1796–1836 (Banns 1920–78) B 1734–1973 **NLW** Mf **Gwent RO**
BT 1696, 1726, 1728–1821, 1823–4, 1826, 1832–76 (see also Llan-arth) **NLW**
Cop ts C 1813–1974 M 1796–1836 B 1813–1973 with index **Gwent RO & Soc Gen**

⋆ BISHTON/TREFESGOB *M*
PR stolen from the church in 1821 (1831 survey). Visitation returns reported no PR CB in 1781 where there had been one ten years earlier
C 1793–1991 M 1800–1967 B 1813–1990 **Gwent RO**
BT 1696, 1725–56, 1758–96, 1798–1819, 1823, 1826–43, 1845–57, 1859–68, 1870–1, 1873–7 **NLW** Mf **Soc Gen**
Cop ts PR C 1793–1899 M 1800–13, 1838–1900 B 1806–11, 1814–1900 **Soc Gen**

BLAENAFON/BLAENAVON   *M*
<Llanofer/Llanover, Llan-ffwyst/Llanfoist, Llanwenarth & Abersychan 1860
C 1804–1950 M 1805–1971 B 1805–74, 1885–1936 **Gwent RO**
BT 1806–42, 1847–51 **NLW**
Cop ts index PR B 1805–19 & ts PR B 1813–96 with index **Gwent RO**

BLAINA gweler/see ABERYSTRUTH

BRYNBUGA/USK   *M*
At visitation in 1771 the incumbent claimed that 'the most antient date I can find in the parish is from 1701'
C 1742–1963 M 1742–1957 (Banns 1824–1965) B 1742–1953 **Gwent RO**
BT 1696, 1725–1858, 1865–1900 **NLW**
Cop ms PR/BT (extracts) CMB 1696–1785 **NLW**

BRYNGWYN   *M*
C 1660–1934 M 1665–1738, 1751–2, 1755–1811, 1813–1995 (Banns 1824–1994) B 1666–1740, 1744–70, 1772–1925 **Gwent RO**
BT 1696, 1725–1823, 1826–72, 1874–92 **NLW**
Cop ms PR (extracts) CMB 1664–1802 **NLW** ts PR C 1641–1900 M 1634–1738, 1751–2, 1755–1811, 1813–96 B 1644–1740, 1742–69, 1772–1900 with index **Gwent RO & Soc Gen**

CAERLEON gweler/see LLANGATTOCK-JUXTA-CAERLEON

CAERLLION gweler/see LLANGADOG

CAER-WENT   *M*
C 1704–13, 1752–1944 M 1706–13, 1753–1834, 1839–1970 B 1568–1711, 1752–1811, 1813–1915 **Gwent RO** Fac C 1704–13 M 1706–13 B 1568–1713 **NLW**
BT 1725–50, 1752–1881 **NLW**
Cop printed PR C 1704–12 & extracts 1752–1812 M 1706–13, 1753–1812 B 1568–1605, 1630–60 with gaps, 1661–1711 & extracts 1753–1811 (ed J A Bradney 1920)
Cop ts index to Bradney's printed version of PR **Gwent RO** PR C extracts 1660–1712 C 1752–1900 M 1706–13, 1753–1834, 1839–1900 B 1568–1646, 1661–1711, 1752–1811, 1813–1900 **Soc Gen**

CALDICOT   *M*
C 1716–1888 M 1719–1837 (Banns 1900–35) B 1716–1976 **Gwent RO**
BT 1725–39, 1741–61, 1763–1870, 1872–4, 1879–80 **NLW**
Cop ts PR CB 1791–1900 M 1754–1900 **Soc Gen**

CAS-GWENT/CHEPSTOW   *M*
CB 1595–1757, 1761–1924 M 1595–1611, 1695–1925 (Banns 1912–26, 1953–66) **Gwent RO**
BT 1725–30, 1732–63, 1765–1812, 1875–96 **NLW** 1813–21, 1823–30, 1833–68 **Gwent RO**

Cop printed PR (extracts) C 1595–1743 M 1595–1819 B 1595–1924 (ed I Waters)
Cop ts PR C 1813–1900 M 1754–1900 (Banns 1779–1813) B 1813–39 with index **Gwent
RO** ts PR (extracts) 1558–1924 & ts PR CMB 1595–1900 **Soc Gen**

CASNEWYDD/NEWPORT All Saints   *M*
<St Woolos 1899
C 1898–1952 M 1899–1978 (Banns 1899–1908, 1913–62) **Gwent RO**

CASNEWYDD/NEWPORT Holy Trinity   *M*
<St Woolos 1864. C 1857–64 entered in PR St Paul. Closed 1975
C 1852–7, 1864–1975 St Peter 1887–1984 M 1862–1975 (Banns 1887–1956, 1960–7)
Gwent RO
BT 1864–84 **NLW**

CASNEWYDD/NEWPORT St John Evangelist & St Mary   *M*
<Eglwys y Drindod/Christchurch 1860. St Mary acted as parish church 1949–52 owing to
fire damage at St John
C 1866–1975 St Mary 1899–1952 M 1861–1977 St Mary 1949–52 **Gwent RO**

CASNEWYDD/NEWPORT St Julian   *M*
<Eglwys y Drindod/Christchurch & St John Evangelist 1921
C 1899–1990 M 1922–95 (Banns 1921–96) **Gwent RO**

CASNEWYDD/NEWPORT St Mark   *M*
<St Woolos 1875
C 1875–1968 M 1875–1971 (Banns 1932–46) **Gwent RO**

CASNEWYDD/NEWPORT St Mary gweler/see CASNEWYDD/NEWPORT St John
Evangelist

CASNEWYDD/NEWPORT St Matthew   *M*
<St John Evangelist 1911
C 1896–1938 M 1911–71 (Banns 1911–74) **Gwent RO**

CASNEWYDD/NEWPORT St Paul   *M*
<St Woolos 1839
C 1837–1962 St Thomas 1950–83 M 1840–1985 (Banns 1978–84) B 'register of funerals'
1953–84 **Gwent RO**

CASNEWYDD/NEWPORT St Peter gweler/see CASNEWYDD/NEWPORT Holy
Trinity

CASNEWYDD/NEWPORT St Stephen   *M*
<Holy Trinity 1921. Joined with Holy Trinity 1970
C 1884–95, 1921–81 M 1922–72 **Gwent RO**

CASNEWYDD/NEWPORT St Teilo   *M*
<Eglwys y Drindod/Christchurch, St Andrew & Llan-wern 1966
M 1966–84 (Banns 1966–86) **Gwent RO**

CASNEWYDD/NEWPORT St Thomas gweler/see CASNEWYDD/NEWPORT St Paul

CASNEWYDD/NEWPORT St Woolos   *M*
C 1702–42, 1769–1931 M 1702–49, 1754–1930 B 1702–43, 1769–1882 **Gwent RO**
BT 1725–75, 1777–1837, 1843–50, 1852–87 **NLW**
Cop ms PR (extracts) CMB 1702–1835 **NLW** ts PR C 1702–42, 1769–1905 M 1702–49,
1754–1900 B 1692, 1702–43, 1769–1825, 1829–71 with index **Gwent RO & Soc Gen**

CEMAIS/KEMEYS INFERIOR   *M*
At visitation in 1781 it was claimed that the register went back to 1662
C 1701–1951 M 1701–52, 1756–1906, 1910–47 (Banns 1823–1924) B 1701–1959 **NLW**
Mf **Gwent RO**
BT 1725–1819, 1821, 1823–9, 1831–67, 1869–79, 1881, 1886–8 **NLW**
Cop ts PR/BT C 1701–1840 M 1701–1837 B 1701–1838 **NLW & Soc Gen**

CEMAIS COMAWNDWR/KEMEYS COMMANDER   *M*
At visitation in 1771 a PR 'bear[ing] date 1740' was recorded, but by 1781 it was said that
'this affair has been greatly neglected by former ministers, nor is there any register found
prior to the year 1780 of births and burials. At present [1781] there is one duly kept'.
Neither of these registers nor that of marriages said to be then in use seems to have survived
C 1813–1973 M 1813–1970 (Banns 1920–78) B 1813–1984 **NLW** Mf **Gwent RO**
BT 1696, 1726–57, 1759–60, 1762–1811, 1813–65, 1867–75, 1877–8 **NLW**
Cop ts PR C 1813–1973 M 1813–1970 with index **Gwent RO & Soc Gen**

CENDL/BEAUFORT   *M*
<Llangatwg/Llangattock & Llangynidr, co Brecknock, Aberystruth & Bedwellte/Bedwellty
1846. New church of St David replaced St John as parish church 1890
C 1843–1958 M 1891–1975 St John 1873–1946 (Banns 1891–1971) B 1896–1961 St John
1843–1915 **Gwent RO**

CHAPEL HILL/LLANANDRAS (ABATY TYNDYRN/TINTERN ABBEY)   *M*
C 1695–1957 M 1695–1970 B 1695–1880 **Gwent RO**
BT 1725–1828, 1830–69 **NLW**
Cop ts PR CB 1813–1900 M 1837–1900 **Soc Gen**

CHEPSTOW/CAS-GWENT   *M*
CB 1595–1757, 1761–1924 M 1595–1611, 1695–1925 (Banns 1912–26, 1953–66) **Gwent
RO**
BT 1725–30, 1732–63, 1765–1812, 1875–96 **NLW** 1813–21, 1823–30, 1833–68 **Gwent
RO**
Cop printed PR (extracts) C 1595–1743 M 1595–1819 B 1595–1924 (ed I Waters)

Cop ts PR C 1813–1900 M 1754–1900 (Banns 1779–1813) B 1813–39 with index **Gwen**
RO ts PR (extracts) 1558–1924 & ts PR CMB 1595–1900 **Soc Gen**

* CHRISTCHURCH/EGLWYS Y DRINDOD   *M*
PR CMB 1695–1736 B 1767–77 C 1778–85 CB 1794–1812 M 1926–34 irredeemably
damaged by fire in 1949
C 1695–1736, 1743–68, 1778–85, 1794–1949 M 1695–1736, 1743–1961 (Banns 1824–73)
B 1695–1736, 1743–77, 1794–1974 **NLW** Mf C 1743–68, 1813–1931 M 1743–1926
(Banns 1824–73) B 1743–68, 1813–1974 **Gwent RO**
BT 1725–54, 1757–1888 **NLW**
Cop ms PR 1695–1736, 1743–89 **NLW**

CILGWRRWG/KILGWRRWG   *M*
At visitation in 1771 this chapel, apparently annexed to Llan-gwm, was said to have no PR
of its own. 'The Ecclesiastical Court takes no notice of this chapel […]' claimed the
incumbent
C 1806–1990 M 1816–1958 B 1774–1991 **Gwent RO**
BT 1814, 1817–19, 1821–53, 1857–60 **NLW**
Cop ts PR C 1806–1900 M 1816–98 B 1774–1900 **Soc Gen**

COEDCERNYW/COEDKERNEW   *M*
C 1654–1976 M 1654–1969, 1981 (Banns 1825–1972) B 1654–1987 **NLW** Mf **Gwen**
RO
BT 1696, 1725–55, 1757–75, 1777–8, 1780–1837, 1839–42, 1844, 1847–8, 1852–5, 1857
1860–73 **NLW**

COEDYMYNACH/MONKSWOOD   *M*
At visitation in 1771 the curate wrote, 'We have no register books. The parishioners expec
the impropriator to furnish them with those books which he refuses to do. I always keep a
book of my own and return yearly copies of it to the registrar's office'. Neither his book
nor his returns seem to have survived
C 1783–1802, 1807–1961 M 1783–1837, 1839–1924, 1926–57 B 1783–1804, 1807–1962
Gwent RO
BT 1813–19, 1821–63, 1865–9, 1874–1900 **NLW**

CRYMLYN/CRUMLIN   *M*
<Pen-maen, Llanhiledd/Llanhilleth, Trefddyn/Trevethin, & Mynyddislwyn 1921
C 1845–1940 M 1904–40 **Gwent RO**

CWM   *M*
<Glynebwy/Ebbw Vale 1900
C 1882–98, 1900–67 M 1883–1971 (Banns 1932–72) **Gwent RO**

CWMBRÂN Fairwater   *M*
<Created 1971; incorporated into Cwmbrân Rectorial Benefice. Previously (from 1969)
Conventional District. Church closed 1995

C 1971–95 M 1971–86 (Banns 1971–87) **Gwent RO**

CWMBRÂN St Gabriel   *M*
<Llanfihangel Llantarnam 1971
C 1896–1987 M 1971–84 (Banns 1971–90) **Gwent RO**
BT see Llanfrechfa

CWMCARFAN/CWMCARVAN   *M*
C 1660–5, 1668–73, 1681–90, 1693–1705, 1741–1976 M 1660–3, 1681–90, 1693–1705,
    1741–1969 B 1662–3, 1668–73, 1681–1705, 1741–1976 **NLW** Mf **Gwent RO**
BT 1696, 1726–43, 1745–1868, 1874–85 **NLW**
Cop ts PR/BT C 1660–1705, 1728–1900 MB 1660–1705, 1743–1900 **Soc Gen**

CWM-CARN   *M*
<Mynyddislwyn, Rhisga/Risca 1922
C 1919–49 M 1923–71 (Banns 1923–66) **Gwent RO**

CWM-IOU/CWMYOY   *M*
Pre-1840 BT filed with St David's diocesan records, post-1840 with Llandaf/Llandaff's
C 1708–92, 1798–1801, 1805–1950 M 1708–1971 (Banns 1823–1958) B 1708–94,
    1798–1801, 1805–1976 **Gwent RO**
BT 1687, 1701, 1708, 1713–95, 1797–1809, 1813, 1815–19, 1821–34, 1836–9, 1843–67,
    1873, 1875–6 **NLW**
Cop ts PR C 1803–1900 M 1754–1900 (Banns 1809–21) B 1805–1900 **Soc Gen**

CWMTYLERI/CWMTILLERY St Paul   *M*
<Abertyleri/Abertillery 1923
CB 1891– M 1890– incumbent
Cop ts index PR B 1891–1986 **Gwent RO**

CHWILGRUG/WILCRICK   *M*
PR C 1786–1812 M 1755–85, 1804 B 1781–4 recorded in 1831 as being 'chiefly on loose
    paper' now apparently lost
C 1814–1967 M 1814–1961 B 1824–1974 **Gwent RO**
BT 1725–41, 1743–54, 1756–75, 1777, 1779–95, 1797–1800, 1802–17, 1819–31, 1833–68,
    1870–6 **NLW**

⭑ DEVAUDEN/Y DDEFAWDON   *M*
<Yr Eglwys Newydd ar y Cefn/Newchurch 1838
C 1839–1955 M 1958–70 **Gwent RO**
BT 1839–48, 1851–73 **NLW**
Cop ts PR C 1839–1900 **Soc Gen**

⭑ DINGESTOW/LLANDDINGAD   *M*
C 1742–1965 M 1742–1811, 1814–37 B 1742–1983 **NLW** M (Banns 1824–1973) Mf C
    1742–1965 M 1742–1811, 1814–37 B 1742–1983 **Gwent RO**

BT 1696, 1725–30, 1733–46, 1750–1818, 1820–64, 1874–90 **NLW**
Cop ts BT CMB 1696–1799 with index **Gwent RO** ts PR C 1742–1900 M 1755–75,
1779–1811, 1814–1900 B 1755–1900 **Soc Gen**

DIXTON   *H*
C 1661–1870 M 1661–1837 B 1661–1852 **HRO** Mf **Gwent RO & Soc Gen**
BT 1661–9, 1671–94, 1696–1813, 1815–33, 1836 **HRO** 1843–62, 1864–71, 1873–7,
1879–81 **NLW** Mf 1814, 1817–36 **Soc Gen**
Cop ts PR C 1813–69 M 1813–37 B 1813–52 with index **NLW Gwent RO & Soc Gen**
ts PR/BT M 1754–1812 **NLW & Gwent RO**

DRENEWYDD GELLI-FARCH/SHIRENEWTON   *M*
C 1730–69, 1771–1971 M 1733–1971 (Banns 1803–7, 1848–1928) B 1730–1955 **Gwent
RO**
BT 1725, 1729–38, 1740–1867, 1881–7 **NLW**
Cop ts PR CB 1730–1900 M 1732–1900 (Banns 1803–7, 1848–1900) with index **Gwent
RO & Soc Gen**

DDEFAWDON, Y/DEVAUDEN   *M*
<Yr Eglwys Newydd ar y Cefn/Newchurch 1838
C 1839–1955 M 1958–70 **Gwent RO**
BT 1839–48, 1851–73 **NLW**
Cop ts PR C 1839–1900 **Soc Gen**

★ EBBW VALE/GLYNEBWY Christ Church   *M*
<Tredegar, Aberystruth, Cendl/Beaufort 1870
C 1858–1967 M 1870–1976 (Banns 1954–64) B 1900–29 **Gwent RO**

★ EBBW VALE/GLYNEBWY St John   *M*
<Glynebwy/Ebbw Vale Christ Church 1909
C 1902–54 M 1910–70 **Gwent RO**

EGLWYS NEWYDD AR Y CEFN, YR/NEWCHURCH   *M*
C 1710–78, 1780–1942 M 1710–1970 B 1711–78, 1780–1897 **Gwent RO**
BT 1725–1868 **NLW**
Cop ts PR C 1710–1942 M 1710–1970 B 1710–1897 with index **Gwent RO & Soc Gen**

EGLWYS Y DRINDOD/CHRISTCHURCH   *M*
PR CMB 1695–1736 B 1767–77 C 1778–85 CB 1794–1812 M 1926–34 irredeemably
damaged by fire in 1949
C 1695–1736, 1743–68, 1778–85, 1794–1949 M 1695–1736, 1743–1961 (Banns 1824–73)
B 1695–1736, 1743–77, 1794–1974 **NLW** Mf C 1743–68, 1813–1931 M 1743–1926
(Banns 1824–73) B 1743–68, 1813–1974 **Gwent RO**
BT 1725–54, 1757–1888 **NLW**
Cop ms PR 1695–1736, 1743–89 **NLW**

FENNI, Y/ABERGAVENNY Holy Trinity   M
<St Mary 1895
C 1888–1976 M 1895–1971 (Banns 1923–50, 1972–88) B 1895–1958 **Gwent RO**

FENNI, Y/ABERGAVENNY St Mary   M
C 1653–89, 1692–1707, 1719–1968 M 1653–8, 1663–88, 1695–1706, 1719–1990 (Banns
1905–26, 1941–72) B 1653–89, 1691–1707, 1710–1957 **Gwent RO**
BT 1696, 1725–1835, 1863–86 **NLW**
Cop ts PR C 1652–1707, 1719–1900 M 1653–8, 1663–78, 1719–1900 (Banns 1754–1855)
B 1653–1900 **Soc Gen**

* FLEUR-DE-LIS/TRE-LYN   M
<Mynyddislwyn, Bedwellte/Bedwellty, Bedwas & Gelli-gaer 1896
C 1897–1961 M 1897–1978 (Banns 1897–1938, 1943–50) B 1904–67 **Gwent RO**

GARNDIFFAITH   M
<Abersychan 1921
M 1922–88 (Banns 1922–63) B 1926–68 **Gwent RO** C 1921– incumbent

GLYNEBWY/EBBW VALE Christ Church   M
<Tredegar, Aberystruth, Cendl/Beaufort 1870
C 1858–1967 M 1870–1976 (Banns 1954–64) B 1900–29 **Gwent RO**

GLYNEBWY/EBBW VALE St John   M
<Glynebwy/Ebbw Vale Christ Church 1909
C 1902–54 M 1910–70 **Gwent RO**

GOETRE   M
C 1695–1728, 1732–1960 M 1695–1728, 1732–1971 B 1695–1728, 1732–1957 **Gwent
RO**
BT 1696, 1725–1865, 1899 **NLW**
Cop ms PR CB 1695–1776 M 1695–1768 **NLW** ms PR CB 1695–1844 M 1695–1869
Soc Gen ts index PR B 1695–1727, 1777–1851 **Gwent RO**

* GOLDCLIFF/ALLTEURYN   M
C 1728–1924 M 1728–1900, 1903–55 B 1728–1981 **Gwent RO**
BT 1725–50, 1753–6, 1758–98, 1800–19, 1824–48, 1850, 1852–7, 1859–68, 1870,
1872–80, 1882–92 **NLW**
Cop ts PR B 1813–1981 with index **Gwent RO & Soc Gen**

GRIFFITHSTOWN   M
<Llanfrechfa & Pant-teg/Panteg 1898
C 1888–1961 M 1888–1971 (Banns 1888–1949) **Gwent RO**

GRYSMWNT, Y/GROSMONT   M
C 1589–1638, 1662–72, 1678–1860 M 1589–1638, 1662–72, 1678–1913 B 1589–1638,

1662–72, 1678–1954 **NLW** Mf **Gwent RO**
BT 1698–9, 1725–31, 1734–46, 1749–1835, 1837–43, 1845, 1848, 1855–61, 1863–4, 1868–73 **NLW**
Cop printed PR CMB 1589–1812 (ed J A Bradney 1921)
Cop ts index to Bradney's printed version of PR **Gwent RO** ts PR CMB 1589–1672, 1678–1900 **Soc Gen**

GWERNESNI/GWERNESNEY   *M*
PR CB 1758–82 M 1757–82 recorded in 1831 apparently lost. At visitation in 1771 the register was said to go back to 1728
C 1783–1990 M 1783–1840 B 1783–1990 **NLW** Mf **Gwent RO**
BT 1725–55, 1757–1817, 1819–21, 1824–5, 1827, 1829–68, 1874 **NLW**
Cop ts PR M 1788–1899 B 1813–1900 with index ts BT C 1725–98 M 1730–96 B 1726–99 with index **Gwent RO** ts BT C 1750–98 M 1758–96 B 1750–99 ts PR C 1784–1900 M 1788–1899 B 1783–1900 **Soc Gen**

GWNDY/UNDY   *M*
C 1760–1891 M 1754–1971 B 1760–1800, 1813–1924 **Gwent RO**
BT 1696, 1725–1869, 1871–90, 1892–5 **NLW**
Cop ts PR C 1813–91 M 1754–1812, 1838–1900 B 1813–1900 **Soc Gen**

HENGASTELL/OLDCASTLE   *M*
C 1784–1976 M 1773–1804, 1815–35, 1837–1960 B 1784–1812, 1816–1974 **Gwent RO**
BT 1702–4, 1707–11, 1714–17, 1723–1809, 1813, 1815–17, 1821–38, 1845–78, 1880, 1882–3 **NLW**
Cop ts PR C 1784–1812, 1814–98 M 1773–1804, 1815–35, 1837–85 B 1784–1812, 1816–1900 **Soc Gen**

HENLLYS   *M*
C 1765–1974 M 1754–1812, 1814–36, 1838–1971 (Banns 1825–1974) B 1765–1976 **Gwent RO**
BT 1696, 1725–75, 1777–1865, 1871–2, 1874–5 **NLW**

HOLLYBUSH gweler/see BEDWELLTE/BEDWELLTY

IFFTWN/IFTON   *M*
There are no visible remains of this church, and the parish has long been associated with Roggiet. No separate records survive

★ ITTON/LLANDDINOL   *M*
At visitation in 1781 the registers were said to begin in 1702
C 1773–1990 M 1775–1836 B 1773–1991 **Gwent RO**
BT 1725–1820, 1822–32, 1834, 1836–62, 1864–8 **NLW** Mf 1725–1868 **Soc Gen**
Cop ts PR CB 1813–1900 M 1838–98 **Soc Gen**

* KEMEYS COMMANDER/CEMAIS COMAWNDWR M

At visitation in 1771 a PR 'bear[ing] date 1740' was recorded, but by 1781 it was said that 'this affair has been greatly neglected by former ministers, nor is there any register found prior to the year 1780 of births and burials. At present [1781] there is one duly kept'. Neither of these registers nor that of marriages said to be then in use seems to have survived
C 1813–1973 M 1813–1970 (Banns 1920–78) B 1813–1984 **NLW** Mf **Gwent RO**
BT 1696, 1726–57, 1759–60, 1762–1811, 1813–65, 1867–75, 1877–8 **NLW**
Cop ts PR C 1813–1973 M 1813–1970 with index **Gwent RO & Soc Gen**

* KEMEYS INFERIOR/CEMAIS M

At visitation in 1781 it was claimed that the register went back to 1662
C 1701–1951 M 1701–52, 1756–1906, 1910–47 (Banns 1823–1924) B 1701–1959 **NLW**
Mf **Gwent RO**
BT 1725–1819, 1821, 1823–9, 1831–67, 1869–79, 1881, 1886–8 **NLW**
Cop ts PR/BT C 1701–1840 M 1701–1837 B 1701–1838 **NLW & Soc Gen**

* KILGWRRWG/CILGWRRWG M

At visitation in 1771 this chapel, apparently annexed to Llan-gwm, was said to have no PR of its own. 'The Ecclesiastical Court takes no notice of this chapel [...]' claimed the incumbent
C 1806–1990 M 1816–1958 B 1774–1991 **Gwent RO**
BT 1814, 1817–19, 1821–53, 1857–60 **NLW**
Cop ts PR C 1806–1900 M 1816–98 B 1774–1900 **Soc Gen**

LANGSTONE M

At visitation in 1781 there was here 'an ancient register book', but no starting date was given
C 1758–1979 M 1755–1971 (Banns 1824–1972) B 1755, 1763–97, 1802, 1805–11, 1813–1979 **Gwent RO**
BT 1696, 1725–51, 1753–1877, 1879–80 **NLW** 1881 (B only) **Gwent RO**
Cop ms PR CB 1763–1812 M 1755–1812 **NLW**

* LISWERRY/LLYSWYRY M

<Eglwys y Drindod/Christchurch & Casnewydd/Newport St John Evangelist 1922
C 1899–1944 M 1923–41 **Gwent RO**

LLANANDRAS/CHAPEL HILL (ABATY TYNDYRN/TINTERN ABBEY) M
C 1695–1957 M 1695–1970 B 1695–1880 **Gwent RO**
BT 1725–1828, 1830–69 **NLW**
Cop ts PR CB 1813–1900 M 1837–1900 **Soc Gen**

LLAN-ARTH M
C 1598–1729, 1734–79, 1789–1896 M 1598–1729, 1734–1837 (Banns 1824–1914) B 1598–1729, 1734–79, 1789–1895 **Gwent RO**
BT 1696, 1725–1876, 1878–82, 1896–1907 **NLW**
Cop ts PR C 1598–1729, 1734–79, 1789–1896 M 1598–1729, 1734–1899 (Banns 1824–99) B 1598–1729, 1734–79, 1789–1895 with index **Gwent RO & Soc Gen**

LLANBADOG   *M*
CB 1582–1709 M 1592–1708 **University College Cardiff** C 1710–1893 M 1710–52
1754–1969 B 1710–1905 **NLW** Mf C 1710–1893 M 1710–52, 1754–1969 B 1710–1905
Gwent RO
BT 1696, 1725–1870, 1876 **NLW**
Cop printed PR 1582–1709 (ed J A Bradney 1919) Cop ms PR 1582–1709 **Cardiff
Central Library** (MS.1.14) ms PR CB 1710–1812 M 1711–54 **NLW** ts index to
Bradney's printed version of PR **Gwent RO**

LLANBEDR GWYNLLŴG/PETERSTONE WENTLLOOG   *M*
PR 1707–84, 1800–12 recorded in 1831 apparently lost
C 1813–1985 M 1754–1812, 1816–35, 1845–1954 B 1817–1958 **NLW** Mf **Gwent RO**
BT 1725–75, 1777–92, 1794–1865 **NLW**

LLANDEGFEDD   *M*
At visitation in 1771 the register was said to go back 'as far as the year 1652 but imperfect'
C 1746–1986 M 1747–95, 1815–16, 1838–1966 B 1747–1985 **Gwent RO**
BT 1725–1813, 1815–73 **NLW**
Cop ms/ts PR C 1746/7–1859 M 1747–1832 B 1747–1850 **NLW Gwent RO & Soc
Gen**

LLANDEILO BERTHOLAU/LLANTILIO PERTHOLEY   *M*
C 1591–1973 M 1591–1981 (Banns 1831–1942) B 1591–1925 **Gwent RO**
BT 1725–1811, 1813–75 **NLW**
Cop ts PR C 1591–1899 M 1591–1893 B 1591–1900 **Soc Gen**

LLANDEILO GRESYNNI/LLANTILIO CROSSENNY   *M*
PR 1609–44 transcribed by Walter Powell (1582–1656) is now lost
C 1719–1967 M 1719–1971 B 1719–1876 **Gwent RO**
BT 1696, 1725–84, 1787–1836, 1838–40, 1842–50, 1852–5, 1857, 1859, 1861–2, 1865
1867, 1869, 1871, 1887–8 **NLW**
Cop printed PR C 1629–44 B 1609–28 (ed J A Bradney, 1916 from Powell's ms copy a
the Bodleian Library, Oxford)
Cop ts PR C 1719–1900 M 1719–1900 B 1719–1877 with index **Gwent RO & Soc Gen**
ts index to Bradney's printed version of PR **Gwent RO**

LLANDENNI/LLANDENNY   *M*
C 1710–15, 1722–42, 1764–1957 M 1711–15, 1723–49, 1754–1970, 1973–92 (Banns
1823–1991) B 1710–15, 1722–49, 1764–1957 **Gwent RO**
BT 1725–1815, 1817–30, 1832–7, 1839–68, 1871–2 **NLW**
Cop ms PR CB 1710–49, 1764–1812 M 1710–49 **NLW** ts PR CB 1710–1900 M
1711–42, 1754–1900 (Banns 1823–1900) with index **Gwent RO & Soc Gen**

LLANDEVAUD M
At visitation in 1771 this was described as 'a chapel of ease belonging to Langwm. We have no register book. We never have any marriages here.' By 1809 only the chancel remained standing (NLW, LL/VC/38). PR begin with the opening of the new church built on the old foundations in 1843
C 1843–1990 M 1849–1925, 1930–70 B 1846–1991 **Gwent RO**
BT 1848–67, 1869–70, 1872–81 **NLW**

LLANDOGO M
C 1694–1942 M 1698–1748, 1750–2, 1755–1971 (Banns 1835–1974) B 1694–1811, 1813–87 **Gwent RO**
BT 1725–9, 1731–1872 **NLW**
Cop ts PR CB 1813–1900 M 1755–1900 **Soc Gen**

LLANDDEWI FACH M
C 1741–98, 1813–1984 M 1741–54, 1813–36, 1838–1966 (Banns 1826–1956) B 1741–1987 **Gwent RO**
BT 1725–6, 1728–1868, 1870–6 **NLW**
Cop ms/ts PR C 1741–98, 1813–61 M 1741–54, 1813–36 B 1741–1845 **NLW Gwent RO & Soc Gen**

LLANDDEWI NANT HODNI/LLANTHONY M
<Cwm-iou/Cwmyoy. See Cwm-iou/Cwmyoy for pre-1840 BT
C 1769–98, 1813–1976 M 1832–7, 1866–1969 B 1769–94, 1813–1973 **Gwent RO**
BT 1708, 1721–3, 1725–6, 1732–5, 1738, 1740–1, 1743–4, 1746–78, 1781, 1783–8, 1790, 1793, 1800–1, 1813, 1815–19, 1821–32, 1834–8, 1840, 1843, 1845–53, 1855–66, 1873, 1875–6 **NLW**
Cop ts PR C 1769–98, 1813–1900 M 1832–7, 1866–96 B 1769–94, 1813–1900 **Soc Gen**

LLANDDEWI RHYDDERCH M
C 1670–1732, 1735–1923 M 1695–1730, 1736–1810, 1813–1970 B 1670–1732, 1735–1978 **Gwent RO**
BT 1725–32, 1735–1817, 1819–58, 1864–74, 1876–7 **NLW**
Cop printed PR CB 1670–1732 M 1695–1730, 1754–83 (ed J A Bradney 1919)
Cop ts PR C 1670–1731 M 1697–1783 B 1670–1732 with index **Gwent RO** ts PR C 1670–1731, 1735–1900 M 1697–1900 B 1670–1899 **Soc Gen**

LLANDDEWI YSGYRYD/LLANDDEWI SKIRRID M
PR M 1754–1806 the only volume to be found in 1831 now apparently lost
C 1550–1729 with gaps, 1813–1978 M 1551–1729 with gaps, 1813–1971 B 1549–1729 with gaps, 1813–1982 **NLW** Mf **Gwent RO**
BT 1725–33, 1735–1847, 1852–6, 1858–78 **NLW**
Cop ts PR CMB 1549–1729, 1813–1900 **NLW & Soc Gen**

LLANDDINGAD/DINGESTOW M
C 1742–1965 M 1742–1811, 1814–37 B 1742–1983 **NLW** M (Banns 1824–1973) Mf C

1742–1965 M 1742–1811, 1814–37 B 1742–1983 **Gwent RO**
BT 1696, 1725–30, 1733–46, 1750–1818, 1820–64, 1874–90 **NLW**
Cop ts BT CMB 1696–1799 with index **Gwent RO** ts PR C 1742–1900 M 1755–75,
1779–1811, 1814–1900 B 1755–1900 **Soc Gen**

LLANDDINOL/ITTON   *M*
At visitation in 1781 the registers were said to begin in 1702
C 1773–1990 M 1775–1836 B 1773–1991 **Gwent RO**
BT 1725–1820, 1822–32, 1834, 1836–62, 1864–8 **NLW** Mf 1725–1868 **Soc Gen**
Cop ts PR CB 1813–1900 M 1838–98 **Soc Gen**

LLANEIRWG/ST MELLONS   *M*
CMB 1717–20 in PR Llanedern/Llanedeyrn (Morgannwg/Glamorgan)
C 1722–1900 M 1722–1844 B 1722–1904 **NLW** C 1900–85 M 1837–1993 (Banns
1823–1996) B 1904–63 Mf C 1722–1900 M 1722–1844 B 1722–1904 **Gwent RO** Fac
C 1900–58 M 1837–1961 B 1904–63 **NLW**
BT 1725–75, 1777–1844, 1846–61, 1864–9 **NLW**
Cop ts PR CMB 1717–20 **NLW**

LLANELEN   *M*
C 1766–1959 M 1754–1971 (Banns 1825–1976) B 1766–1922 **NLW** Mf **Gwent RO**
BT 1696, 1725–31, 1733–45, 1747–1860, 1862–70 **NLW**
Cop ts PR C 1766–1959 M 1754–1971 B 1766–1812 **NLW**

LLANFABLE/LLANVAPLEY   *M*
C 1699–1977 M 1699–1752, 1754–1812, 1815–37, 1840–1965 (Banns 1824–1976) B
1699–1973 **Gwent RO**
BT 1725–1810, 1813–53, 1855, 1859, 1864–70, 1879–83, 1898–1912 **NLW** 1875–8
Gwent RO
Cop ts PR CB 1699–1900 M 1699–1812, 1815–37, 1840–97 **Soc Gen**

LLANFACHES/LLANVACHES   *M*
PR CMB in current use at visitation in 1771 & 1781 apparently lost
C 1796–1973 M 1796–1971 (Banns 1826–1973) B 1796–1992 **Gwent RO**
BT 1725–44, 1746–8, 1750–3, 1755–1865, 1867–70, 1872–85 **NLW**

LLANFAIR CILGEDIN/LLANFAIR KILGEDDIN   *M*
C 1733–1978 M 1733–53, 1757–1811, 1813–1982 (Banns 1824–1979) B 1733–198
Gwent RO Fac C 1813–1978 M 1777–1811 **NLW**
BT 1696, 1725–42, 1744–1870, 1872 **NLW**
Cop ts PR CM 1733–1900 B 1733–1812 **Soc Gen**

LLANFAIR ISGOED/LLANFAIR DISGOED   *M*
C 1681–1991 M 1680–1811, 1813–36, 1840–1969 B 1681–1986 **Gwent RO**
BT 1725–1878, 1880–1 **NLW**
Cop printed PR C 1681–1796, 1803–12 M 1680–1726, 1758–95 B 1680–1803 (ed J A

Bradney 1920)
Cop ts index to Bradney's printed version of PR **Gwent RO**   ts C (1568–1812)–1900 M
(1568–1812)–1836 B (1568–1812)–1900 **Soc Gen**

LLANFARTHIN/LLANMARTIN   *M*
PR CB 1778–1812 recorded in 1831 apparently lost. M 1755–1837 badly damaged by damp
(Gwent RO survey 1979). At visitation in 1805 PR went back to 1736
C 1813–1979 M 1839–1970 B 1813–1979 **Gwent RO**
BT 1725–44, 1746–1801, 1803–17, 1819–76 **NLW** Mf **Gwent RO**

LLANFIHANGEL (NEAR ROGGIET)   *M*
At visitation in 1805 the registers were said to go back to 1739
C 1754–1812, 1814–1975 M 1757–1810 (Banns 1863–?4) B 1813–1991 **Gwent RO**
BT 1725–1808, 1810, 1812–67, 1869 **NLW**
Cop ts PR C 1814–99 M 1757–1810, 1838–98 B 1816–99 **Soc Gen**

LLANFIHANGEL CRUCORNAU/LLANFIHANGEL CRUCORNEY   *M*
C 1727–1900 M 1727–49, 1755–1971 (Banns 1790–1958) B 1629–40, 1678–1921 **Gwent
RO**
BT 1696, 1725–1872 **NLW**
Cop ts PR/BT C 1727–1802 M 1727–49 B 1629–40, 1678–1802 **Gwent RO & Soc
Gen** ts PR CB 1813–1900 M 1789–1900 **Soc Gen**

⋆ LLANFIHANGEL GOBION/LLANFIHANGEL-Y-GOFION   *M*
C 1752–1977 M 1755–1811, 1813–36, 1844–1968 B 1751–1975 **Gwent RO**
BT 1696, 1725–32, 1734–47, 1749–54, 1756–1827, 1829–39, 1841–59, 1863–4, 1866–71
NLW
Cop ms PR/BT (extracts) CMB 1696–1812 **NLW** ts PR C 1813–1977 M 1813–36,
1844–1968 B 1813–1975 with index **Gwent RO & Soc Gen** ts PR C 1752–86,
1794–1900 M 1755–1836, 1844–1900 B 1751–84, 1793–1900 **Soc Gen**

LLANFIHANGEL-JUXTA-USK   gweler/see   LLANFIHANGEL-Y-
GOFION/LLANFIHANGEL GOBION

LLANFIHANGEL LLANTARNAM   *M*
C 1727–1883, 1894–1927 M 1727–1971 (Banns 1824–90, 1894–1915, 1961–74) B
1727–1889, 1897–1945 **Gwent RO**
BT 1725–7, 1729–1855 **NLW**
Cop ms PR (extracts) CMB 1727–1809 **NLW**

LLANFIHANGEL   NIGH   USK   gweler/see   LLANFIHANGEL-Y-
GOFION/LLANFIHANGEL GOBION

LLANFIHANGEL PONT-Y-MOEL   *M*
C 1739–1976 M 1754–1970 B 1754–1806, 1813–1944, 1950–64 **Gwent RO**
BT see Mamheilad/Mamhilad

Cop ms PR C 1739–1869 MB 1739–1855 **Soc Gen** ts index PR B 1754–1950 **Gwent RO**

LLANFIHANGEL ROGGIET gweler/see LLANFIHANGEL(NEAR ROGGIET)

LLANFIHANGEL TORYMYNYDD *M*
C 1594–1707, 1713, 1723–5, 1733–46, 1770–1806, 1813–1989 M 1699, 1721, 1724, 1736
1739, 1742, 1745–7, 1754–1812, 1819, 1837–1962 (Banns 1915–38) B 1594–1604, 1640
1655, 1662–71, 1678, 1695–1707, 1720–4, 1735–47, 1766–73, 1785–1803, 1813–1990
NLW Mf **Gwent RO**
BT 1725–1819, 1821–2, 1824–5, 1827–62 **NLW**
Cop ms PR CMB 1602–1773 **NLW** ts PR C 1602–1806, 1813–1900 M 1671–1748
1754–1819, 1837–1900 B 1594–1769, 1785–1803, 1813–1900 with index **Gwent RO &**
Soc Gen ts BT CB 1725–1800 M 1737–1800 with index **Gwent RO**

LLANFIHANGEL TRODDI/MITCHEL TROY *M*
C 1590–1717, 1728–1994 M 1590–1717, 1728–1970 B 1590–1717, 1728–1994 **Gwent RO**
BT 1725–1865, 1879–83 **NLW**
Cop ms PR CB (extracts) 1732–1812 M 1736–54 **NLW** ts PR C 1720–1889 M
1727–1811, 1813–1900 B 1720–1900 **Soc Gen**

LLANFIHANGEL-Y-FEDW/MICHAELSTON-Y-FEDW *M*
C 1660–1713, 1742–1926 M 1660–1715, 1743–1983 B 1658–1714, 1734, 1742–1967
Gwent RO Fac **Glam RO** Fac C 1660–1713, 1742–1926 M 1660–1715, 1743–1983
(Banns 1754–1812, 1821–51) B 1658–1714, 1734, 1742–1967 **Gwent RO**
BT 1696, 1725–75, 1777–1886, 1889–91 **NLW**

LLANFIHANGEL-Y-GOFION/LLANFIHANGEL GOBION *M*
C 1752–1977 M 1755–1811, 1813–36, 1844–1968 B 1751–1975 **Gwent RO**
BT 1696, 1725–32, 1734–47, 1749–54, 1756–1827, 1829–39, 1841–59, 1863–4, 1866–7.
NLW
Cop ms PR/BT (extracts) CMB 1696–1812 **NLW** ts PR C 1813–1977 M 1813–36
1844–1968 B 1813–1975 with index **Gwent RO & Soc Gen** ts PR C 1752–86
1794–1900 M 1755–1836, 1844–1900 B 1751–84, 1793–1900 **Soc Gen**

LLANFIHANGEL YSTUM LLYWERN/LLANFIHANGEL YSTERN LLEWERN *M*
C 1695–1739, 1754–1991 M 1696–1736, 1755–1811, 1813–34, 1842–1969 B 1695–1739
1755–1975 **Gwent RO**
BT 1725–41, 1743–6, 1748–1818, 1820–81 **NLW**
Cop printed PR 1695–1812 (ed J A Bradney 1920)
Cop ms PR CB 1695–1812 M 1695–1772 **NLW** ts index to Bradney's printed version o
PR **Gwent RO**

LLANFOCHA/ST MAUGHAN'S   M
C 1733–1992 M 1733–1841 (Banns 1824–1988) B 1733–1990 NLW Mf Gwent RO
BT 1696, 1725–1847, 1850–73 NLW
Cop ts PR CB 1733–1900 M 1734–1841 Soc Gen

LLANFOIST/LLAN-FFWYST   M
C 1736–1975 M 1736–1971 (Banns 1824–47, 1890–1933) B 1736–1945 NLW Mf Gwent
RO
BT 1725–32, 1734–51, 1753–4, 1756–75, 1777–1806, 1808–10, 1813, 1815–16, 1820–37,
1841–58, 1862–5, 1869, 1880 (see also Blaenafon/Blaenavon) NLW
Cop ms BT/PR 1725–1810 NLW

LLANFRECHFA   M
C 1727–1971 M 1727–1963 (Banns 1839–1965) B 1727–68, 1777–1905 Gwent RO
BT 1725–41, 1743–1852, 1854–68, 1870–4 including Cwmbrân from 1860 NLW
Cop ms PR CB (extracts) 1727–1812 M 1754–1812 NLW

LLANFRECHFA UCHAF/LLANFRECHFA UPPER   M
<Llanfrechfa 1885. Alias Pontnewydd, Holy Trinity
C 1860–1922 M 1860–1953 B 1860–1924 Gwent RO

LLAN-FFWYST/LLANFOIST   M
C 1736–1975 M 1736–1971 (Banns 1824–47, 1890–1933) B 1736–1945 NLW Mf Gwent
RO
BT 1725–32, 1734–51, 1753–4, 1756–75, 1777–1806, 1808–10, 1813, 1815–16, 1820–37,
1841–58, 1862–5, 1869, 1880 (see also Blaenafon/Blaenavon) NLW
Cop ms BT/PR 1725–1810 NLW

LLANGADOG/LLANGATTOCK-JUXTA-CAERLEON   M
C 1695–1838 M 1695–1752, 1755–1837 B 1695–1858 NLW C 1838–1971 M
1837–1971 B 1858–1957 Mf C 1695–1838 M 1695–1752, 1755–1837 B 1695–1858
Gwent RO
BT 1696, 1725–1905 NLW
Cop ts C 1695–1878 M 1695–1753, 1755–1924 B 1695–1893 with index Gwent RO &
Soc Gen

LLANGATWG DYFFRYN WYSG/LLANGATTOCK NIGH USK   M
C 1598–1716, 1727–1977 M 1598–1707, 1727–1812, 1814–1970 (Banns 1905–69) B
1598–1716, 1727–1978 Gwent RO
BT 1696, 1725–36, 1738–1829, 1833–5, 1848–55, 1864–74 NLW
Cop ts PR C to 1900 M to 1837 B to 1900 with index Gwent RO & Soc Gen

LLANGATWG FEIBION AFEL/LLANGATTOCK VIBON AVEL   M
C 1683–1991 M 1683–1812, 1814–1934 (Banns 1824–1934) B 1683–1914 NLW Mf
Gwent RO
BT 1696, 1725–9, 1731–1847, 1850–69 NLW

Cop ts PR C 1683–1900 M 1683–1752, 1754–1812, 1814–99 B 1683–1787, 1813–1900
Soc Gen

LLANGATWG LINGOED/LLANGATTOCK LINGOED *M*
C 1696–1980 M 1696–1837, 1840–1970 (Banns 1819–37) B 1696–1810, 1812–1982 **NLW**
Mf **Gwent RO**
BT 1696, 1725–1868, 1870–80 **NLW**
Cop ms PR CB 1696–1810 M 1696–1812 **NLW** ts PR CB 1696–1900 M 1696–1753,
1755–1837, 1840–1900 **Soc Gen**

* LLANGEVIEW/LLANGYFIW *M*
C 1709–31, 1755–1992 M 1713–1958 (Banns 1823–1960) B 1711–1991 **NLW** Mf **Gwent
RO**
BT 1725–1858, 1860–7 **NLW**
Cop ts BT CB 1725–1800 M 1725–99 with index **Gwent RO** ts PR CB 1813–1900 M
1755–1898 **Soc Gen**

* LLANGIBBY/LLANGYBI FAWR *M*
C 1679–1812 M 1679–1839 B 1679–1812 **NLW** Mf **Gwent RO**
BT 1696, 1725–1868 **NLW**
Cop ms/ts PR C 1679–1838 M 1679–1839 B 1678–1840 with index **NLW & Soc Gen** ts
index PR B 1813–1993 & ts PR B 1813–1910 with index **Gwent RO**

LLANGIWA/LLANGUA *H*
C 1714–63, 1768–1810 M 1714–1763, 1768–1810, 1817–43 B 1714–63, 1768–1810
HRO Mf **Gwent RO & Soc Gen**
BT 1696, 1725–32, 1734–56, 1758–1805, 1807–9, 1811–15, 1817–44, 1850, 1855 **NLW**

LLANGOFEN/LLANGOVAN *M*
C 1689–1715, 1720–3, 1727–8, 1733–1982 M 1689–1715, 1720–3, 1727–8, 1733–49
1755–1968 (Banns 1826–1982) B 1689–1715, 1720–3, 1727–8, 1733–1982 **NLW** Mf
Gwent RO
BT 1725–1875 **NLW**
Cop ts PR CB 1689–1812 M 1696–1812 with index ts BT C 1728–1800 M 1730–1800
B 1725–1800 with index **Gwent RO** ts PR C 1689–1900 M 1689–1749, 1755–1900 B
1689–1900 **Soc Gen**

LLANGUA gweler/see LLANGIWA

LLAN-GWM ISAF *M*
At visitation in 1848 the church had been in ruins for many years, only burial services having
been held there in living memory. The *Parliamentary Returns 1875* indicate that it was
rebuilt in 1851
M 1853–1967 **NLW** Mf **Gwent RO**

LLAN-GWM UCHAF   *M*
C 1663–1986 M 1663–1752, 1755–1810, 1813–1970 B 1663–1965 **NLW** Mf CB
1663–1812 M 1663–1752, 1755–1810, 1813–40 **Gwent RO**
BT 1696, 1725–1861 **NLW**
Cop ms/ts PR 1663–1812 **NLW** ts PR 1663–1733 **Cardiff Central Library** ts PR C
1666–1900 M 1663–1733, 1748–52, 1755–1810, 1813–1900 B 1663–1900 **Soc Gen**

LLANGYBI FAWR/LLANGIBBY   *M*
C 1679–1812 M 1679–1839 B 1679–1812 **NLW** Mf **Gwent RO**
BT 1696, 1725–1868 **NLW**
Cop ms/ts PR C 1679–1838 M 1679–1839 B 1678–1840 with index **NLW & Soc Gen** ts
index PR B 1813–1993 & ts PR B 1813–1910 with index **Gwent RO**

LLANGYFIW/LLANGEVIEW   *M*
C 1709–31, 1755–1992 M 1713–1958 (Banns 1823–1960) B 1711–1991 **NLW** Mf **Gwent
RO**
BT 1725–1858, 1860–7 **NLW**
Cop ts BT CB 1725–1800 M 1725–99 with index **Gwent RO** ts PR CB 1813–1900 M
1755–1898 **Soc Gen**

LLANHENWG/LLANHENNOCK   *M*
C 1695–1737, 1753–1811, 1813–1991 M 1697–1726, 1737, 1753, 1758 B 1695–1740,
1753–1809, 1817–1991 **NLW** M 1760–1812, 1814–1970 (Banns 1826–1971) **Gwent RO**
Mf C 1695–1737, 1753–1811, 1813–1991 M 1697–1726, 1737, 1753, 1758 B
1695–1740, 1753–1809, 1817–1991 **Gwent RO**
BT 1725–49, 1751–73, 1775–1874 **NLW**
Cop ms PR CB 1695–1738, 1753–1810 M 1695–1738, 1753–60 **NLW**

LLANHILEDD/LLANHILLETH   *M*
C 1733–1913 Aber-big/Aberbeeg 1909-25 M 1733–90, 1802, 1813–1911 Aber-
big/Aberbeeg 1911-71 B 1733–1930 Aber-big/Aberbeeg 1911–34 **Gwent RO**
BT 1725–1861 **NLW**
Cop ms PR (extracts) CMB 1733–1838 **NLW** ts index PR B 1813–1930 & Aber-
big/Aberbeeg B 1911–34 **Gwent RO**

LLANISIEN/LLANISHEN   *M*
C 1597–1731, 1738–1951 M 1663–1725, 1738–1812, 1815–1971 (Banns 1824–1914) B
1596–1731, 1738–1992 **Gwent RO**
BT 1696, 1725–1819, 1821–76 **NLW**
Cop ts PR CMB to 1900 with index **Gwent RO & Soc Gen** ts BT C 1696–1801 MB
1696–1800 with index **Gwent RO**

LLANLLYWEL/LLANLLOWELL   *M*
C 1666, 1676–1811, 1813–1991 M 1676–1770, 1815–35, 1839–1968 B 1664, 1679–1753,
1774–1811, 1813–1989 **NLW** Mf **Gwent RO & Soc Gen**
BT 1696, 1725–33, 1735, 1737–8, 1740–1, 1743–1829, 1832–67, 1874 **NLW**

Cop ms PR C 1676–1811 M 1695–1753 B 1677–1811 **NLW**

* LLANMARTIN/LLANFARTHIN *M*
PR CB 1778–1812 recorded in 1831 apparently lost. M 1755–1837 badly damaged by damp
(Gwent RO survey 1979). At visitation in 1805 PR went back to 1736
C 1813–1979 M 1839–1970 B 1813–1979 **Gwent RO**
BT 1725–44, 1746–1801, 1803–17, 1819–76 **NLW** Mf **Gwent RO**

LLANOFER/LLANOVER *M*
PR 1661–1706 recorded in 1935 apparently lost
C 1708–1973 M 1708–1837 (Banns 1823–94) B 1708–1930 **NLW** Mf **Gwent RO**
BT 1696–7, 1725–34, 1737–8, 1741–1865, 1869–70, 1906 (see also Blaenafon/Blaenavon)
NLW
Cop ts PR C 1661–1852 M 1661–1837 B 1661–1896 **Soc Gen**

LLANRHYMNI/LLANRUMNEY *M*
<Llaneirwg/St Mellons 1976
C 1958–87 M 1970–89 (Banns 1975–6, 1980–4) **Gwent RO** Fac M 1970–9 **Glam RO**

LLANSANFFRAID/LLANSANTFRAED *M*
At visitation in 1781 the rector noted that, on taking up the incumbency in 1770, he had
'establish'd a proper register here'. Being unable to 'find any prior to that time', he
surmised that 'the parish being so very small, and of so few inhabitants, I suppose very little
attention was paid to this article by my predecessors'
C 1753–1807, 1819–1988 M 1772–1805, 1815–37, 1846–1965 B 1753–1811, 1813–1990
Gwent RO
BT 1772–3, 1775–99, 1801–16, 1819, 1822–7, 1829–46, 1849–57, 1864–6 **NLW**
Cop ts PR C 1753–1807, 1819–96 M 1772–1837, 1846–94 B 1753–1811, 1813–95 with
index **Gwent RO & Soc Gen**

LLANSANFFRAID GWYNLLŴG/ST BRIDE'S WENTLLOOG *M*
C [?1695]–1725, 1732–1985 M 1695–1810, 1813–1971 B 1695–1714, 1729–1989 **NLW**
Mf **Gwent RO**
BT 1725–66, 1768–75, 1777–1821, 1823–8, 1830–7, 1840, 1844, 1847, 1852–5, 1857,
1860–73 **NLW**

LLANSANTFRAED gweler/see LLANSANFFRAID

LLAN-SOE/LLANSOY *M*
C 1592–1652, 1654, 1659–60, 1663–1710, 1747–54, 1760, 1764–1984 M 1592–1647,
1664–9, 1697–1705, 1749, 1752–3, 1755–1812, 1814–1969 B 1593–1650, 1653, 1663–8,
1671, 1674, 1679, 1688–9, 1695–1730, 1747, 1750, 1752–3, 1765–1984 **NLW** Mf **Gwent
RO**
BT 1697, 1725–1868, 1870–9, 1881–4 **NLW**
Cop ms PR CB 1594–1812 M 1594–1754 **NLW** ts PR C 1588, 1594–1900 M
1592–1647, 1664–9, 1697–1705, 1711–22, 1753–1899 B 1593–1900 with index **Gwent**

RO & Soc Gen ts BT C 1730–60 M 1732–58 B 1729–60 with index **Soc Gen**

LLANTARNAM gweler/see LLANFIHANGEL LLANTARNAM

* LLANTHONY/LLANDDEWI NANT HODNI   *M*
<Cwm-iou/Cwmyoy. See Cwm-iou/Cwmyoy for pre-1840 BT
  C 1769–98, 1813–1976 M 1832–7, 1866–1969 B 1769–94, 1813–1973 **Gwent RO**
  BT 1708, 1721–3, 1725–6, 1732–5, 1738, 1740–1, 1743–4, 1746–78, 1781, 1783–8, 1790,
    1793, 1800–1, 1813, 1815–19, 1821–32, 1834–8, 1840, 1843, 1845–53, 1855–66, 1873,
    1875–6 **NLW**
  Cop ts PR C 1769–98, 1813–1900 M 1832–7, 1866–96 B 1769–94, 1813–1900 **Soc Gen**

* LLANTILIO CROSSENNY/LLANDEILO GRESYNNI   *M*
  PR 1609–44 transcribed by Walter Powell (1582–1656) is now lost
  C 1719–1967 M 1719–1971 B 1719–1876 **Gwent RO**
  BT 1696, 1725–84, 1787–1836, 1838–40, 1842–50, 1852–5, 1857, 1859, 1861–2, 1865,
    1867, 1869, 1871, 1887–8 **NLW**
  Cop printed PR C 1629–44 B 1609–28 (ed J A Bradney, 1916 from Powell's ms copy at
    the Bodleian Library, Oxford)
  Cop ts PR C 1719–1900 M 1719–1900 B 1719–1877 with index **Gwent RO & Soc Gen**
    ts index to Bradney's printed version of PR **Gwent RO**

* LLANTILIO PERTHOLEY/LLANDEILO BERTHOLAU   *M*
  C 1591–1973 M 1591–1981 (Banns 1831–1942) B 1591–1925 **Gwent RO**
  BT 1725–1811, 1813–75 **NLW**
  Cop ts PR C 1591–1899 M 1591–1893 B 1591–1900 **Soc Gen**

LLANTRISAINT FAWR/LLANTRISSENT   *M*
At visitation in 1781 it was claimed that the register went back to 1702
  C 1743–1991 M 1743–1970 B 1743–1812, 1814–1992 **NLW** Mf **Gwent RO & Soc
    Gen**
  BT 1725–9, 1731–49, 1751–1864, 1866–8 **NLW**
  Cop ts PR C 1813–43 B 1813–40 with index **NLW & Soc Gen** ts BT CB 1725–1800 M
    1727–99 with index **Gwent RO**

LLANVACHES/LLANFACHES   *M*
PR CMB in current use at visitation in 1771 & 1781 apparently lost
  C 1796–1973 M 1796–1971 (Banns 1826–1973) B 1796–1992 **Gwent RO**
  BT 1725–44, 1746–8, 1750–3, 1755–1865, 1867–70, 1872–85 **NLW**

LLANVAPLEY/LLANFABLE   *M*
  C 1699–1977 M 1699–1752, 1754–1812, 1815–37, 1840–1965 (Banns 1824–1976) B
    1699–1973 **Gwent RO**
  BT 1725–1810, 1813–53, 1855, 1859, 1864–70, 1879–83, 1898–1912 **NLW** 1875–8
    Gwent RO
  Cop ts PR CB 1699–1900 M 1699–1812, 1815–37, 1840–97 **Soc Gen**

* LLANVETHERINE/LLANWYTHERIN   *M*
PR CMB 1693–1812 in one volume recorded in 1831 now apparently lost
C 1745–52, 1813–1980 M 1754–1810, 1813–1970 B 1813–1981 **NLW** Mf **Gwent RO**
BT 1696–7, 1725–1875 **NLW**
Cop ts PR C 1746–52, 1813–1900 M 1754–1900 B 1813–1900 **Soc Gen**

LLANWARW/WONASTOW   *M*
C 1674–1752, 1759–62, 1765–1989 M 1675–1752, 1754–1812, 1814–36, 1838–1970 B
1674–1747, 1759–62, 1765–1992 **NLW** Mf **Gwent RO**
BT 1725–50, 1752–5, 1758–1861 **NLW**
Cop ts BT CB 1725–1801 M 1725–99 with index **Gwent RO** ts PR CB 1674–1900 M
1675–1895 **Soc Gen**

LLANWENARTH CITRA   *M*
C 1725–1811, 1813–1996 M 1725–1901, 1903–71, 1975–84 (Banns 1823–82) B
1725–1996 **Gwent RO**
BT 1725–1870 (see also Blaenafon/Blaenavon) **NLW**
Cop ms PR (extracts) CMB 1726–1808 **NLW** ts PR C 1725–1811, 1813–99 M
1725–1900 (Banns 1823–46) B 1725–1900 **Soc Gen**

LLANWENARTH ULTRA (GOFILON/GOVILON)   *M*
<Llanwenarth Citra 1865
C 1860–1961 M 1866–1980 (Banns 1887–1971) B 1860–1936 **Gwent RO**

LLAN-WERN   *M*
C 1750–1811, 1814–1991 M 1763–1975 B 1755–86, 1815–1986 **Gwent RO**
BT 1725–31, 1759, 1762–1816, 1818–21, 1834–67, 1869, 1871 **NLW**
Cop ts PR C 1750–1811, 1814–1900 M 1820–1900 B 1755–86, 1815–1900 **Soc Gen**

LLANWYNELL/WOLVESNEWTON   *M*
At visitation in 1771 it was claimed that the register went back to 1680
C 1716–1990 M 1716–1970 B 1716–1812, 1814–1990 **Gwent RO**
BT 1725–52, 1755–97, 1799–1807, 1809–16, 1818–27, 1829–30, 1832, 1834–62 **NLW**
Cop ts PR C 1678–1900 M 1716–1898 B 1680–1900 **Soc Gen**

LLANWYTHERIN/LLANVETHERINE   *M*
PR CMB 1693–1812 in one volume recorded in 1831 now apparently lost
C 1745–52, 1813–1980 M 1754–1810, 1813–1970 B 1813–1981 **NLW** Mf **Gwent RO**
BT 1696–7, 1725–1875 **NLW**
Cop ts PR C 1746–52, 1813–1900 M 1754–1900 B 1813–1900 **Soc Gen**

LLYSWYRY/LISWERRY   *M*
<Eglwys y Drindod/Christchurch & Casnewydd/Newport St John Evangelist 1922
C 1899–1944 M 1923–41 **Gwent RO**

MACHEN *M*
C 1670–1984 M 1688–1983 (Banns 1823–1966) St John Baptist 1899–1988 B 1671–1996
Gwent RO Mf/Fac C 1670–1850 M 1688–1837 B 1671–1849 **NLW**
BT 1696, 1725–68, 1770–5, 1777–1828, 1830–77 **NLW**

MAENDY gweler/see CASNEWYDD/NEWPORT St John Evangelist

MAERUN/MARSHFIELD *M*
C 1653–1713, 1715–27, 1732–5, 1742–1938 M 1653–1713, 1715–27, 1732–5, 1742–1964
(Banns 1824–1974) B 1653–1713, 1715–27, 1732–5, 1742–1973 **NLW** Mf **Gwent RO**
BT 1725–1867 **NLW**

MAGWYR/MAGOR *M*
At visitation in 1771 it was recorded that 'the new book' went 'about twenty years back'.
Neither that register nor the implied older one seem to have survived
C 1799–1984 M 1754–1812, 1814–1974 B 1799–1914 **Gwent RO**
BT 1725–9, 1733–40, 1742–1880 **NLW**
Cop ms PR (extracts) CB 1799–1835 M 1754–1813 **NLW** ts PR C 1799–1900 M
1814–1900 (Banns 1830–1900) B 1793–1900 **Soc Gen**

MAINDEE gweler/see CASNEWYDD/NEWPORT St John Evangelist

MALPAS *M*
PR 1733–1812 recorded in 1831 apparently lost
C 1813–1930 M 1759–1986 (Banns 1834–1985) B 1813–1925 **Gwent RO**
BT 1725–75, 1777–90, 1792–1809, 1811–15, 1817–26, 1828–34, 1836–42, 1844–8,
1851–2, 1854 **NLW**
Cop ts PR C 1813–1930 M 1759–1932 B 1813–1925 with index **Gwent RO & Soc Gen**

MAMHEILAD/MAMHILAD *M*
C 1686–1954 M 1699–1811, 1813–1963, 1966–9, 1979–89 B 1686–1936 **Gwent RO**
BT 1725–71, 1773–4, 1776–1861 **NLW**
Cop ms PR CMB 1682–1837 **Soc Gen**

MARKHAM gweler/see BEDWELLTE/BEDWELLTY

＊MARSHFIELD/MAERUN *M*
C 1653–1713, 1715–27, 1732–5, 1742–1938 M 1653–1713, 1715–27, 1732–5, 1742–1964
(Banns 1824–1974) B 1653–1713, 1715–27, 1732–5, 1742–1973 **NLW** Mf **Gwent RO**
BT 1725–1867 **NLW**

MATHARN/MATHERN *M*
PR CB 1792–1812 recorded in 1831 apparently lost
C 1576–1630, 1656, 1661, 1663–4, 1669–1739, 1742–92, 1813–84 M 1565–1632, 1644–7,
1651, 1676, 1680, 1684–1739, 1754–1835, 1837–1942 (Banns 1819–35) B 1565–1645,
1664–7, 1676, 1679–80, 1684–1739, 1742–92, 1813–1915 **NLW** Mf **Gwent RO**

BT 1696, 1725–34, 1736–43, 1745–9, 1751–2, 1754–1826, 1828–76 **NLW**
Cop ms PR/BT CB 1565–1792 M 1565–1812 **NLW** ts PR CB 1565–1739, 1742–92,
1813–1900 M 1565–1739, 1754–1835, 1837–1900 **Soc Gen**

* MICHAELSTON-Y-FEDW/LLANFIHANGEL-Y-FEDW *M*
C 1660–1713, 1742–1926 M 1660–1715, 1743–1983 B 1658–1714, 1734, 1742–1967
Gwent RO Fac **Glam RO** Fac C 1660–1713, 1742–1926 M 1660–1715, 1743–1983
(Banns 1754–1812, 1821–51) B 1658–1714, 1734, 1742–1967 **Gwent RO**
BT 1696, 1725–75, 1777–1886, 1889–91 **NLW**

* MITCHEL TROY/LLANFIHANGEL TRODDI *M*
C 1590–1717, 1728–1994 M 1590–1717, 1728–1970 B 1590–1717, 1728–1994 **Gwent
RO**
BT 1725–1865, 1879–83 **NLW**
Cop ms PR CB (extracts) 1732–1812 M 1736–54 **NLW** ts PR C 1720–1889 M
1727–1811, 1813–1900 B 1720–1900 **Soc Gen**

* MONKSWOOD/COEDYMYNACH *M*
At visitation in 1771 the curate wrote, 'We have no register books. The parishioners expect
the impropriator to furnish them with those books which he refuses to do. I always keep a
book of my own and return yearly copies of it to the registrar's office.' Neither his book
nor his returns seem to have survived
C 1783–1802, 1807–1961 M 1783–1837, 1839–1924, 1926–57 B 1783–1804, 1807–1962
Gwent RO
BT 1813–19, 1821–63, 1865–9, 1874–1900 **NLW**

* MONMOUTH/TREFYNWY St Mary *M*
C 1598–1608, 1610–52, 1654, 1656–86, 1690–1754 M 1598–1603, 1606–8, 1610–49,
1651, 1657–83, 1690–1754 B 1598–1608, 1610–50, 1658, 1660, 1662–78, 1690–1754
NLW C 1755–1908 M 1754–1918 (Banns 1823–47, 1915–64) B 1755–1918 Mf CMB
to 1754 **Gwent RO**
BT 1660–88, 1690–4, 1696–1833, 1836–42 **HRO** 1843–59, 1862–9 **NLW** Mf 1839–42
Soc Gen
Cop ts PR CB 1755–1812 M 1754–63 with index **Gwent RO** ts PR C 1598–1686,
1690–1900 M 1598–1682, 1690–1782, 1795–1900 B 1598–1678, 1690–1900 **Soc Gen**

* MONMOUTH/TREFYNWY St Thomas Overmonnow *M*
<St Mary 1831
C 1846–1910 M 1846–1942 (Banns 1846–1939) B 1850–4 **Gwent RO**
BT 1846–60, 1862, 1865, 1867 **NLW**
Cop ts PR CM 1846–1900 B 1850–4 **Soc Gen**

MOUNTON *M*
At visitation in 1805 it was stated that no register was kept at this chapel before the
appointment of Edward Lewis to the curacy in 1789
C 1790–1811, 1813–1991 B 1790–1811, 1813–1991 **NLW** M 1845– incumbent Mf CB

1790–1811, 1813–1991 **Gwent RO**
BT 1813–16, 1818, 1820–2, 1824–58, 1860–75 **NLW**
Cop ts PR C 1813–1900 M 1845–1900 B 1790–1811, 1813–98 **Soc Gen**

MYNYDDISLWYN   *M*
C 1664–1918 M 1656–84, 1687–1743, 1750–1922 (Banns 1911–51) B 1664–1743,
1745–1933 **Gwent RO**
BT 1717, 1725–75, 1777–1842 **NLW**

NANT-Y-GLO   *M*
<Aberystruth 1844
C 1844–1925 M 1855–1958 (Banns 1932–55) **Gwent RO**
BT 1844–55, 1857–63 **NLW**

* NASH/TREFONNEN   *M*
C 1733–1943 M 1733–1970 B 1733–1984 **Gwent RO**
BT 1725–50, 1753–5, 1758–1819, 1823, 1827–62, 1864–70 **NLW** Mf 1726–1837 **Glam
RO**
Cop ts PR C 1813–1943 M 1758–1970 with index **Gwent RO & Soc Gen**

* NEWBRIDGE/TRECELYN   *M*
<Pen-maen 1914
C 1888–1960 M 1922–77 (Banns 1922–55) **Gwent RO**

* NEWCHURCH/YR EGLWYS NEWYDD AR Y CEFN   *M*
C 1710–78, 1780–1942 M 1710–1970 B 1711–78, 1780–1897 **Gwent RO**
BT 1725–1868 **NLW**
Cop ts PR C 1710–1942 M 1710–1970 B 1710–1897 with index **Gwent RO & Soc Gen**

NEWPORT/CASNEWYDD All Saints   *M*
<St Woolos 1899
C 1898–1952 M 1899–1978 (Banns 1899–1908, 1913–62) **Gwent RO**

NEWPORT/CASNEWYDD Holy Trinity   *M*
<St Woolos 1864. C 1857–64 entered in PR St Paul. Closed 1975
C 1852–7, 1864–1975 St Peter 1887–1984 M 1862–1975 (Banns 1887–1956, 1960–7)
Gwent RO
BT 1864–84 **NLW**

NEWPORT/CASNEWYDD St John Evangelist & St Mary   *M*
<Eglwys y Drindod/Christchurch 1860. St Mary acted as parish church 1949–52 owing to
fire damage at St John
C 1866–1975 St Mary 1899–1952 M 1861–1977 St Mary 1949–52 **Gwent RO**

NEWPORT/CASNEWYDD St Julian   *M*
<Eglwys y Drindod/Christchurch & St John Evangelist 1921

C 1899–1990 M 1922–95 (Banns 1921–96) **Gwent RO**

* NEWPORT/CASNEWYDD St Mark   *M*
<St Woolos 1875
C 1875–1968 M 1875–1971 (Banns 1932–46) **Gwent RO**

* NEWPORT/CASNEWYDD St Mary gweler/see CASNEWYDD/NEWPORT St John
Evangelist

* NEWPORT/CASNEWYDD St Matthew   *M*
<St John Evangelist 1911
C 1896–1938 M 1911–71 (Banns 1911–74) **Gwent RO**

* NEWPORT/CASNEWYDD St Paul   *M*
<St Woolos 1839
C 1837–1962 St Thomas 1950–83 M 1840–1985 (Banns 1978–84) B ('register of funerals'
1953–84 **Gwent RO**

* NEWPORT/CASNEWYDD St Peter gweler/see CASNEWYDD/NEWPORT Holy
Trinity

* NEWPORT/CASNEWYDD St Stephen   *M*
<Holy Trinity 1921. Joined with Holy Trinity 1970
C 1884–95, 1921–81 M 1922–72 **Gwent RO**

* NEWPORT/CASNEWYDD St Teilo   *M*
<Eglwys y Drindod/Christchurch, St Andrew & Llan-wern 1966
M 1966–84 (Banns 1966–86) **Gwent RO**

* NEWPORT/CASNEWYDD St Thomas gweler/see CASNEWYDD/NEWPORT St Paul

* NEWPORT/CASNEWYDD St Woolos   *M*
C 1702–42, 1769–1931 M 1702–49, 1754–1930 B 1702–43, 1769–1882 **Gwent RO**
BT 1725–75, 1777–1837, 1843–50, 1852–87 **NLW**
Cop ms PR (extracts) CMB 1702–1835 **NLW** ts PR C 1702–42, 1769–1905 M 1702–49
1754–1900 B 1692, 1702–43, 1769–1825, 1829–71 with index **Gwent RO & Soc Gen**

* NEW TREDEGAR/TREDEGAR NEWYDD   *M*
<Tredegar & Bedwellte/Bedwellty 1900
C 1896–1974 M 1897–1982 (Banns 1961–82) **Gwent RO**

OAKDALE   *M*
<Pen-maen; parish church of Pen-maen since 1970
M 1956–71 **Gwent RO**

* OLDCASTLE/HENGASTELL   *M*
C 1784–1976 M 1773–1804, 1815–35, 1837–1960 B 1784–1812, 1816–1974 **Gwent RO**
BT 1702–4, 1707–11, 1714–17, 1723–1809, 1813, 1815–17, 1821–38, 1845–78, 1880, 1882–3 **NLW**
Cop ts PR C 1784–1812, 1814–98 M 1773–1804, 1815–35, 1837–85 B 1784–1812, 1816–1900 **Soc Gen**

PANT-TEG/PANTEG   *M*
C 1598–1969 M 1598–1982 (Banns 1935–68) B 1598–1999 **Gwent RO**   Fac CMB 1598–1785 **NLW**
BT 1725–51, 1753–1848, 1850–2, 1854 **NLW**
Cop ts PR C 1598–1838 MB 1598–1837 **Soc Gen** ms CMB 1598–1812 **Gwent RO**

PEN-ALLT   *M*
At visitation in 1781 there was here 'an imperfect register so far back as 1695'
C 1779–1869 M 1765–1812, 1815–1970 B 1779–1902 **Gwent RO**
BT 1725–91, 1793–1849, 1851–70 **NLW**
Cop ts PR CB 1779–1836 M 1765–1836 with index ts BT CMB 1725–1800 with index **Gwent RO** ts PR CB 1779–1900 M 1765–1900 **Soc Gen**

PEN-CLAWDD/PEN-Y-CLAWDD   *M*
C 1730–1982 M 1731–1811, 1815–1912, 1915–69 (Banns 1826–1982) B 1727–1981 **NLW** Mf **Gwent RO**
BT 1696, 1725–32, 1734–86, 1788–94, 1796–1875 **NLW**
Cop ts BT C 1729–1810 M 1731, 1758–1804 B 1696, 1725–1810 ts PR CB 1727–1900 M 1727–1811, 1815–1900 **Soc Gen**

PEN-HW/PENHOW   *M*
C 1725–1961 M 1725–1975 B 1725–1992 **Gwent RO**
BT 1725–1839, 1846–51, 1853–4, 1857, 1860–72, 1875, 1880–5 **NLW**
Cop ms PR CB 1725–1812 M 1725–60 **NLW**

PEN-MAEN   *M*
<Mynyddislwyn 1845. See also Oakdale
C 1852–1934 M 1858–1969 B 1858–1930 **Gwent RO**
BT 1852–72 **NLW**

PEN-RHOS   *M*
PR 1560–1641 transcribed by Walter Powell (1582–1656) was 'much mouseaten' *c*1650 and is now entirely lost
C 1721–1816 M 1718–46, 1755–1808, 1814–35 B 1718–53, 1765–1815 **NLW** C 1813–1915 M 1837–1969 B 1813–1990 Mf C to 1816 M to 1835 B to 1815 **Gwent RO**
BT 1696, 1725–1834, 1836, 1838–87 **NLW**
Cop printed PR C 1560, 1565, 1573–98, 1606–41 M 1573–98, 1611–39 B 1573–98, 1611–40 (ed J A Bradney, 1916 from Powell's ms copy at the Bodleian Library, Oxford)

Cop ts PR C 1813–1900 M 1837–99 B 1813–99 with index & ts index to Bradney's printed version of PR **Gwent RO** ts PR C 1723–1900 M 1718–1808, 1814–99 B 1718–1899 **Soc Gen**

PENTERI/PENTERRY   *M*
C 1726–1988 M 1721–1805, 1813–34 B 1723–1809, 1813–1992 **Gwent RO**
BT 1727, 1729–70, 1772, 1776–1815, 1817–24, 1826–76 **NLW** 1877 **Gwent RO**
Cop ts PR C 1813–99 M 1841–96 B 1814–99 **Soc Gen**

⋆ PEN-Y-CLAWDD/PEN-CLAWDD   *M*
C 1730–1982 M 1731–1811, 1815–1912, 1915–69 (Banns 1826–1982) B 1727–1981 **NLW**
  Mf **Gwent RO**
BT 1696, 1725–32, 1734–86, 1788–94, 1796–1875 **NLW**
Cop ts BT C 1729–1810 M 1731, 1758–1804 B 1696, 1725–1810 ts PR CB 1727–1900
M 1727–1811, 1815–1900 **Soc Gen**

⋆ PETERSTONE WENTLLOOG/LLANBEDR GWYNLLŴG   *M*
PR 1707–84, 1800–12 recorded in 1831 apparently lost
C 1813–1985 M 1754–1812, 1816–35, 1845–1954 B 1817–1958 **NLW** Mf **Gwent RO**
BT 1725–75, 1777–92, 1794–1865 **NLW**

PILLGWENLLI gweler/see CASNEWYDD/NEWPORT Holy Trinity

PONTNEWYDD gweler/see LLANFRECHFA UCHAF/LLANFRECHFA UPPER

PONTNEWYNYDD   *M*
<Trefddyn/Trevethin 1845
C 1845–1954 M 1845–1971 (Banns 1936–47, 1957–71) **Gwent RO**
BT 1857–63, 1866, 1868–9, 1871 **NLW**

PONT-Y-PŴL/PONTYPOOL St James   *M*
<Pant-teg/Panteg & Trefddyn/Trevethin 1915
C 1906–48 M 1915–71 **Gwent RO**

PORTHSGIWED/PORTSKEWETT   *M*
C 1593–1926 M 1593–1953 B 1593–1771, 1776–1911 **Gwent RO**
BT 1725–57, 1760–90, 1792–1829, 1831–70, 1873, 1875, 1879–82 **NLW**
Cop ts PR CB 1593–1900 M 1593–1753, 1814–1900 **Soc Gen**

⋆ RAGLAN/RHAGLAN   *M*
At visitation in 1781 there was 'an old register here that goes as far back as very near the tim
of registers being first established'
C 1722–1984 M 1722–44, 1754–1989 (Banns 1824–1950) B 1722–1958 **Gwent RO**
BT 1725–42, 1744–1873 **NLW**
Cop ts PR CB 1711–1900 M 1722–1900 (Banns 1824–1900) with index **Gwent RO &**
  Soc Gen

REDWICK *M*
At visitation in 1781 PR CB was said to begin in 1752
C 1699–1721, 1785–1938 M 1719–21, 1754–1811, 1813–1969 B 1785–1813 **Gwent RO**
BT 1725–37, 1739, 1741–9, 1751–1879 **NLW**
Cop ts PR CB 1785–1900 M 1754–1811, 1813–1900 (Banns 1830–92) **Soc Gen**

★ RISCA/RHISGA *M*
PR C 1736–1812 B 1779–1812 recorded in 1831 apparently lost
C 1813–1946 M 1754–1823, 1825–1958 (Banns 1834–1925, 1942–72) B 1813–1935
Gwent RO
BT 1696, 1725–75, 1777–1840, 1842, 1845–52, 1876 **NLW**

ROCKFIELD *M*
PR C 1813–1927 missing in 1994
C 1696–1712, 1737–1812, 1927–1991 M 1696–1711, 1737–1977 B 1696–1712,
1737–1992 **NLW** Mf **Gwent RO**
BT 1696, 1725–61, 1763–75, 1777–89, 1791–1851, 1854–68, 1873–87 **NLW**
Cop ms PR CB 1697–1712, 1737–1812 M 1697–1712, 1737–53 **NLW** ts PR C
1696–1712, 1737–1812 M 1696–1711, 1737–1839 B 1696–1712, 1737–1900 **Soc Gen**

ROGGIET *M*
C 1752–1960 M 1754–1811, 1814–38 (Banns 1825–78, 1898–1946) B 1750–1812,
1814–1993 **Gwent RO**
BT 1725–1867 **NLW**
Cop ts PR C 1752–1900 M 1751–1896 B 1750–1812 **Soc Gen**

RUMNEY/TREDELERCH *M*
PR M 1754–1812 recorded in 1831 apparently lost. At visitation in 1781 there was here a
register going back 'about 120 years but in very bad preservation'
C 1744–1812 M 1744–86, 1804–37 B 1744–1812 **NLW** Mf **Gwent RO**
BT 1696, 1725–75, 1777, 1779–1865 **NLW**
Cop Mfc index B 1696–1840 **Soc Gen**

RHAGLAN/RAGLAN *M*
At visitation in 1781 there was 'an old register here that goes as far back as very near the time
of registers being first established'
C 1722–1984 M 1722–44, 1754–1989 (Banns 1824–1950) B 1722–1958 **Gwent RO**
BT 1725–42, 1744–1873 **NLW**
Cop ts PR CB 1711–1900 M 1722–1900 (Banns 1824–1900) with index **Gwent RO &**
Soc Gen

RHISGA/RISCA *M*
PR C 1736–1812 B 1779–1812 recorded in 1831 apparently lost
C 1813–1946 M 1754–1823, 1825–1958 (Banns 1834–1925, 1942–72) B 1813–1935
Gwent RO
BT 1696, 1725–75, 1777–1840, 1842, 1845–52, 1876 **NLW**

RHYMNI/RHYMNEY   *M*
<Bedwellte/Bedwellty 1843
C 1843–1942 M 1843–1971 (Banns 1947–54) B 1843–1916 **Gwent RO**
BT 1843–61, 1863–5 **NLW**

SAIN PŶR/ST PIERRE   *M*
PR 1686–1812 recorded in 1831 apparently lost. At visitation in 1771 it was said that CMB
were 'register'd in the register book belonging to Portskewett'
C 1813–1992 M 1813–40 B 1813–1991 **NLW** Mf **Gwent RO**
BT 1696, 1725–35, 1737–43, 1745, 1757–8, 1774, 1789, 1794–6, 1800, 1803–6, 1808–70,
1873, 1877–81 **NLW**
Cop ts BT C 1725–1820 M 1697–1820 B 1696–1818 with index **Gwent RO** ts PR CMB
1813–1900 **Soc Gen**

ST ARVANS   *M*
PR destroyed by fire *c*1708. The entries for years before that date were recorded from
memory in 1708 (see earliest extant PR)
C 1684–1890 M 1683–1917 (Banns 1861–1959) B 1694–1912 **Gwent RO**
BT 1725–47, 1749–56, 1758–1824, 1826–70 **NLW**
Cop ts PR CB 1802–1900 M 1792–1900 **Soc Gen**

* ST BRIDE'S NETHERWENT/SAINT-Y-BRID   *M*
At visitation in 1771 the PR was said to go back 'about a hundred years'. PR CB
1771–1812 recorded in 1831 apparently lost
C 1813–1991 M 1754–1817, 1819–1966 B 1813–1992 **Gwent RO**
BT 1725–9, 1731–54, 1756–1822, 1824–79, 1881–90 **NLW**
Cop ts PR CB 1813–1900 M 1819–1900 **Soc Gen**

* ST BRIDE'S WENTLLOOG/LLANSANFFRAID GWYNLLŴG   *M*
C [?1695]–1725, 1732–1985 M 1695–1810, 1813–1971 B 1695–1714, 1729–1989 **NLW**
Mf **Gwent RO**
BT 1725–66, 1768–75, 1777–1821, 1823–8, 1830–7, 1840, 1844, 1847, 1852–5, 1857,
1860–73 **NLW**

* ST MAUGHAN'S/LLANFOCHA   *M*
C 1733–1992 M 1733–1841 (Banns 1824–1988) B 1733–1990 **NLW** Mf **Gwent RO**
BT 1696, 1725–1847, 1850–73 **NLW**
Cop ts PR CB 1733–1900 M 1734–1841 **Soc Gen**

* ST MELLONS/LLANEIRWG   *M*
CMB 1717–20 in PR Llanedern/Llanedeyrn (Morgannwg/Glamorgan)
C 1722–1900 M 1722–1844 B 1722–1904 **NLW** C 1900–85 M 1837–1993 (Banns
1823–1996) B 1904–63 Mf C 1722–1900 M 1722–1844 B 1722–1904 **Gwent RO** Fa
C 1900–58 M 1837–1961 B 1904–63 **NLW**
BT 1725–75, 1777–1844, 1846–61, 1864–9 **NLW**
Cop ts PR CMB 1717–20 **NLW**

ST PIERRE/SAIN PŶR **M**
PR 1686–1812 recorded in 1831 apparently lost. At visitation in 1771 it was said that CMB
were 'register'd in the register book belonging to Portskewett'
C 1813–1992 M 1813–40 B 1813–1991 **NLW** Mf **Gwent RO**
BT 1696, 1725–35, 1737–43, 1745, 1757–8, 1774, 1789, 1794–6, 1800, 1803–6, 1808–70,
1873, 1877–81 **NLW**
Cop ts BT C 1725–1820 M 1697–1820 B 1696–1818 with index **Gwent RO** ts PR CMB
1813–1900 **Soc Gen**

ST THOMAS OVERMONNOW gweler/see TREFYNWY/MONMOUTH

SAINT-Y-BRID/ST BRIDE'S NETHERWENT **M**
At visitation in 1771 the PR was said to go back 'about a hundred years'. PR CB
1771–1812 recorded in 1831 apparently lost
C 1813–1991 M 1754–1817, 1819–1966 B 1813–1992 **Gwent RO**
BT 1725–9, 1731–54, 1756–1822, 1824–79, 1881–90 **NLW**
Cop ts PR CB 1813–1900 M 1819–1900 **Soc Gen**

SHIRENEWTON/DRENEWYDD GELLI-FARCH **M**
C 1730–69, 1771–1971 M 1733–1971 (Banns 1803–7, 1848–1928) B 1730–1955 **Gwent
RO**
BT 1725, 1729–38, 1740–1867, 1881–7 **NLW**
Cop ts PR CB 1730–1900 M 1732–1900 (Banns 1803–7, 1848–1900) with index **Gwent
RO & Soc Gen**

SKENFRITH/YNYSGYNWRAIDD **M**
C 1639–1745 with gaps, 1751–65, 1767–1925, 1928 M 1639–1731 with gaps, 1755–1837
(Banns 1824–1947) B 1639–1745 with gaps, 1751–65, 1767–1917 **NLW** Mf **Gwent RO**
BT 1726–84, 1786–7, 1789–1860 **NLW**
Cop ts PR CMB 1639–1900 **Soc Gen**

TINTERN PARVA/TYNDYRN **M**
PR 1694–1812 recorded in 1831 apparently lost
C 1813–1922 M 1756–1811, 1814–1970 **Gwent RO** B 1813– incumbent (Gwent RO
survey 1970)
BT 1725–1867 **NLW**
Cop ts BT CB 1726–1800 M 1728–99 with index **Gwent RO** ts PR CB 1813–1900 M
1756–1811, 1814–1900 **Soc Gen**

TRECELYN/NEWBRIDGE **M**
<Pen-maen 1914
C 1888–1960 M 1922–77 (Banns 1922–55) **Gwent RO**

TREDEGAR St George **M**
<Bedwellte/Bedwellty 1836

C 1838–1969 M 1840–1974 (Banns 1943–77) B 1851–1937 **Gwent RO**
BT 1838–61 **NLW**

TREDEGAR NEWYDD/NEW TREDEGAR   *M*
<Tredegar & Bedwellte/Bedwellty 1900
C 1896–1974 M 1897–1982 (Banns 1961–82) **Gwent RO**

TREDELERCH/RUMNEY   *M*
PR M 1754–1812 recorded in 1831 apparently lost. At visitation in 1781 there was here
  register going back 'about 120 years but in very bad preservation'
C 1744–1812 M 1744–86, 1804–37 B 1744–1812 **NLW** Mf **Gwent RO**
BT 1696, 1725–75, 1777, 1779–1865 **NLW**
Cop Mfc index B 1696–1840 **Soc Gen**

TREDYNOG/TREDUNNOCK   *M*
C 1695–1990 M 1695–1837, 1843–1970 (Banns 1827–1926, 1950, 1965–90)]
  1695–1812, 1814–1916, 1939–92 **NLW** Mf **Gwent RO**
BT 1696, 1725–70, 1772–1849, 1851–74, 1876–7, 1879 **NLW**
Cop ms/ts PR C 1695–1847 M 1695–1767, 1813–37 B 1695–1848 **NLW & Soc Gen**

TREFDDYN/TREVETHIN   *M*
C 1665–1709, 1726–1939 M 1655–1709, 1715, 1726–1923 (Banns 1823–55, 1891–1903
  1907–46) B 1655–1709, 1726–1933 **Gwent RO** Fac 1690–1709 **NLW**
BT 1696, 1725–1844 (see also Blaenafon/Blaenavon) **NLW**
Cop ms PR CMB 1652–69, 1695–1709 & ts PR CB 1714, 1726–1812 M 1714, 1726–9
  with index **NLW** ts PR CM 1652–1709, 1714–1837 B 1652–1709, 1806–34 **Soc Gen** t
  index PR B 1806–1908 **Gwent RO**

TREFESGOB/BISHTON   *M*
PR stolen from the church in 1821 (1831 survey). Visitation returns reported no PR CB i
  1781 where there had been one ten years earlier
C 1793–1991 M 1800–1967 B 1813–1990 **Gwent RO**
BT 1696, 1725–56, 1758–96, 1798–1819, 1823, 1826–43, 1845–57, 1859–68, 1870–1
  1873–7 **NLW** Mf **Soc Gen**
Cop ts PR C 1793–1899 M 1800–13, 1838–1900 B 1806–11, 1814–1900 **Soc Gen**

TREFONNEN/NASH   *M*
C 1733–1943 M 1733–1970 B 1733–1984 **Gwent RO**
BT 1725–50, 1753–5, 1758–1819, 1823, 1827–62, 1864–70 **NLW** Mf 1726–1837 **Glan**
  RO
Cop ts PR C 1813–1943 M 1758–1970 with index **Gwent RO & Soc Gen**

TREFYNWY/MONMOUTH St Mary   *M*
C 1598–1608, 1610–52, 1654, 1656–86, 1690–1754 M 1598–1603, 1606–8, 1610–49
  1651, 1657–83, 1690–1754 B 1598–1608, 1610–50, 1658, 1660, 1662–78, 1690–175
  NLW C 1755–1908 M 1754–1918 (Banns 1823–47, 1915–64) B 1755–1918 Mf **CM**

to 1754 **Gwent RO**
BT 1660–88, 1690–4, 1696–1833, 1836–42 **HRO**   1843–59, 1862–9 **NLW**   Mf 1839–42
Soc Gen
Cop ts PR CB 1755–1812   M 1754–63 with index **Gwent RO**   ts PR C 1598–1686,
1690–1900 M 1598–1682, 1690–1782, 1795–1900 B 1598–1678, 1690–1900 **Soc Gen**

TREFYNWY/MONMOUTH St Thomas Overmonnow   M
<St Mary 1831
C 1846–1910 M 1846–1942 (Banns 1846–1939) B 1850–4 **Gwent RO**
BT 1846–60, 1862, 1865, 1867 **NLW**
Cop ts PR CM 1846–1900 B 1850–4 **Soc Gen**

TREGARE/TRE'R-GAER   M
There are references to and extracts from the lost sixteenth-century register in *The Diary of
Walter Powell of Llantilio Crossenny* (ed J A Bradney: Bristol, 1907)
C 1751–1983 M 1751–1837 (Banns 1914–82) B 1751–1984 **NLW** Mf **Gwent RO**
BT 1725–36, 1738–1818, 1820–65, 1867–77 **NLW**
Cop ms BT (extracts) CMB 1696–1805 **NLW**   ts BT CMB 1760–1800 with index **Gwent
RO** ts PR C 1751–1812   MB 1751–1900 **Soc Gen**

TRELLECK/TRYLEG   M
At visitation in 1781 it was claimed that the register went back to 1602
C 1763–1976 M 1773–1971 (Banns 1824–1963) B 1763–1966 **NLW** Mf **Gwent RO**
BT 1696, 1725–1876, 1879–81 **NLW**
Cop ts BT CMB 1696, 1725–1800 with index **Gwent RO**   ts PR CB 1763–1900   M
1773–1900 **Soc Gen**

TRELLECK GRANGE   M
At visitation in 1771 it was claimed that 'there is no register book of births and burials (as for
burials there are none here); there are no returns made to the registrar's office, nor has the
Court at any time (as far as I know) taken any notice of this chapel'
C 1770–1811, 1813–1991 M 1771–1811, 1813–1946, 1950–63 B 1830–1989 **Gwent RO**
BT 1813–14, 1816–19, 1821–30, 1832–57, 1859–74 **NLW**
Cop ts PR C 1770–1811, 1813–99   M 1771–1811, 1813–1900   B 1830–99 with index
Gwent RO & Soc Gen

TRE-LYN/FLEUR-DE-LIS   M
<Mynyddislwyn, Bedwellte/Bedwellty, Bedwas & Gelli-gaer 1896
C 1897–1961 M 1897–1978 (Banns 1897–1938, 1943–50) B 1904–67 **Gwent RO**

TRE'R-GAER/TREGARE   M
There are references to and extracts from the lost sixteenth-century register in *The Diary of
Walter Powell of Llantilio Crossenny* (ed J A Bradney: Bristol, 1907)
C 1751–1983 M 1751–1837 (Banns 1914–82) B 1751–1984 **NLW** Mf **Gwent RO**
BT 1725–36, 1738–1818, 1820–65, 1867–77 **NLW**

Cop ms BT (extracts) CMB 1696–1805 **NLW**   ts BT CMB 1760–1800 with index **Gwent RO**   ts PR C 1751–1812 MB 1751–1900 **Soc Gen**

★ TREVETHIN/TREFDDYN   *M*
C 1655–1709, 1726–1939 M 1655–1709, 1715, 1726–1923 (Banns 1823–55, 1891–1903,
1907–46) B 1655–1709, 1726–1933 **Gwent RO**   Fac 1690–1709 **NLW**
BT 1696, 1725–1844 (see also Blaenafon/Blaenavon) **NLW**
Cop ms PR CMB 1652–69, 1695–1709 & ts PR CB 1714, 1726–1812 M 1714, 1726–94
with index **NLW**   ts PR CM 1652–1709, 1714–1837 B 1652–1709, 1806–34 **Soc Gen**

TROSTRE/TROSTREY   *M*
C 1723–33, 1758–66, 1779–1801, 1805–1975 M 1732, 1761–1802, 1804–12, 1816–36
1838–1970 (Banns 1824–?1979) B 1723–33, 1758–66, 1779–1801, 1805–1975 **NLW**   M
Gwent RO
BT 1725, 1728–34, 1737–1876 **NLW**
Cop ts PR C 1723–1801, 1805–1975 M 1732, 1761–1802, 1804–12, 1816–36 E
1731–1801, 1805–1975 with index **Gwent RO & Soc Gen**

TRYLEG/TRELLECK   *M*
At visitation in 1781 it was claimed that the register went back to 1602
C 1763–1976 M 1773–1971 (Banns 1824–1963) B 1763–1966 **NLW**   Mf **Gwent RO**
BT 1696, 1725–1876, 1879–81 **NLW**
Cop ts BT CMB 1696, 1725–1800 with index **Gwent RO**   ts PR CB 1763–1900 M
1773–1900 **Soc Gen**

TYNDYRN/TINTERN PARVA   *M*
PR 1694–1812 recorded in 1831 apparently lost
C 1813–1922 M 1756–1811, 1814–1970 **Gwent RO**   B 1813– incumbent (Gwent RO
survey 1970)
BT 1725–1867 **NLW**
Cop ts BT CB 1726–1800 M 1728–99 with index **Gwent RO**   ts PR CB 1813–1900 M
1756–1811, 1814–1900 **Soc Gen**

★ UNDY/GWNDY   *M*
C 1760–1891 M 1754–1971 (Banns 1758–89) B 1760–1800, 1813–1924 **Gwent RO**
BT 1696, 1725–1869, 1871–90, 1892–5 **NLW**
Cop ts PR C 1813–91 M 1754–1812, 1838–1900 B 1813–1900 **Soc Gen**

★ USK/BRYNBUGA   *M*
At visitation in 1771 the incumbent claimed that 'the most antient date I can find in the
parish is from 1701'
C 1742–1963 M 1742–1957 (Banns 1824–1965) B 1742–1953 **Gwent RO**
BT 1696, 1725–1858, 1865–1900 **NLW**
Cop ms PR/BT (extracts) CMB 1696–1785 **NLW**

VICTORIA   M
<Glynebwy/Ebbw Vale 1900
C 1908–68 M 1901–68 (Banns 1907–28) **Gwent RO**

WHITSON   M
C 1728–1991 M 1728–1970 B 1728–1984 **Gwent RO**
BT 1725–52, 1754, 1758–1825, 1827–68, 1870, 1872, 1875–80, 1882–9, 1891–2 **NLW**
Cop ts PR C 1744–1986 M 1729–1970 B 1728–1815 with index **Gwent RO & Soc Gen**

WILCRICK/CHWILGRUG   M
PR C 1786–1812 M 1755–85, 1804 B 1781–4 recorded in 1831 as being 'chiefly on loose
paper' now apparently lost
C 1814–1967 M 1814–1961 B 1824–1974 **Gwent RO**
BT 1725–41, 1743–54, 1756–75, 1777, 1779–95, 1797–1800, 1802–17, 1819–31, 1833–68,
1870–6 **NLW**

WOLVESNEWTON/LLANWYNELL   M
At visitation in 1771 it was claimed that the register went back to 1680
C 1716–1990 M 1716–1970 B 1716–1812, 1814–1990 **Gwent RO**
BT 1725–52, 1755–97, 1799–1807, 1809–16, 1818–27, 1829–30, 1832, 1834–62 **NLW**
Cop ts PR C 1678–1900 M 1716–1898 B 1680–1900 **Soc Gen**

WONASTOW/LLANWARW   M
C 1674–1752, 1759–62, 1765–1989 M 1675–1752, 1754–1812, 1814–36, 1838–1970 B
1674–1747, 1759–62, 1765–1992 **NLW** Mf **Gwent RO**
BT 1725–50, 1752–5, 1758–1861 **NLW**
Cop ts BT CB 1725–1801 M 1725–99 with index **Gwent RO** ts PR CB 1674–1900 M
1675–1895 **Soc Gen**

YNYS-DDU   M
<Mynyddislwyn 1925
C 1916–66 M 1927–71 (Banns 1927–74) **Gwent RO**

YNYSGYNWRAIDD/SKENFRITH   M
C 1639–1745 with gaps, 1751–65, 1767–1925, 1928 M 1639–1731 with gaps, 1755–1837
(Banns 1824–1947) B 1639–1745 with gaps, 1751–65, 1767–1917 **NLW** Mf **Gwent RO**
BT 1726–84, 1786–7, 1789–1860 **NLW**
Cop ts PR CMB 1639–1900 **Soc Gen**

PENFRO
PEMBROKESHIRE

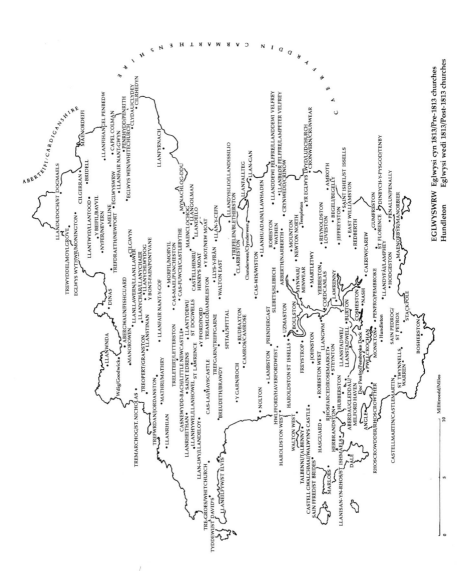

EGLWYSWRW Eglwysi cyn 1813/Pre-1813 churches

Hundleton Eglwysi wedi 1813/Post-1813 churches

ABERDAUGLEDDAU/MILFORD HAVEN   *SD*
<Steynton 1891.   Consecrated 1808
C 1808–33, 1860–1960 M 1891–1975 (Banns 1921–75) B 1877–1955 **Pemb RO**
BT see Steynton

ABERGWAUN/FISHGUARD   *SD*
Diocesan records suggest that *c*1790 this parish had a register going back to 1761
C 1799–1949 M 1785–1964 (Banns 1902–40) B 1799–1854, 1934–95 **NLW** Mf **Pemb RO**
BT 1685, 1799–1829, 1831–47, 1863–4 **NLW**
Cop ms PR C 1783–1854 M 1785–1837 B 1799–1854 **NLW** ts PR M 1813–37 with index **NLW Pemb RO & Soc Gen**

* AMBLESTON/TREAMLOD   *SD*
C 1765–1974 M 1776–1968 B 1765–1974 **NLW** Mf **Pemb RO**
BT 1685, 1799–1862, 1864 **NLW**
Cop ts PR M 1813–36 with index **NLW Pemb RO & Soc Gen**

AMROTH   *SD*
PR C –1785 recorded in 1831 as having been destroyed
C 1786–1913 M 1754–1970 B 1786–1874 **Pemb RO**
BT 1799–1835, 1837–51, 1853–89 **NLW**
Cop ts PR M 1813–37 with index **NLW Pemb RO & Soc Gen**

ANGLE   *SD*
PR ancient volumes reputedly destroyed by fire (1831 survey; cf Castellmartin/Castlemartin).
A few entries C 1763–83 are in PR CB 1784–1812. PR CB 1779–85 is a draft register
C 1779–1993 M 1755–1983 (Banns 1856–1962) B 1779–1993 **NLW** Mf **Pemb RO**
BT 1685–6, 1799–1807, 1809–99 **NLW**
Cop ts PR/BT M pre-1813 with index **NLW & Pemb RO** ts PR M 1814–37 with index **NLW Pemb RO & Soc Gen**

ARBERTH/NARBERTH   *SD*
C 1676–1703, 1762–1918 M 1676–1703, 1754–1808, 1811–1964 (Banns 1811–42, 1896–1966) B 1676–1703, 1762–1898 **Pemb RO** Fac 1676–1845 **NLW**
BT 1799–1801, 1803, 1805, 1807–67, 1872–3 **NLW**
Cop ts PR (extracts) C 1681–1844, 1854–84 M 1756–1837 **NLW** ts PR M 1813–37 with index **NLW Pemb RO & Soc Gen**

BAYVIL gweler/see BEIFIL, Y

BEGELI/BEGELLY   *SD*
C 1759–1934 M 1771–1933 B 1759–1934 **NLW** Mf **Pemb RO**
BT 1685–6, 1799–1809, 1811–88, 1892, 1896–7 **NLW**
Cop ts PR/BT 1757–1800 **Pemb RO & Soc Gen** ts PR M 1813–37 with index **NLW Pemb RO & Soc Gen**

BEIFIL, Y/BAYVIL   *SD*
Diocesan records suggest that *c*1790 this parish had registers going back to 1767
C 1813–93 M 1814–37, 1839–77 (Banns 1828–71, 1929–93) B 1813–1908 **NLW** Mf
(except Banns) **Pemb RO**
BT 1674–6, 1679–82, 1685–6, 1688–9, 1700–1, 1703, 1799–1802, 1804–15, 1821–60,
1862, 1864–5, 1867–8, 1870–5, 1877, 1879, 1882–3, 1885–8 **NLW**
Cop ts PR/BT M 1814–37 with index **NLW Pemb RO & Soc Gen**

* BLETHERSTON/TREFELEN   *SD*
CB 1653–1812 M 1653–1753 entered in PR Llanhuadain/Llawhaden
C 1653–1980 M 1653–1971 B 1653–1980 **NLW** Mf **Pemb RO**
BT 1772, 1799, 1801–38, 1840–57, 1859–70, 1872–3, 1875–9, 1881–3 **NLW**
Cop ts PR M 1813–37 with index **NLW Pemb RO & Soc Gen**

BONT-FAEN, Y/PONTVANE   *SD*
Diocesan records suggest that *c*1790 this parish had registers going back to 1748
C 1813–1993 M 1815–1971 B 1813–1986 **Pemb RO**
BT 1676, 1678–9, 1681–4, 1686, 1800–13, 1815–19, 1821–40, 1845–7, 1850, 1853, 1855
NLW
Cop ts PR M 1815–35 with index **NLW Pemb RO & Soc Gen**

BOSHERSTON   *SD*
C 1670–1991 M 1670–1752, 1754–1906 B 1670–1783, 1787–1990 **NLW** Mf/Fac **Pemb**
RO
BT 1799–1807, 1809–87 **NLW**
Cop ts PR CMB 1670–1991 arranged alphabetically **NLW & Pemb RO** ts PR M pre-
1813 with index **NLW & Pemb RO** ts PR/BT M 1813–37 with index **NLW Pemb**
RO & Soc Gen

BOULSTON   *SD*
C 1799–1939 M 1754–1928 (Banns 1837–1923) B 1799–1913 **Pemb RO** Mf M
1754–1809 **NLW**
BT 1813–22, 1837, 1839 **NLW**
Cop ts PR C 1799–1939 M 1754–1809 B 1813–1913 with index **Pemb RO & Soc Gen**
ts PR M 1813–36 with index **NLW Pemb RO & Soc Gen**

BREUDETH/BRAWDY   *SD*
PR CB 1783–1812 M 1754–1812 recorded in 1831 apparently lost. M 1813–37 B
1813–82 were missing in 1933 and are also apparently lost. For some entries *c*1784 see PR
Tre-groes/Whitchurch. Diocesan records suggest that *c*1790 the registers went back to
1764
C 1813–1915 M 1837–1966 (Banns 1935–60) B 1882–1915 **Pemb RO**
BT 1799–1800, 1802, 1804–9, 1811–67, 1872–82, 1884–5, 1887–96 **NLW**
Cop ts PR (extracts) C 1813–96 **NLW** ts BT M 1813–37 with index **NLW Pemb RO &**
Soc Gen

BRIDELL   SD
PR CMB 1705–1809 recorded in 1831 apparently lost
C 1810–1993 M 1810–1970 (Banns 1824–79, 1912–80) B 1810–11, 1814–1993 **NLW** Mf
Pemb RO
BT 1674–5, 1678–81, 1683, 1685–6, 1689, 1700, 1709, 1799–1801, 1806–7, 1809–43,
1846–52, 1854–73, 1875–80 **NLW**
Cop ts PR/BT M pre-1813 with index **NLW & Pemb RO** ts PR M 1814–36 with index
NLW Pemb RO & Soc Gen

BURTON   SD
C 1689–99, 1716–1922 M 1689–99, 1716–1837 (Banns 1823–1905) B 1689–99,
1716–1895 **NLW** Mf **Pemb RO**
BT 1799–1807, 1809–67, 1869–73 **NLW**
Cop ts PR (extracts) C 1689–1804 M 1695–1808 B 1695–1811 **NLW** ts PR M
1754–1837 **Pemb RO & Soc Gen** ts PR M 1813–37 with index **NLW Pemb RO &
Soc Gen**

CAERIW/CAREW   SD
C 1718–1951 M 1718–1971 (Banns 1811–1932) B 1718–1966 **Pemb RO**
BT 1685–6, 1799–1801, 1803–68, 1870–9, 1884–9, 1896–9, 1901–5 **NLW**
Cop ts PR/BT 1779–1819 **Pemb RO & Soc Gen** ts PR M 1813–37 with index **NLW
Pemb RO & Soc Gen**

CAMROS/CAMROSE   SD
Diocesan records suggest that c1790 the registers went back to 1749. PR B includes entries
for Cas-lai/Hayscastle from 1977
C 1795–1934 M 1754–1929 B 1813–1992 **NLW** Mf/Fac C 1795–1982 M 1754–1953 B
1813–1992 **Pemb RO**
BT 1799–1804, 1806, 1809–48, 1852–83, 1888–97 **NLW**
Cop ts PR (extracts) C 1813–1906 M 1838–96 B 1861–1907 **NLW** ts PR M 1813–37
with index **NLW Pemb RO & Soc Gen**

CAPEL COLMAN   SD
PR CB 1777–1812 recorded in 1831 apparently lost. M 1770–90 entered in PR
Llanfihangel Penbedw
C 1813–1987 M 1770–1834, 1840–1970 (Banns 1824–85, 1931–89) B 1824–1991 **NLW**
Mf **Pemb RO**
BT 1806, 1810–11, 1813–17, 1820, 1823–36, 1838, 1840–56, 1858–67, 1870–1, 1873–8
NLW
Cop ts PR/BT M pre-1813 with index **NLW & Pemb RO** ts PR M 1813–34 with index
NLW Pemb RO & Soc Gen

CAREW/CAERIW   SD
C 1718–1951 M 1718–1971 (Banns 1811–1932) B 1718–1966 **Pemb RO**
BT 1685–6, 1799–1801, 1803–68, 1870–9, 1884–9, 1896–9, 1901–5 **NLW**

Cop ts PR/BT 1779–1819 **Pemb RO & Soc Gen** ts PR M 1813–37 with index **NLW**
Pemb RO & Soc Gen

CARNHEDRYN gweler/see LLANHYWEL/LLANHOWEL

CAS-FUWCH/CASTLEBYTHE   *SD*
Civil register 1653–7 (**Cardiff Central Library** MS.4.44)   Mf **NLW**
C 1777–1894, 1959 M 1752, 1756–72, 1775–1920 B 1777–1980 **NLW** Mf **Pemb RO**
BT 1677–80, 1685–6, 1799, 1801, 1803, 1805–11, 1813–16, 1819–20, 1825–9, 1831–9
1841, 1843, 1845–80, 1885–98 **NLW**
Cop ts PR (extracts) CMB 1781–1883 **NLW** ts PR M 1813–37 with index **NLW Pemb**
RO & Soc Gen

CAS-LAI/HAYSCASTLE   *SD*
PR C 1800–12 M 1810–37 B 1798–1812 recorded in 1933 and M 1787–1812 recorded in
1831 apparently lost. Diocesan records suggest that c1790 the registers went back to 1764
B 1977– entered in PR Camros/Camrose
C 1813–1992 M 1837–1968 B 1813–1941 **Pemb RO**
BT 1799–1808, 1810–66, 1872–89, 1891–6 **NLW**
Cop ts PR C 1800–12 M 1810 B 1798–1812 **NLW** ts BT M 1813–37 with index **NLW**
Pemb RO & Soc Gen

CAS-MAEL/PUNCHESTON   *SD*
Civil register 1653–9 (**Cardiff Central Library** MS.4.44)   Mf **NLW**. PR M 1813–3
recorded in 1933 apparently lost
C 1789–1807, 1813–1985 M 1797–1810, 1838–1967 B 1789–1807, 1813–1974 **NLW M**
Pemb RO
BT 1675–6, 1678–83, 1686, 1688, 1799, 1801–4, 1806–7, 1809–11, 1813–43, 1845–8
1852–9 **NLW**
Cop ts BT M 1813–37 with index **NLW Pemb RO & Soc Gen**

CASNEWYDD-BACH/LITTLE NEWCASTLE   *SD*
Civil register 1654–8 (**Cardiff Central Library** MS.4.44) Mf **NLW**
C 1783–1813 M 1813–1966 B 1783–1813 **NLW** Mf **Pemb RO**
BT 1679–80, 1685, 1799, 1801, 1803, 1805–9, 1811–79, 1885 **NLW**
Cop ts PR M 1813–36 with index **NLW Pemb RO & Soc Gen**

CASTELLAN   *SD*
An ancient chapelry in the parish of Penrhydd/Penrith. No separate PR

CASTELL GWALCHMAI/WALWYN'S CASTLE   *SD*
C 1767–1920 M 1755–1808, 1812–1962 B 1755–1993 **NLW** Mf **Pemb RO**
BT 1772, 1801–6, 1809–14, 1818–74 **NLW**
Cop ts BT M 1813–37 with index **NLW Pemb RO & Soc Gen**

CASTELLHENRI/HENRY'S MOAT   SD
A note written on the front cover of PR B 1813–1986 states that PR CB 1715–1813 was
extant in 1844
C 1813–1993 M 1755–1970 B 1813–1986 **NLW** Mf/Fac **Pemb RO**
BT 1674–6, 1678–84, 1686, 1689, 1799, 1803–5, 1807–16, 1818–37, 1839–48, 1850, 1853,
1855, 1858–9, 1861–7, 1871, 1874, 1878–89, 1897–1906 **NLW**
Cop ts PR M 1813–37 with index **NLW Pemb RO & Soc Gen**

CASTELLMARTIN/CASTLEMARTIN   SD
Earlier PR reputedly destroyed in a fire at 'the old rectory' (NLW survey 1933; cf Angle)
C 1783–1992 M 1783–1810, 1813–1991 (Banns 1782–1809, 1824–1993) B 1783–1975
NLW Mf **Pemb RO**
BT 1685–6, 1799–1805, 1807, 1809–57, 1859–60, 1864–90 **NLW**
Cop ts PR/BT M pre-1813 with index **NLW & Pemb RO** ts PR M 1813–37 with index
NLW Pemb RO & Soc Gen

CASTLEBYTHE/CAS-FUWCH   SD
Civil register 1653–7 (**Cardiff Central Library** MS.4.44) Mf **NLW**
C 1777–1894, 1959 M 1752, 1756–72, 1775–1920 B 1777–1980 **NLW** Mf **Pemb RO**
BT 1677–80, 1685–6, 1799, 1801, 1803, 1805–11, 1813–16, 1819–20, 1825–9, 1831–9,
1841, 1843, 1845–80, 1885–98 **NLW**
Cop ts PR (extracts) CMB 1781–1883 **NLW** ts PR M 1813–37 with index **NLW Pemb
RO & Soc Gen**

CASTLEMARTIN gweler/see CASTELLMARTIN

CAS-WIS/WISTON   SD
CMB 1653–66 entered in PR Llanhuadain/Llawhaden
C 1653–66, 1715–1993 M 1653–66, 1715–1970 B 1653–66, 1715–1921 **NLW** Mf/Fac
Pemb RO
BT 1799–1806, 1808–82 **NLW**
Cop ts PR M 1813–37 with index **NLW Pemb RO & Soc Gen**

CILGERRAN   SD
C 1708–96, 1806–1992 M 1708–1970 B 1708–96, 1806–1961 **NLW** Mf **Pemb RO**
BT 1674–6, 1678–85, 1687, 1689, 1702–3, 1705, 1799–1805, 1807–62, 1871, 1873–80,
1882, 1885–7 **NLW**
Cop ts PR/BT M pre-1813 with index **NLW & Pemb RO** ts PR M 1813–37 with index
NLW Pemb RO & Soc Gen

CILGWYN   SD
<Nyfer/Nevern
C 1775–1811 M 1754–1811, 1934–68 (Banns 1823–1902) B 1775–1811 **NLW** Mf CB
1775–1811 M 1759–82 **Pemb RO** Mf M 1759–82 **Soc Gen**
BT see Nyfer/Nevern

CILRHEDYN   *SD*
Most of this parish was in Carmarthenshire. Church closed 1981. Diocesan records sugges
that *c*1790 this parish had registers going back to 1701
C 1800–1978 M 1754–1963 B 1800–12 **NLW** Mf **Pemb RO**
BT 1676, 1678–81, 1683, 1685–9, 1702–3, 1705, 1799–1807, 1809–57, 1861, 1864–5
1868–70, 1872–4 **NLW**
Cop ts PR (extracts) CMB 1771–1904 **NLW** ts PR C 1813–75 M 1754–1875 B 1813–7!
arranged alphabetically **Pemb RO** ts PR/BT M pre-1813 with index **NLW & Peml**
RO ts PR M 1813–37 with index **NLW Pemb RO & Soc Gen**

CLARBESTON   *SD*
No mention of PR M 1813–37 in 1933 survey
C 1718–1993 M 1724–1813, 1837–1970 (Banns 1755–1812, 1825–1952) B 1725–199:
Pemb RO
BT 1799–1806, 1809–67, 1878–82 **NLW**
Cop ts BT M 1813–36 with index **NLW Pemb RO & Soc Gen**

CLUNDERWEN/CLYNDERWEN   *SD*
<Llanfallteg
M 1956–71 **Pemb RO**

CLYDAU/CLYDEY   *SD*
C 1701–1991 M 1701–1970 B 1701–1991 **NLW** Mf **Pemb RO**
BT 1674, 1676, 1678–80, 1682–5, 1687–9, 1702, 1705, 1799–1803, 1805–14, 1816–67
1869, 1873 **NLW**
Cop ts PR/BT M pre-1813 with index **NLW & Pemb RO** ts PR M 1813–37 with inde:
NLW Pemb RO & Soc Gen

CLYNDERWEN gweler/see CLUNDERWEN

COEDCANLAS   *SD*
A small ancient parish, its church was rebuilt 1718 after being a ruin for half a century, an
was again a ruin by the 1920s. PR included in those of Martletwy and Lawrenny

COSHESTON   *SD*
C 1723–42, 1752–1944 M 1723–40, 1752–1970 (Banns 1755–99, 1882–1967) B 1723–42
1752–1891 **Pemb RO**
BT 1799–1886 **NLW**
Cop ts PR/BT C 1723–1825 M 1723–1812 B 1723–1812 **Pemb RO & Soc Gen** ts PF
M pre-1813 with index **NLW & Pemb RO** ts PR M 1813–36 with index **NLW Peml**
RO & Soc Gen

CRINOW gweler/see CRYNWEDD

CRONWERN/CRUNWEAR   *SD*
PR CB 1725–83 M 1725–53 recorded in 1831 apparently lost

C 1783–1979 M 1754–1969 B 1783–1978 **Pemb RO** Fac 1725–62 **NLW**
BT 1799–1839, 1841–91, 1893–1900 **NLW**
Cop ts PR M 1813–36 with index **NLW Pemb RO & Soc Gen**

CRYNWEDD/CRINOW   *SD*
M 1757–72, 1776, 1786–8, 1792, 1815–36, 1838–1970 **NLW** Mf **Pemb RO** CB 1813–
   incumbent
BT 1829–30, 1832–9, 1841–55, 1857–72 **NLW**
Cop ts PR M 1815–36 with index **NLW Pemb RO & Soc Gen**

DALE   *SD*
C 1723–1887 M 1723–1958 B 1723–1958 **NLW** Mf **Pemb RO**
BT 1799–1800, 1802–78 **NLW**
Cop ts PR M 1813–36 with index **NLW Pemb RO & Soc Gen**

DINAS   *SD*
C 1676–1972 M 1676–1804, 1813–1970 B 1676–1993 **NLW** Mf C 1804–12 M 1755–91
   B 1804–12 **Pemb RO**
BT 1675–6, 1678, 1680, 1682–6, 1688–9, 1699, 1702–3, 1799–1809, 1811–37, 1839–45,
   1848–58, 1865, 1867–81 **NLW**
Cop ms PR CMB 1676–1812 **NLW** ts BT M 1813–37 with index **NLW Pemb RO &
   Soc Gen**

DINBYCH-Y-PYSGOD/TENBY   *SD*
C 1711–1930 M 1711–1971 (Banns 1823–66, 1877–1963) B 1711–1971 **Pemb RO** Fac
   1711–28 **NLW**
BT 1685, 1762, 1799–1804, 1806–7, 1811–51, 1853–94 **NLW**
Cop ts PR M 1813–37 with index **NLW Pemb RO & Soc Gen**

DOCKYARD gweler/see DOC PENFRO/PEMBROKE DOCK

DOC PENFRO/PEMBROKE DOCK St John   *SD*
<Penfro/Pembroke St Mary 1844
C 1844–1927 Garrison 1856–1906 Dockyard 1875–1926 Pennar 1895–1967 M 1848–1951,
   1965–76 (Banns 1848–1971) B 1844–1977 Garrison 1861–1922 **Pemb RO**
BT 1844–86 **NLW**

EAST WILLIAMSTON   *SD*
An ancient chapelry whose PR are included in those of Begeli/Begelly

EGLWYS LWYD, YR/LUDCHURCH   *SD*
C 1732–1992 M 1732–1971 B 1732–1993 **NLW** Mf **Pemb RO**
BT 1799–1839, 1842–54, 1857–60, 1865–77 **NLW**
Cop ts PR/BT CMB 1779–1839 **Pemb RO & Soc Gen** ts PR M 1813–37 with index
   NLW Pemb RO & Soc Gen

EGLWYS WEN/WHITECHURCH   *SD*
C 1704–1992 M 1704–53, 1755–9, 1813–1933, 1948–70 B 1704–1812, 1814–1992 **NLW**
Mf **Pemb RO**
BT 1674–5, 1678, 1680–3, 1685–90, 1699, 1701–3, 1799–1800, 1803–39, 1844–6
1851–60, 1863, 1865, 1869–70, 1872–80, 1882, 1885, 1890 **NLW**
Cop ts PR M 1813–37 with index **NLW Pemb RO & Soc Gen**

EGLWYSWRW   *SD*
PR CMB 1731–9 recorded in 1831 apparently lost. Diocesan records suggest that *c*1790 thi
parish had registers going back to 1685
C 1740–1992 M 1740–1970, 1973–87 (Banns 1824–73, 1921–9, 1957–93) B 1740–199.
NLW Mf **Pemb RO**
BT 1674, 1676, 1680, 1683–7, 1689, 1703, 1799–1863, 1865–7, 1869–74, 1879–80 **NLW**
Cop ts BT M 1813–37 with index **NLW Pemb RO & Soc Gen**

EGLWYS WYTHWR/MONINGTON   *SD*
Diocesan records suggest that *c*1790 this parish had registers going back to 1751
C 1813–1993 M 1773–1809, 1816–33, 1837–1968 B 1813–1993 **NLW** Mf **Pemb RO**
BT 1674–6, 1679–81, 1686–7, 1689, 1697, 1703, 1799–1800, 1802–24, 1826–40, 1842
1844–7, 1849–54, 1860, 1865–9, 1871–3, 1875 **NLW**
Cop ts PR (extracts) C 1818–44 B 1802–87 **NLW** ts PR M 1816–33 with index **NLW**
Pemb RO & Soc Gen

★ FISHGUARD/ABERGWAUN   *SD*
Diocesan records suggest that *c*1790 this parish had a register going back to 1761
C 1799–1949 M 1785–1964 (Banns 1902–40) B 1799–1854, 1934–95 **NLW** Mf **Peml**
RO
BT 1685, 1799–1829, 1831–47, 1863–4 **NLW**
Cop ms PR C 1783–1854 M 1785–1837 B 1799–1854 **NLW** ts PR M 1813–37 witl
index **NLW Pemb RO & Soc Gen**

FREYSTROP   *SD*
C 1729–1876 M 1740–3, 1754–84, 1813–1969 (Banns 1863–1947) B 1729–1891 **Peml**
RO
BT 1799–1801, 1804–7, 1809–70, 1883–5 **NLW**
Cop ts PR M 1813–37 with index **NLW Pemb RO & Soc Gen**

FFORD, Y/FORD   *SD*
Odd entries CMB 1801–49 with PR Treamlod/Ambleston and Casnewydd-bach/Littl
Newcastle
C 1885–1944 M 1837–1963 B 1866–1945 **Pemb RO**
BT 1839–42, 1844–54, 1856–65, 1875, 1885 **NLW**

GARN, Y/ROCH   *SD*
C 1677–1737, 1763–1974 M 1677–1737, 1754–1922, 1926–82 (Banns 1823–99)]
1677–1737, 1763–1901 **Pemb RO** Fac C 1813–1974 M 1837–1922 **NLW**

BT 1799–1800, 1802–63, 1865–8, 1871–86 **NLW**
Cop ts PR CB 1677–1737, 1763–1812 M 1677–1737, 1783–1812 **NLW** ts PR M 1813–37
with index **NLW Pemb RO & Soc Gen**

GARRISON gweler/see DOC PENFRO/PEMBROKE DOCK

★ GOODWICK/WDIG *SD*
<Llanwnda
M 1913–74 (Banns 1923–74) **Pemb RO**

★ GRANSTON/TREOPERT *SD*
Diocesan records suggest that *c*1790 the registers went back to 1727
C 1793–1990 M 1778–1970 (Banns 1778–1814, 1828–1908) B 1793–1805, 1813–1991
   Pemb RO
BT 1799–1843, 1846, 1865–7 **NLW**
Cop ms PR C 1785–1811 M 1778–1813 B 1784–1813 ts PR (extracts) CB 1785–1902 M
   1778–1817 **NLW** ts PR M 1813–35 with index **NLW Pemb RO & Soc Gen**

GUMFRESTON *SD*
C 1647–1966 M 1655–1970 (Banns 1843–1949) B 1651–1790, 1813–1954 **Pemb RO**
BT 1799–1831, 1833–50, 1853–9, 1861–73 **NLW**
Cop PR CMB 1799–1806 incomplete **Pemb RO & Soc Gen** ts PR M 1813–36 with
   index **NLW Pemb RO & Soc Gen**

HAKIN gweler/see HUBBERSTON

HAROLDSTON ST ISSELLS *SD*
PR CMB 1765–[1812] recorded in 1933 apparently lost
C 1813–1990 M 1814–1969 B 1813–98 **Pemb RO**
BT 1798–1802, 1807, 1809–57, 1859–70 **NLW**
Cop ts PR M 1814–37 with index **NLW Pemb RO & Soc Gen**

HAROLDSTON WEST *SD*
C 1748–1991 M 1751–86, 1813–1959 B 1750–1992 **Pemb RO**
BT 1800–1, 1803–18, 1820–46, 1849 **NLW**
Cop ts PR M 1813–34 with index **NLW Pemb RO & Soc Gen**

HASGUARD *SD*
PR C 1764–1812 M 1756–1812 B 1792–1812 recorded in 1831 apparently lost. M
   1813–37 not recorded in 1933
C 1813–1968 M 1837–1957 B 1814–1969 **Pemb RO**
BT 1800–3, 1805–13, 1816–20, 1823–40, 1842, 1854–6, 1868–70, 1876–8 **NLW**
Cop ts BT M 1816–37 with index **NLW Pemb RO & Soc Gen**

HAVERFORDWEST/HWLFFORDD St Martin *SD*
C 1721–36, 1745–85, 1793–1887 M 1721–1917 (Banns 1824–1952) B 1721–36, 1745–85,

1793–1974 **Pemb RO**
BT 1800–7, 1809–19, 1823–71 **NLW**
Cop ts PR (extracts) C 1722–1812 M 1729–1884 B 1721–1839 ts PR M 1813–37 with
index **NLW Pemb RO & Soc Gen** Mf cop ms PR CB 1745–73 M 1745–72 (**Cardif
Central Library** MS.2.116) **NLW**

* HAVERFORDWEST/HWLFFORDD St Mary   *SD*
  C 1602–43, 1678–1725, 1728–1955 M 1600–48, 1686, 1699–1706, 1716–23, 1728–196!
  (Banns 1754–1967) B 1590–1643, 1683–1706, 1716–24, 1728–1966 **Pemb RO** M
  1590–1644, 1713–25 **NLW**
  BT 1799–1801, 1804–6, 1808–82 **NLW**
  Cop ms/ts PR 1590–1812 **NLW** ts PR M 1813–37 with index **NLW Pemb RO & So**
  Gen ms/ts PR 1594–1850 incomplete and partly with index **Pemb RO & Soc Gen**

* HAVERFORDWEST/HWLFFORDD St Thomas   *SD*
  C 1714–1962 M 1714–1952 B 1710–1901 **Pemb RO**
  BT 1813–18, 1823, 1825–73 **NLW**
  Cop ts PR (extracts) C 1716–1907 M 1713–1892 B 1712–1879 ts PR M 1813–37 with
  index **NLW Pemb RO & Soc Gen**

* HAYSCASTLE/CAS-LAI   *SD*
  PR C 1800–12 M 1810–37 B 1798–1812 recorded in 1933 and M 1787–1812 recorded i
  1831 apparently lost. Diocesan records suggest that c1790 the registers went back to 1764
  B 1977– entered in PR Camros/Camrose
  C 1813–1992 M 1837–1968 B 1813–1941 **Pemb RO**
  BT 1799–1808, 1810–66, 1872–89, 1891–6 **NLW**
  Cop ts PR C 1800–12 M 1810 B 1798–1812 **NLW** ts BT M 1813–37 with index **NLW**
  Pemb RO & Soc Gen

* HENRY'S MOAT/CASTELLHENRI   *SD*
  A note written on the front cover of PR B 1813–1986 states that PR CB 1715–1813 wa
  extant in 1844
  C 1813–1993 M 1755–1970 B 1813–1986 **NLW** Mf/Fac **Pemb RO**
  BT 1674–6, 1678–84, 1686, 1689, 1799, 1803–5, 1807–16, 1818–37, 1839–48, 1850, 1853
  1855, 1858–9, 1861–7, 1871, 1874, 1878–89, 1897–1906 **NLW**
  Cop ts PR M 1813–37 with index **NLW Pemb RO & Soc Gen**

HERBRANDSTON   *SD*
C 1717–20, 1729–1908 M 1729–1970 (Banns 1813–52) B 1717–20, 1729–1992 **Pem
RO**
BT 1799–1804, 1806–63, 1865–70 **NLW**
Cop ts PR M 1813–37 with index **NLW Pemb RO & Soc Gen**

HODGESTON   *SD*
C 1766–1812 M 1755–1801, 1814–1961 (Banns 1755–1848) B 1766–1812 **Pemb RO**
BT 1686, 1799–1807, 1809–67, 1869–79, 1889–93, 1895 **NLW**

Cop ts PR/BT M pre-1813 with index **NLW & Pemb RO** ts PR M 1814–35 with index **NLW Pemb RO & Soc Gen**

HUBBERSTON *SD*
C 1702–1970 M 1702–1986 (Banns 1783–1869) Hakin, St Mary 1955–70 (Banns 1956–75) B 1702–1958 **NLW** Mf/Fac **Pemb RO**
BT 1800, 1803–4, 1807–9, 1811–59, 1862–7 **NLW**
Cop ts PR M 1813–37 with index **NLW Pemb RO & Soc Gen**

HUNDLETON *SD*
<Monkton
C 1897–1935 M 1954–70 B 1897–1959 **Pemb RO**

HWLFFORDD/HAVERFORDWEST St Martin *SD*
C 1721–36, 1745–85, 1793–1887 M 1721–1917 (Banns 1824–1952) B 1721–36, 1745–85, 1793–1974 **Pemb RO**
BT 1800–7, 1809–19, 1823–71 **NLW**
Cop ts PR (extracts) C 1722–1812 M 1729–1884 B 1721–1839 ts PR M 1813–37 with index **NLW Pemb RO & Soc Gen** Mf cop ms PR CB 1745–73 M 1745–72 (**Cardiff Central Library** MS.2.116) **NLW**

HWLFFORDD/HAVERFORDWEST St Mary *SD*
C 1602–43, 1678–1725, 1728–1955 M 1600–48, 1686, 1699–1706, 1716–23, 1728–1965 (Banns 1754–1967) B 1590–1643, 1683–1706, 1716–24, 1728–1966 **Pemb RO** Mf 1590–1644, 1713–25 **NLW**
BT 1799–1801, 1804–6, 1808–82 **NLW**
Cop ms/ts PR 1590–1812 **NLW** ts PR M 1813–37 with index **NLW Pemb RO & Soc Gen** ms/ts PR 1594–1850 incomplete and partly with index **Pemb RO & Soc Gen**

HWLFFORDD/HAVERFORDWEST St Thomas *SD*
C 1714–1962 M 1714–1952 B 1710–1901 **Pemb RO**
BT 1813–18, 1823, 1825–73 **NLW**
Cop ts PR (extracts) C 1716–1907 M 1713–1892 B 1712–1879 ts PR M 1813–37 with index **NLW Pemb RO & Soc Gen**

JEFFREYSTON *SD*
C 1695–1945 M 1695–1971 B 1695–1977 **NLW** Mf **Pemb RO**
BT 1799–1876, 1879, 1881, 1885–6, 1888–9, 1903–4 **NLW**
Cop ts PR (extracts) 1715–1801 **NLW** ts PR 1730–1837 incomplete and with index **Pemb RO & Soc Gen** ts PR M 1813–37 with index **NLW Pemb RO & Soc Gen**

JOHNSTON *SD*
CB 1637–1804 M 1637–1755 entered in PR Steynton
C 1637–1804, 1813–1956 M 1637–1809, 1813–1971 (Banns 1839–1976) B 1637–1803, 1813–1987 **Pemb RO**

BT 1799–1801, 1804–7, 1809–12, 1814–66 **NLW**
Cop ts PR M 1814–36 with index **NLW Pemb RO & Soc Gen**

* JORDANSTON/TREFWRDAN   *SD*
  C 1802–13 M 1803–51 (Banns 1812–96) B 1802–13 **NLW** Mf **Pemb RO**
  BT 1799–1800, 1802–10, 1812–21, 1823–37, 1839–40, 1843–7, 1857–8, 1866 **NLW**
  Cop ts PR (extracts) C 1811–39 M 1834–9 B 1808–97 **NLW** ts PR M 1814–36 wit
  index **NLW Pemb RO & Soc Gen**

LAMBSTON   *SD*
C 1737–1991 M 1741–1968 (Banns 1755–1833) B 1737–1957 **Pemb RO**
BT 1799–1804, 1806–41, 1843, 1845, 1849, 1868 **NLW**
Cop ts PR M 1813–36 with index **NLW Pemb RO & Soc Gen**

* LAMPETER VELFREY/LLANBEDR FELFFRE   *SD*
  PR CB 1779–1812 recorded in 1831 apparently lost
  C 1813–1923 M 1755–1980 (Banns 1853–1919, 1931–47) Princes Gate 1949–64 (Banr
  1948–71) B 1813–1992 **Pemb RO**
  BT 1677, 1679, 1681, 1686, 1698–9, 1720–2, 1724–5, 1727, 1729, 1735, 1737–4?
  1763–70, 1774–6, 1780, 1782–4, 1786–9, 1793–9, 1803–81, 1885–6 **NLW**
  Cop ts PR M 1813–37 with index **NLW Pemb RO & Soc Gen**

* LAMPHEY/LLANDYFÁI   *SD*
  C 1776–1883 M 1755–1975 B 1776–1962 **Pemb RO**
  BT 1799–1807, 1809–75, 1877–8, 1880–9 **NLW**
  Cop ts PR M pre-1813 with index **NLW & Pemb RO** ts PR M 1813–37 with inde
  NLW Pemb RO & Soc Gen

LAWRENNY   *SD*
C 1708–1895 M 1717–1970 (Banns 1824–1919) B 1717–1812 **Pemb RO**
BT 1685, 1800, 1808–9, 1811–16, 1818–37, 1839–60, 1862–4, 1866–9, 1871, 1873–
NLW
Cop ts PR 1716–1837 **Pemb RO & Soc Gen** ts PR M 1813–37 with index **NLW**
Pemb RO & Soc Gen

* LETTERSTON/TRELETERT   *SD*
  The earliest registers reputedly destroyed at the time of the French invasion 1797 (183
  survey). Diocesan records suggest that *c*1790 the registers went back only 36 years
  C 1801–1975 M 1801–1982 (Banns 1801–1941) B 1801–1976 **Pemb RO**
  BT 1773, 1799, 1802–65, 1886–9, 1891 **NLW**
  Cop ts PR (extracts) C 1813–70 **NLW** ts PR M 1813–37 with index **NLW Pemb RO** ◢
  Soc Gen

* LITTLE NEWCASTLE/CASNEWYDD-BACH   *SD*
  Civil register 1654–8 (**Cardiff Central Library** MS.4.44) Mf **NLW**
  C 1783–1813 M 1813–1966 B 1783–1813 **NLW** Mf **Pemb RO**

BT 1679–80, 1685, 1799, 1801, 1803, 1805–9, 1811–79, 1885 **NLW**
Cop ts PR M 1813–36 with index **NLW Pemb RO & Soc Gen**

LOVESTON *SD*
C 1791–1977 M 1783–1957 B 1791–1977 **Pemb RO**
BT 1799–1820, 1823–36, 1838–64, 1866–9, 1871–3, 1876, 1878, 1880, 1884–5, 1888,
1890–1, 1893–9, 1901–2, 1907–9 **NLW**
Cop ts PR/BT 1799–1836 **Pemb RO & Soc Gen** ts PR M 1813–34 with index **NLW**
Pemb RO & Soc Gen

LUDCHURCH/YR EGLWYS LWYD *SD*
C 1732–1992 M 1732–1971 B 1732–1993 **NLW** Mf **Pemb RO**
BT 1799–1839, 1842–54, 1857–60, 1865–77 **NLW**
Cop ts PR/BT CMB 1779–1839 **Pemb RO & Soc Gen** ts PR M 1813–37 with index
NLW Pemb RO & Soc Gen

LLANBEDR FELFFRE/LAMPETER VELFREY *SD*
PR CB 1779–1812 recorded in 1831 apparently lost
C 1813–1923 M 1755–1980 (Banns 1853–1919, 1931–47) Princes Gate 1949–64 (Banns
1948–71) B 1813–1992 **Pemb RO**
BT 1677, 1679, 1681, 1686, 1698–9, 1720–2, 1724–5, 1727, 1729, 1735, 1737–43,
1763–70, 1774–6, 1780, 1782–4, 1786–9, 1793–9, 1803–81, 1885–6 **NLW**
Cop ts PR M 1813–37 with index **NLW Pemb RO & Soc Gen**

LLANDEILO *SD*
The church was a ruin by 1930. The following note appears in Llangolman BT 1811: 'I
hereby certify that there are no registers in the parish of Llandilo and that all [CMB] were
for these last twenty years entered in the register of the parish of Llangolman'
C 1814–60 M 1813–34 B 1814–45 **NLW** Mf **Pemb RO**
BT see Llangolman
Cop ts PR M 1813–34 with index **NLW Pemb RO & Soc Gen**

LLANDELOY/LLAN-LWY *SD*
CMB 1754–97 **NLW** C 1796–1973 M 1796–1967 B 1796–1974 Mf CMB 1754–97
Pemb RO
BT 1799–1811, 1813–44, 1846–9, 1851–69, 1872–3 **NLW**
Cop ts PR (extracts) C 1813–72 M 1807–55 B 1813–89 **NLW** ts PR M 1813–36 with
index **NLW Pemb RO & Soc Gen**

LLANDISSILIO/LLANDYSILIO (-YN-NYFED) *SD*
CMB 1720–50 **NLW** C 1751–1812 M 1783–1969 B 1751–1948 Fac CMB 1720–50
Carm RO Mf/Fac CB 1720–96 M 1720–53, 1837–1969 **Pemb RO**
BT 1671–2, 1677–9, 1681–2, 1684–7, 1689–90, 1693–5, 1697–9, 1707, 1715, 1717,
1719–22, 1724–54, 1756–90, 1792–4, 1796, 1798, 1802–36, 1841–3, 1847–8, 1850–4,
1863–70, 1875–6 **NLW**
Cop ts PR M 1813–37 with index **NLW Pemb RO & Soc Gen**

LLANDUDOCH/ST DOGMAELS   *SD*
C 1699–1967 M 1699–1762, 1791–1970 (Banns 1823–97, 1957–93) B 1699–1952 **NLW**
Mf (except Banns) **Pemb RO**
BT 1674–5, 1679–87, 1689, 1691–2?, 1703, 1705, 1757, 1799–1804, 1806–38, 1845–7
1849–60, 1865–76 **NLW**
Cop ts PR/BT M 1813–37 with index **NLW Pemb RO & Soc Gen**

LLANDYFÁI/LAMPHEY   *SD*
C 1776–1883 M 1755–1975 B 1776–1962 **Pemb RO**
BT 1799–1807, 1809–75, 1877–8, 1880–9 **NLW**
Cop ts PR M pre-1813 with index **NLW & Pemb RO** ts PR M 1813–37 with index
NLW Pemb RO & Soc Gen

LLANDYSILIO (-YN-NYFED)/LLANDISSILIO   *SD*
CMB 1720–50 **NLW** C 1751–1812 M 1783–1969 B 1751–1948 Fac CMB 1720–50
Carm RO Mf/Fac CB 1720–96 M 1720–53, 1837–1969 **Pemb RO**
BT 1671–2, 1677–9, 1681–2, 1684–7, 1689–90, 1693–5, 1697–9, 1707, 1715, 1717
1719–22, 1724–54, 1756–90, 1792–4, 1796, 1798, 1802–36, 1841–3, 1847–8, 1850–4
1863–70, 1875–6 **NLW**
Cop ts PR M 1813–37 with index **NLW Pemb RO & Soc Gen**

LLANDDEWI FELFFRE/LLANDDEWI VELFREY   *SD*
C 1727–70, 1778–1992 M 1727–1970 B 1727–70, 1778–1990 **NLW** Mf **Pemb RO**
BT 1676, 1680–7, 1689, 1697–9, 1702–3, 1705–8, 1713, 1717, 1724–6, 1728–30, 1732–85
1790–6, 1798–1800, 1802–3, 1806–7, 1809–39, 1841–73, 1876–8, 1880 **NLW**
Cop ts PR M 1813–37 with index **NLW Pemb RO & Soc Gen**

LLANEILFYW/ST ELVIS   *SD*
C 1784–1811 M 1791–1811 entered in PR Tre-groes/Whitchurch. The church was a ruin
by 1900
C 1784–1811, 1817–36 M 1791–1839 **Pemb RO** B nil
BT 1813, 1817–22, 1824, 1829, 1833–7 **NLW**
Cop ts PR C 1784–1811 (extracts to 1824) M 1791–1811 (extracts to 1839) **NLW**
PR/BT M 1813–35 with index **NLW Pemb RO & Soc Gen**

LLANFAIR NANT-GWYN   *SD*
Diocesan records suggest that *c*1790 this parish had 'no register of births and burials', and that
it had been at one time united with Eglwys Wen/Whitechurch
C 1795–1992 M 1776–1837 (Banns 1824–77, 1973–91) B 1795–1812, 1816–1989 **NLW**
Mf **Pemb RO**
BT 1674–5, 1678, 1680, 1683, 1685–90, 1699, 1701–3, 1800, 1803–9, 1812–37, 1839–40
1844–53, 1855–65, 1868, 1870–2, 1874–80, 1890 **NLW**
Cop ts BT M pre-1813 with index **NLW & Pemb RO** ts PR M 1813–37 with index
NLW Pemb RO & Soc Gen

LLANFAIR NANT-Y-GOF   *SD*
Civil register 1655–8 (**Cardiff Central Library** MS.4.44) Mf **NLW**
C 1801–1975 M 1802–1969 (Banns 1823–1973) B 1801–1975 **Pemb RO**
BT 1681, 1799, 1802–7, 1809–40, 1843–4, 1846–53, 1855–64, 1886–91 **NLW**
Cop ts PR M 1813–36 with index **NLW Pemb RO & Soc Gen**

LLANFALLTEG   *SD*
C 1711–1978 M 1755–1969 B 1711–1978 **Pemb RO** Mf CB 1711–1812 M 1759–1969
Carm RO
BT 1671–2, 1677–9, 1681–4, 1686–7, 1690–1, 1693, 1695–9, 1707, 1713, 1717, 1719,
1724–6, 1728–31, 1733–1800, 1802–12, 1814–43 **NLW**
Cop ts PR M 1813–35 with index **NLW Pemb RO & Soc Gen**

LLANFIHANGEL PENBEDW   *SD*
C 1680–1908 M 1680–1970 (Banns 1824–1966) B 1680–1916 **NLW** Mf **Pemb RO**
BT 1676, 1678–81, 1683–8, 1701–3, 1799–1801, 1804–6, 1809–26, 1828–36, 1839,
1847–9, 1852–6, 1858, 1860, 1865–6, 1870–3, 1875–6, 1878 **NLW**
Cop ts PR/BT M pre-1813 with index **NLW & Pemb RO** ts PR M 1813–36 with index
NLW Pemb RO & Soc Gen

LLANFYRNACH   *SD*
Diocesan records suggest that *c*1790 this parish had registers going back to 1714
C 1765–1993 M 1754–1968, 1973–94 (Banns 1823–44, 1908–56) B 1765–1992 **Pemb
RO**
BT 1675–6, 1678–83, 1685–8, 1703, 1799–1813, 1815–20, 1823–63, 1865–7, 1869–71,
1875–7 **NLW**
Cop ts PR C 1765–1993 M 1754–1968 B 1765–1992 **Soc Gen** ts C 1813–1992 B
1813–1993 with index **Pemb RO** ts PR M 1813–37 with index **NLW Pemb RO &
Soc Gen**

LLAN-GAN   *SD*
C 1768–93, 1813–1989 M 1769–1963 B 1768–94, 1813–1992 **Pemb RO** Mf **Carm RO**
BT 1677–9, 1681–5, 1690–1, 1693–5, 1697–9, 1704–5, 1707–8, 1711, 1713, 1715–18,
1720–2, 1725–7, 1729–83, 1785–92, 1794–5, 1805, 1807–31, 1833, 1837, 1840 **NLW**
Cop ts PR M 1813–37 with index **NLW Pemb RO & Soc Gen**

LLANGOLMAN   *SD*
C 1813–1985 M 1755–1958 B 1813–1991 **NLW** Mf/Fac **Pemb RO**
BT 1685–6, 1799–1807, 1809–37, 1840–52, 1854–9, 1861 **NLW**
Cop ts PR (extracts) C 1762–1812 M 1824–30 B 1776–1811 **NLW** ts PR C 1813–1971
B 1813–1977 with index **Pemb RO** ts PR M 1814–37 with index **NLW Pemb RO &
Soc Gen**

LLANGWM   *SD*
C 1716–1949 M 1716–1966 (Banns 1811–18, 1865–1948) B 1716–1949 **Pemb RO**

BT 1799–1807, 1809–83 **NLW**
Cop ts PR M 1813–37 with index **NLW Pemb RO & Soc Gen**

LLANHOWEL gweler/see LLANHYWEL

LLANHUADAIN/LLAWHADEN *SD*
C 1653–1980 M 1653–1971 (Banns 1823–1930) B 1653–1956 **NLW** Mf **Pemb RO**
BT 1772, 1799, 1801–77, 1879–81, 1883 **NLW**
Cop ts PR M 1754–1837 **Soc Gen** ts PR M 1813–37 with index **NLW Pemb RO &**
Soc Gen

LLANHYWEL/LLANHOWEL *SD*
C 1797–1993 Carnhedryn 1880–1921 M 1796–1837 (Banns 1823–1956) Carnhedryr
1881–1906 B 1797–1985 **NLW** Mf/Fac **Pemb RO**
BT 1799–1841, 1843–4, 1846, 1848–69, 1872–3 **NLW**
Cop ts PR (extracts) C 1838–94 M 1805–82 B 1826–1902 **NLW** ts PR M 1813–37 witl
index **NLW Pemb RO & Soc Gen**

LLANISAN-YN-RHOS/ST ISHMAELS *SD*
C 1761–1946 M 1755–1970 (Banns 1855–1933) B 1761–1926 **Pemb RO**
BT 1799, 1801–3, 1805–79 **NLW**
Cop ts PR M 1813–37 with index **NLW Pemb RO & Soc Gen**

LLAN-LWY/LLANDELOY *SD*
CMB 1754–97 **NLW** C 1796–1973 M 1796–1967 B 1796–1974 Mf CMB 1754–97
Pemb RO
BT 1799–1811, 1813–44, 1846–9, 1851–69, 1872–3 **NLW**
Cop ts PR (extracts) C 1813–72 M 1807–55 B 1813–89 **NLW** ts PR M 1813–36 witl
index **NLW Pemb RO & Soc Gen**

LLANLLAWERN/LLANLLAWER *SD*
C 1770–1968 M 1781–1964 B 1770–1968 **NLW** Mf **Pemb RO**
BT see Llanychlwydog
Cop printed BT CMB 1674–5, 1680–9, 1699 & PR CB 1771–1812 M 1781–1812 (ed Rev
J Meredith Williams, Fishguard, 1925)
Cop ts PR M 1814–37 with index **NLW Pemb RO & Soc Gen**

LLANRHEITHAN *SD*
PR M 1786–98 recorded in 1831 apparently lost. Diocesan records suggest that *c*1790 the
registers went back 25 years
C 1803–1968 M 1799–1952 (Banns 1799–1823) B 1799–1977 **Pemb RO**
BT 1799, 1801–5, 1807–27, 1829–48, 1850–3, 1855–8, 1862–5, 1867, 1869, 1871–7 **NLW**
Cop ts PR (extracts) CMB 1799–1907 **NLW** ts PR M 1813–36 with index **NLW Pemb**
RO & Soc Gen

LLANRHIAN   *SD*
A few entries CMB 1686– included in earliest extant PR
C 1729–1957 M 1729–1970 (Banns 1878–1905) B 1729–1993 **NLW** Mf/Fac **Pemb RO**
BT 1739, 1798–1801, 1803, 1806–79 **NLW**
Cop ts PR C 1686–1812 (extracts to 1903) M 1729–1807 (extracts to 1862) B 1731–1812
(extracts to 1880) **NLW** ts PR M 1814–37 with index **NLW Pemb RO & Soc Gen**

LLANSTADWEL/LLANSTADWELL   *SD*
C 1714–1948 M 1714–1892 B 1714–1941 **NLW** Mf **Pemb RO**
BT 1800–3, 1805–7, 1809–13, 1818, 1820–57, 1860–1, 1866–7 **NLW**
Cop ts PR M 1813–37 with index **NLW Pemb RO & Soc Gen**

LLANSTINAN   *SD*
Diocesan records suggest that *c*1790 the registers went back 29 years; and that in 1814 there
were extant C 1784–1812 M 1788–1812 B 1800–13. The only pre-1813 PR seen by
antiquarian, J T Evans, in 1910 was the 'ragged', now lost, first leaf of M 1788–1812
(NLW, Titus and Elizabeth Evans 18)
C 1814–1979 M 1797–1971 (Banns 1823–70) B 1813–1976 **NLW** Mf/Fac **Pemb RO**
BT 1685–6, 1799–1804, 1806–7, 1810–35, 1841–53, 1855–67, 1871–6 **NLW**
Cop ms PR M 1788–97 **NLW** ts PR M 1813–37 with index **NLW Pemb RO & Soc
Gen**

LLANTWYD/LLANTOOD   *SD*
C 1768–93, 1813–1991 M 1813–1968 (Banns 1824–6, 1830) B 1769–77, 1783–5,
1813–1993 **NLW** Mf **Pemb RO**
BT 1674–6, 1678–81, 1684–7, 1700, 1703, 1705, 1799–1800, 1802–40, 1842, 1844–7,
1849–60, 1865–8, 1870–5, 1896–7 **NLW**
Cop ts BT M pre-1813 with index **NLW & Pemb RO** ts PR M 1813–37 with index
NLW Pemb RO & Soc Gen

LLANTYDEWI/ST DOGWELLS   *SD*
C 1718–1973 M 1718–53, 1756–1933, 1939–68 (Banns 1797–1944) B 1722–74,
1783–1966 **NLW** Mf **Pemb RO**
BT 1799–1800, 1802–7, 1811–79, 1885 **NLW**
Cop ts PR M 1813–36 with index **NLW Pemb RO & Soc Gen**

LLANWNDA   *SD*
The earliest PR reputedly destroyed at the time of the French invasion 1797 (1831 survey).
Diocesan records suggest that *c*1790 the register went back only as far as 1777
C 1813–1993 M 1813–1968 (Banns 1823–69, 1907–45, 1973–4) B 1799–1942 **Pemb RO**
BT 1685, 1799–1806, 1808–46, 1864–72, 1877–81, 1883–4, 1887 **NLW**
Cop ms PR B 1799–1812 ts PR (extracts) CMB 1799–1896 **NLW** ts PR M 1813–37 with
index **NLW Pemb RO & Soc Gen**

LLAN-Y-CEFN   *SD*
C 1816–1979 M 1813–1911, 1917–60 B 1816–1980 **NLW** Mf **Pemb RO**

BT 1799–1805, 1807–11, 1813, 1816–37, 1844–6, 1849–57, 1861, 1863–5, 1871–80 **NLW**
Cop ts PR M 1813–35 with index **NLW Pemb RO & Soc Gen**

LLANYCHÂR/LLANYCHAER *SD*
Civil register 1654–9 (**Cardiff Central Library** MS.4.44) Mf **NLW**. Diocesan records
suggest that *c*1790 'the old register [was] lost. The existing register goes back only 2 years'
C 1788–1990 M 1787–1970 (Banns 1824–49) B 1789–1993 **NLW** Mf/Fac **Pemb RO**
BT 1676, 1678–83, 1685–6, 1689, 1705, 1799–1808, 1810–38, 1843–7, 1853–65 **NLW**
Cop printed PR C 1788–1812 M 1787–1811 B 1789–1812 (ed Rev J Meredith Williams
Fishguard [1924]) ts PR M 1813–36 with index **NLW Pemb RO & Soc Gen**

LLANYCHLWYDOG *SD*
C 1770–1812 M 1781–1812 B 1770–1812 **NLW** C 1813–1927 M 1814–1961 B
1813–1965 Mf CB 1770–1812 M 1781–1812 **Pemb RO**
BT 1674–6, 1678–83, 1685–9, 1799–1804, 1806–7, 1809–44, 1874 **NLW**
Cop printed BT CMB 1674–5, 1680–9, 1699 & PR C 1770–1803 M 1780–1812 B
1770–1812 (ed Rev J Meredith Williams, Fishguard, 1925) ts PR M 1814–37 with index
NLW Pemb RO & Soc Gen

* LLAWHADEN/LLANHUADAIN *SD*
C 1653–1980 M 1653–1971 (Banns 1823–1930) B 1653–1956 **NLW** Mf **Pemb RO**
BT 1772, 1799, 1801–77, 1879–81, 1883 **NLW**
Cop ts PR M 1754–1837 **Soc Gen** ts PR M 1813–37 with index **NLW Pemb RO &
Soc Gen**

LLYS-Y-FRÂN *SD*
C 1728–1803, 1813–1993 M 1728–1803, 1813–1903, 1924–63 B 1728–1803, 1813–1992
NLW Mf/Fac **Pemb RO**
BT 1799–1820, 1822–37, 1839–41, 1843–4, 1846–52, 1855, 1858–63, 1865–6, 1868–9
NLW
Cop ts PR M 1813–37 with index **NLW Pemb RO & Soc Gen**

MAENCLOCHOG *SD*
C 1770–1993 M 1770–1970 B 1770–1993 **NLW** Mf/Fac **Pemb RO**
BT 1685, 1799, 1801–36, 1839–52, 1854–61, 1865 **NLW**
Cop ts PR (extracts) C 1771–1832 M 1779–1877 B 1770–1888 **NLW** ts PR M 1813–37
with index **NLW Pemb RO & Soc Gen**

MAENORBŶR/MANORBIER *SD*
C 1761–1993 M 1755–1971 B 1761–1993 **Pemb RO** Fac C 1813–70 M 1755–1837 B
1813–87 **NLW**
BT 1685–6, 1799–1804, 1806–21, 1823–85 **NLW**
Cop ts PR M pre-1813 with index **NLW & Pemb RO** ts PR M 1813–37 with index
NLW Pemb RO & Soc Gen

MAENORDEIFI *SD*
C 1724–70, 1780–1992 M 1724–1970 B 1724–70, 1780–1974 **NLW** Mf **Pemb RO**
BT 1674–6, 1678–9, 1681–2, 1684, 1686–9, 1702–3, 1705, 1799–1856, 1859–75 **NLW**
Cop ts PR CB 1724–70 M 1725–53 **Soc Gen** ts PR/BT M pre-1813 with index **NLW &**
Pemb RO ts PR M 1813–37 with index **NLW Pemb RO & Soc Gen**

MANORBIER gweler/see MAENORBŶR

MANOROWEN (MARNAWAN) *SD*
PR C 1783–1812 M 1786–96 B 1785–1800 recorded in 1831 apparently lost
C 1813–1993 M 1779–85, 1797–1970 (Banns 1797–1818, 1927–67) B 1813–1993 **Pemb**
RO
BT 1799–1800, 1802–4, 1806–48, 1865, 1868, 1870–81, 1883–4, 1887 **NLW**
Cop ms PR M 1779–1814 (Banns 1797–1818) ts PR (extracts) C 1817–1903 M
1779–1801 B 1813–1906 **NLW** ts PR M 1813–36 with index **NLW Pemb RO & Soc**
Gen

MARLOES *SD*
C 1749–51, 1771–1876 M 1749–1969 B 1749–51, 1771–1924 **Pemb RO**
BT 1799–1836, 1838–75, 1877 **NLW**
Cop ts PR M 1813–37 with index **NLW Pemb RO & Soc Gen**

MARTLETWY *SD*
C 1728–31, 1739–45, 1754–8, 1760–1850 M 1728–31, 1739–45, 1754–8, 1762–80,
1813–1971 (Banns 1824–78) B 1728–31, 1739–45, 1754–8, 1762–85, 1809–11, 1813–95
Pemb RO
BT 1799–1803, 1805–47, 1849–60, 1862–75, 1877–8, 1880–4, 1886–8 **NLW**
Cop ts PR CB 1757–1837 M 1757–80 **Soc Gen** ts PR M 1813–36 with index **NLW**
Pemb RO & Soc Gen

MATHRI/MATHRY *SD*
C 1729–30, 1736–42, 1745–1992 M 1729–30, 1735–41, 1745–54, 1776–1969 (Banns
1778–86, 1791–1816, 1824–45, 1895–1916) B 1729–30, 1735–42, 1745–1940 **Pemb RO**
BT 1799–1853, 1855–62, 1864–9, 1875–6 **NLW**
Cop ts PR C 1729–1810 (extracts to 1904) M 1729–54 (extracts 1814–35) B 1729–1810
(extracts to 1873) **NLW** ts PR M 1813–36 with index **NLW Pemb RO & Soc Gen**

MELINE *SD*
C 1702–1989 M 1702–1955 (Banns 1824–86, 1982–9) B 1702–1993 **NLW** Mf **Pemb**
RO
BT 1674–6, 1679–81, 1683–4, 1686–7, 1689–90, 1692, 1700, 1799–1809, 1811–17,
1819–30, 1832–40, 1842, 1844–7, 1849–52, 1855, 1857–9, 1862–4, 1869, 1873–4, 1876,
1878–9 **NLW**
Cop ms PR CB 1702–1812 M 1702–54 **NLW** ts PR M 1813–36 with index **NLW Pemb**
RO & Soc Gen

* MILFORD HAVEN/ABERDAUGLEDDAU   *SD*
<Steynton 1891. Consecrated 1808
C 1808–33, 1860–1960 M 1891–1975 (Banns 1921–75) B 1877–1955 **Pemb RO**
BT see Steynton

* MINWEAR/MYNWAR   *SD*
C 1753–81, 1813–1987 M 1757–1810, 1813–1935 B 1753–1807, 1813–1991 **Pemb RO**
BT 1799–1818, 1820–1, 1823–41, 1844, 1849, 1851–3, 1855–9, 1872, 1874–6, 1879–81
NLW
Cop ts PR C 1753–81 M 1757–98 B 1753–1808 **Soc Gen** ms PR C 1795–1812 E
1784–1812 **Pemb RO** ts PR M 1813–36 with index **NLW Pemb RO & Soc Gen**

* MONINGTON/EGLWYS WYTHWR   *SD*
Diocesan records suggest that *c*1790 this parish had registers going back to 1751
C 1813–1993 M 1773–1809, 1816–33, 1837–1968 B 1813–1993 **NLW** Mf **Pemb RO**
BT 1674–6, 1679–81, 1686–7, 1689, 1697, 1703, 1799–1800, 1802–24, 1826–40, 1842
1844–7, 1849–54, 1860, 1865–9, 1871–3, 1875 **NLW**
Cop ts PR (extracts) C 1818–44 B 1802–87 **NLW** ts PR M 1816–33 with index **NLW**
Pemb RO & Soc Gen

MONKTON (PENFRO/PEMBROKE St Nicholas)   *SD*
CMB 1711–50 entered in PR Penfro/Pembroke St Mary
CMB 1711–50 **NLW** C 1748–1966 M 1748–1970 (Banns 1917–36) B 1748–1900 **Pemb**
RO
BT 1685, ?1774, 1799–1807, 1809–82 **NLW**
Cop ts PR/BT M pre-1813 with index **NLW & Pemb RO** ts PR M 1813–37 with index
NLW Pemb RO & Soc Gen

MORFIL/MORVIL   *SD*
Civil register 1653–8 (**Cardiff Central Library** MS.4.44) Mf **NLW**.   Diocesan recor
suggest that *c*1790 this parish had a register 'begun in the year 1789'. PR B 1813–1918
recorded in 1933 apparently lost
C 1813–1965 M 1814–1953 **Pemb RO**
BT 1674, 1676, 1678–88, 1699, 1804–11, 1813–16, 1819–20, 1823–37, 1839–40 **NLW**
Cop ts PR M 1814–36 with index **NLW Pemb RO & Soc Gen**

MOT, Y/NEW MOAT   *SD*
C 1755–1990 M 1754–1969 B 1755–1993 **Pemb RO**
BT 1799–1800, 1803, 1805, 1809–21, 1823–31, 1833–70, 1878–81, 1884 **NLW**
Cop ts PR CB 1755–1812 M 1754–1836 **Soc Gen** ts PR M 1813–36 with index **NLW**
Pemb RO & Soc Gen

MOUNTON   *SD*
A small parish long associated with Arberth/Narberth and apparently without its own PR

MOYLGROVE/TREWYDDEL   *SD*
C 1769–1812 M 1770–7, 1781–1837 (Banns 1824–84, 1949–90) B 1769–1988 **NLW** Mf
Pemb RO
BT 1675–6, 1678–86, 1688–9, 1702–3, 1708, 1799–1801, 1803–19, 1821–75, 1877–9 **NLW**
Cop ts PR (extracts) C 1770–1818 M 1771–1833 B 1770–1815 **NLW** ts PR M 1813–37
with index **NLW Pemb RO & Soc Gen**

MYNACHLOG-DDU   *SD*
PR C 1802–12 recorded in 1831 apparently lost. M 1813–37 not recorded in 1933.
Diocesan records suggest that *c*1790 the registers went back to 1758
C 1813–1993 M 1837–1951 (Banns 1890–1951) B 1813–1993 **Pemb RO**
BT 1674, 1676, 1678–9, 1681–2, 1685–9, 1705, 1799–1800, 1802–3, 1806–42, 1845,
1848–51, 1865–6, 1871–6, 1878–9 **NLW**
Cop ts BT M 1813–37 with index **NLW Pemb RO & Soc Gen**

MYNWAR/MINWEAR   *SD*
C 1753–81, 1813–1987 M 1757–1810, 1813–1935 B 1753–1807, 1813–1991 **Pemb RO**
BT 1799–1818, 1820–1, 1823–41, 1844, 1849, 1851–3, 1855–9, 1872, 1874–6, 1879–81
NLW
Cop ts PR C 1753–81 M 1757–98 B 1753–1808 **Soc Gen** ms PR C 1795–1812 B
1784–1812 **Pemb RO** ts PR M 1813–36 with index **NLW Pemb RO & Soc Gen**

NARBERTH/ARBERTH   *SD*
C 1676–1703, 1762–1918 M 1676–1703, 1754–1808, 1811–1964 (Banns 1811–42,
1896–1966) B 1676–1703, 1762–1898 **Pemb RO** Fac 1676–1845 **NLW**
BT 1799–1801, 1803, 1805, 1807–67, 1872–3 **NLW**
Cop ts PR (extracts) C 1681–1844, 1854–84 M 1756–1837 **NLW** ts PR M 1813–37 with
index **NLW Pemb RO & Soc Gen**

NASH with UPTON   *SD*
C 1742–1959 M 1744–1969 (Banns 1812, 1826) B 1742–1976 **Pemb RO**
BT 1696, 1800–7, 1809–11, 1813–80, 1882–1903 **NLW**
Cop ts BT 1800–26 **Pemb RO & Soc Gen** ts PR/BT M pre-1813 with index **NLW &
Pemb RO** ts PR M 1813–36 with index **NLW Pemb RO & Soc Gen**

NEVERN/NYFER (NANHYFER)   *SD*
The earliest PR 1663–1710 is an early 19th century copy
C 1663–1992 M 1663–1986 B 1663–1993 **NLW** Mf **Pemb RO** Mf C 1663–1909 M
1663–1754, 1759–82, 1813–37 B 1663–1869 **Soc Gen**
BT 1634, 1674–6, 1678–80, 1682–7, 1689, 1702, 1799–1800, 1802–70, 1878–83, 1885–9
NLW
Cop ms PR 1663–1812 ts PR (extracts) 1663–1850 **NLW** ts PR M 1813–37 with index
NLW Pemb RO & Soc Gen

NEW MOAT/Y MOT   *SD*
C 1755–1990 M 1754–1969 B 1755–1993 **Pemb RO**

BT 1799–1800, 1803, 1805, 1809–21, 1823–31, 1833–70, 1878–81, 1884 **NLW**
Cop ts PR CB 1755–1812 M 1754–1836 **Soc Gen** ts PR M 1813–36 with index **NLW**
Pemb RO & Soc Gen

★ NEWPORT/TREFDRAETH   *SD*
PR CMB 1741–62 recorded in 1831 apparently lost
C 1765–71, 1799–1800, 1807–71 M 1765–1940 (Banns 1824–1962) B 1765–71
1799–1800, 1805–1930 **Pemb RO**
BT 1674–6, 1680–2, 1684–9, 1699, 1702–3, 1800, 1806–73, 1875 **NLW**
Cop ms/ts PR C 1765–1812 M 1778–1895 B 1766–1847 **NLW** ts PR M 1813–37 with
index **NLW Pemb RO & Soc Gen**

NEWTON NORTH (LLYS PRAWST)   *SD*
The church was a ruin by 1900. CB 1784–1812 M 1757–1812 recorded in 1831 apparently
lost
C 1816–90 M 1814–53 B 1815–60 **Pemb RO**
BT 1813–17, 1819, 1821–3, 1825, 1827–30, 1832–3, 1843, 1856–9 **NLW**
Cop ts PR M 1814–33 with index **NLW Pemb RO & Soc Gen**

NOLTON   *SD*
PR earliest date given as 1695 in 1831
C 1704–1991 M 1704–1967 B 1704–1991 **Pemb RO** Fac M 1814–1924 **NLW**
BT 1685–6, 1799–1800, 1802–5, 1807–61, 1863–8, 1871–85 **NLW**
Cop ts PR CB [1695]–1736, 1751–1812 M [1695]–1736, 1781–1812 **NLW** ts PR M
1814–36 with index **NLW Pemb RO & Soc Gen**

NYFER (NANHYFER)/NEVERN   *SD*
The earliest PR 1663–1710 is an early 19th century copy
C 1663–1992 M 1663–1986 B 1663–1993 **NLW** Mf **Pemb RO** Mf C 1663–1909 M
1663–1754, 1759–82, 1813–37 B 1663–1869 **Soc Gen**
BT 1634, 1674–6, 1678–80, 1682–7, 1689, 1702, 1799–1800, 1802–70, 1878–83, 1885–
NLW
Cop ms PR 1663–1812 ts PR (extracts) 1663–1850 **NLW** ts PR M 1813–37 with index
NLW Pemb RO & Soc Gen

★ PEMBROKE/PENFRO St Mary   *SD*
C 1711–1961 M 1711–1915 B 1711–1950 **NLW** M (Banns 1924–68) **Pemb RO** Mf C
1711–1961 M 1711–1915 B 1711–1950 **Pemb RO**
BT 1799–1807, 1809–88 **NLW**
Cop ts PR M pre-1813 with index **NLW & Pemb RO** ts PR M 1813–37 with index
NLW Pemb RO & Soc Gen

★ PEMBROKE/PENFRO St Michael   *SD*
CMB 1711–50 entered in PR Pembroke/Penfro St Mary
C 1711–1901 M 1711–1930 B 1711–1929 **NLW** Mf **Pemb RO**
BT 1799–1807, 1809–81 **NLW**

Cop ts PR M pre-1813 with index **NLW & Pemb RO** ts PR M 1814–37 with index **NLW Pemb RO & Soc Gen**

PEMBROKE/PENFRO St Nicholas gweler/see MONKTON

PEMBROKE DOCK/DOC PENFRO St John   *SD*
<Penfro/Pembroke St Mary 1844
C 1844–1927 Garrison 1856–1906 Dockyard 1875–1926 Pennar 1895–1967 M 1848–1951, 1965–76 (Banns 1848–1971) B 1844–1977 Garrison 1861–1922 **Pemb RO**
BT 1844–86 **NLW**

PENALUN/PENALLY   *SD*
C 1738–86, 1792–1991 M 1739–51, 1754–1966 (Banns 1824-90) B 1738–86, 1792–1993 **Pemb RO** Fac C 1738–86 M 1738–1890 B 1738–86, 1813–1936 **NLW**
BT 1799–1806, 1809–73, 1875, 1877, 1890–2 **NLW**
Cop ts PR M pre-1813 with index **NLW & Pemb RO** ts PR M 1813–37 with index **NLW Pemb RO & Soc Gen**

PENFRO/PEMBROKE St Mary   *SD*
C 1711–1961 M 1711–1915 B 1711–1950 **NLW** M (Banns 1924–68) **Pemb RO** Mf C 1711–1961 M 1711–1915 B 1711–1950 **Pemb RO**
BT 1799–1807, 1809–88 **NLW**
Cop ts PR M pre-1813 with index **NLW & Pemb RO** ts PR M 1813–37 with index **NLW Pemb RO & Soc Gen**

PENFRO/PEMBROKE St Michael   *SD*
CMB 1711–50 entered in PR Penfro/Pembroke St Mary
C 1711–1901 M 1711–1930 B 1711–1929 **NLW** Mf **Pemb RO**
BT 1799–1807, 1809–81 **NLW**
Cop ts PR M pre-1813 with index **NLW & Pemb RO** ts PR M 1814–37 with index **NLW Pemb RO & Soc Gen**

PENFRO/PEMBROKE St Nicholas gweler/see MONKTON

PENNAR gweler/see DOC PENFRO/PEMBROKE DOCK

PENRHYDD/PENRITH   *SD*
PR CB 1771–97 M 1755–1812 recorded in 1831 apparently lost
C 1813–1959 M 1813–1970 B 1813–1973 **NLW** Mf **Pemb RO**
BT 1674, 1676, 1679–85, 1688–9, 1702–3, 1705, 1799, 1802–13, 1815–29, 1832–6, 1838–9, 1842–59, 1866, 1869–71, 1876–80, 1882 **NLW**
Cop ts BT M pre-1813 with index **NLW & Pemb RO** ts PR M 1814–36 with index **NLW Pemb RO & Soc Gen**

PONTVANE/Y BONT-FAEN   *SD*
Diocesan records suggest that *c*1790 this parish had registers going back to 1748

C 1813–1993 M 1815–1971 B 1813–1986 **Pemb RO**
BT 1676, 1678–9, 1681–4, 1686, 1800–13, 1815–19, 1821–40, 1845–7, 1850, 1853, 185.
NLW
Cop ts PR M 1815–35 with index **NLW Pemb RO & Soc Gen**

PRENDERGAST   *SD*
C 1696–1966 M 1696–1985 (Banns 1825–49, 1937–72) B 1696–1977 **NLW** Mf/Fa
Pemb RO
BT 1777, 1801–13, 1815–61, 1865–73 **NLW**
Cop ts PR C 1702–90 incomplete **Pemb RO & Soc Gen** ts PR M 1813–37 with inde
NLW Pemb RO & Soc Gen

* PUNCHESTON/CAS-MAEL   *SD*
Civil register 1653–9 (**Cardiff Central Library** MS.4.44) Mf **NLW**. PR M 1813–3
recorded in 1933 apparently lost
C 1789–1807, 1813–1985 M 1797–1810, 1838–1967 B 1789–1807, 1813–1974 **NLW** M
Pemb RO
BT 1675–6, 1678–83, 1686, 1688, 1799, 1801–4, 1806–7, 1809–11, 1813–43, 1845–8
1852–9 **NLW**
Cop ts BT M 1813–37 with index **NLW Pemb RO & Soc Gen**

PWLLCROCHAN   *SD*
C 1695–1976 M 1695–1811, 1815–36, 1839–1956 (Banns 1886–1940) B 1695–1982 **NLW**
Mf C 1695–1976 M 1695–1811, 1815–36, 1839–1956 (Banns 1886–1940) B 1695–181
Pemb RO
BT 1799–1810, 1812–21, 1823–91 **NLW**
Cop ts PR M pre-1813 with index **NLW & Pemb RO** ts PR M 1815–36 with inde
NLW Pemb RO & Soc Gen

REDBERTH   *SD*
CMB to 1807 entered in PR Caeriw/Carew
C 1794–1993 M 1808–1978 (Banns 1808–12, 1919–86) B 1794–1992 **Pemb RO**
BT 1802–3, 1805–7, 1809–28, 1830–8, 1840–76, 1884–90, 1896–9, 1901–2, 1905 **NLW**
Cop ts PR/BT CB 1802–9 **Pemb RO & Soc Gen** ts PR/BT M 1815–36 with inde
NLW Pemb RO & Soc Gen

REYNOLDSTON (REYNALTON)   *SD*
C 1786–1977 M 1786–1948 B 1786–1953 **NLW** Mf **Pemb RO**
BT 1799–1800, 1802–4, 1806–76, 1879, 1881, 1903–4 **NLW**
Cop ts PR 1786–1802 **Pemb RO & Soc Gen** ts PR M 1814–37 with index **NLW Pem**
RO & Soc Gen

ROBESTON WATHEN   *SD*
PR CB 1737–89 M [1737–54], 1800–5 recorded in 1831 apparently lost. The 1933 retur
claims that a ms copy of PR 1750–1812 made in 1902-3 was kept at the parish church a
Arberth/Narberth

C 1790–1968 M 1814–1970 B 1790–1968 **Pemb RO**
BT 1799–1801, 1803–7, 1809–10, 1812, 1814–67 **NLW**
Cop ts PR (extracts) M 1756–1837 **NLW** ts PR M 1814–37 with index **NLW Pemb RO & Soc Gen**

ROBESTON WEST *SD*
C 1731–1992 M 1731–1836, 1838–1926, 1930–67 B 1731–1992 **NLW** Mf **Pemb RO**
BT 1799, 1801–7, 1809–10, 1813–21, 1823–36, 1840–7, 1849–67, 1869 **NLW**
Cop ts PR C 1731–1812 M 1742–1812 B 1743–1812 **NLW** ts PR M 1813–36 with index **NLW Pemb RO & Soc Gen**

ROCH/Y GARN *SD*
C 1677–1737, 1763–1974 M 1677–1737, 1754–1922, 1926–82 (Banns 1823–99) B 1677–1737, 1763–1901 **Pemb RO** Fac C 1813–1974 M 1837–1922 **NLW**
BT 1799–1800, 1802–63, 1865–8, 1871–86 **NLW**
Cop ts PR CB 1677–1737, 1763–1812 M 1677–1737, 1783–1812 **NLW** ts PR M 1813–37 with index **NLW Pemb RO & Soc Gen**

ROSEMARKET/RHOSFARCED *SD*
PR CB 1777–1804 recorded in 1831 apparently lost. No mention of PR M 1813–37 in 1933 survey. Diocesan records suggest that c1790 the registers went back to 1754
C 1804–12, 1826–89 M 1772–1812, 1837–1969 (Banns 1823–1978) B 1804–89 **Pemb RO**
BT 1799, 1801–31, 1833–6, 1838, 1840–2, 1844–50, 1853–5, 1858 **NLW**
Cop ms PR (extracts) C 1761–1803 **Pemb RO** ts BT M 1813–36 with index **NLW Pemb RO & Soc Gen**

RUDBAXTON *SD*
C 1735–1950 M 1736–1970 (Banns 1755–1836) B 1735–1992 **Pemb RO**
BT 1799–1807, 1809–50, 1852–86 **NLW**
Cop ts PR (extracts) CMB 1735–1810 **NLW** ts PR M 1813–36 with index **NLW Pemb RO & Soc Gen**

RHOSCROWDDER/RHOSCROWTHER *SD*
C 1731–1993 M 1731–1970 (Banns 1813–32) B 1731–1812, 1815–1992 **NLW** Mf **Pemb RO**
BT 1799–1807, 1809, 1811–93 **NLW**
Cop ts PR M pre-1813 with index **NLW & Pemb RO** ts PR M 1813–37 with index **NLW Pemb RO & Soc Gen**

RHOSFARCED/ROSEMARKET *SD*
PR CB 1777–1804 recorded in 1831 apparently lost. No mention of PR M 1813–37 in 1933 survey. Diocesan records suggest that c1790 the registers went back to 1754
C 1804–12, 1826–89 M 1772–1812, 1837–1969 (Banns 1823–1978) B 1804–89 **Pemb RO**
BT 1799, 1801–31, 1833–6, 1838, 1840–2, 1844–50, 1853–5, 1858 **NLW**

Cop ms PR (extracts) C 1761–1803 **Pemb RO** ts BT M 1813–36 with index **NLW Pemb RO & Soc Gen**

SAIN FFRED/ST BRIDES *SD*
C 1725–1992 M 1726–1970 B 1725–1992 **Pemb RO**
BT 1800–1, 1803, 1805–15, 1825–77 **NLW**
Cop ts PR M 1725–1812 (extracts to 1836) **NLW** ts PR 1799–1877 **Soc Gen** ts PR M 1813–36 with index **NLW Pemb RO & Soc Gen**

SAIN PEDROG/ST PETROX *SD*
C 1640–1989 M 1640–1836, 1840–1963 B 1640–1987 **NLW** Mf **Pemb RO**
BT 1685, 1799–1802, 1804–7, 1809, 1811–19, 1821–59, 1861–96 **NLW**
Cop ts PR CMB 1640–1991 arranged alphabetically **NLW & Pemb RO** ts PR M pre-1813 with index **NLW & Pemb RO** ts PR M 1813–36 with index **NLW Pemb RO & Soc Gen**

ST BRIDES gweler/see SAIN FFRED

★ ST DAVID'S/TYDDEWI *SD*
C 1724–1984 M 1724–1966 (Banns 1808–50, 1878–1963) B 1724–1963 **NLW** Mf **Pemb RO**
BT 1813–56, 1864, 1866, 1872–4 **NLW**
Cop ts PR C 1724–1858 M 1724–1837 B 1724–1812 (extracts to 1906) **NLW** ts PR M 1813–37 with index **NLW Pemb RO & Soc Gen**

★ ST DOGMAELS/LLANDUDOCH *SD*
C 1699–1967 M 1699–1762, 1791–1970 (Banns 1823–97, 1957–93) B 1699–1952 **NLW** Mf (except Banns) **Pemb RO**
BT 1674–5, 1679–87, 1689, 1691–2?, 1703, 1705, 1757, 1799–1804, 1806–38, 1845–7 1849–60, 1865–76 **NLW**
Cop ts PR/BT M 1813–37 with index **NLW Pemb RO & Soc Gen**

★ ST DOGWELLS/LLANTYDEWI *SD*
C 1718–1973 M 1718–53, 1756–1933, 1939–68 (Banns 1797–1944) B 1722–74 1783–1966 **NLW** Mf **Pemb RO**
BT 1799–1800, 1802–7, 1811–79, 1885 **NLW**
Cop ts PR M 1813–36 with index **NLW Pemb RO & Soc Gen**

SAINT EDRENS *SD*
Diocesan records suggest that *c*1790 the registers went back to 1770
C 1791–1959 M 1800–09, 1813–25, 1834–1932 (Banns 1809–18) B 1788–1887 **Pemb RO**
BT 1799–1813, 1815–45 **NLW**
Cop ts PR (extracts) C 1785–1829 B 1789–1886 **NLW** ts PR/BT M 1813–37 with index **NLW Pemb RO & Soc Gen**

ST ELVIS/LLANEILFYW   *SD*
C 1784–1811 M 1791–1811 entered in PR Tre-groes/Whitchurch. The church was a ruin by 1900
C 1784–1811, 1817–36 M 1791–1839 **Pemb RO** B nil
BT 1813, 1817–22, 1824, 1829, 1833–7 **NLW**
Cop ts PR C 1784–1811 (extracts to 1824) M 1791–1811 (extracts to 1839) **NLW** ts PR/BT M 1813–35 with index **NLW Pemb RO & Soc Gen**

ST FLORENCE   *SD*
C 1763–1993 M 1755–1987 B 1763–1994 **Pemb RO**
BT 1799–1890, 1892 **NLW**
Cop ts BT 1799–1805 **Pemb RO & Soc Gen** ts PR M pre-1813 with index **NLW & Pemb RO** ts PR M 1813–36 with index **NLW Pemb RO & Soc Gen**

SAINT ISHEL/ST ISSELLS   *SD*
PR CB 1753–66 recorded in 1831 apparently lost
C 1766–83, 1787–1922 M 1778–1938 B 1766–75, 1783–1908 **NLW** Mf **Pemb RO**
BT 1685–6, 1775, 1799–1837, 1839–89, 1892, 1895–8 **NLW**
Cop ts PR (extracts) CMB 1766–1829 ts PR/BT 1656, 1685, 1775, 1799–1837 **Pemb RO & Soc Gen** ts PR M 1813–37 with index **NLW Pemb RO & Soc Gen**

ST ISHMAELS/LLANISAN-YN-RHOS   *SD*
C 1761–1946 M 1755–1970 (Banns 1855–1933) B 1761–1926 **Pemb RO**
BT 1799, 1801–3, 1805–79 **NLW**
Cop ts PR M 1813–37 with index **NLW Pemb RO & Soc Gen**

ST ISSELLS gweler/see SAINT ISHEL

ST LAWRENCE   *SD*
C 1767–99, 1814–1992 M 1766–1954, 1959–70 (Banns 1799–1944) B 1767–99, 1813–1992 **Pemb RO** Mf C 1814–47 M 1800–37 (Banns 1799–1944) B 1813–1946 **NLW**
BT 1799, 1802–54, 1866, 1871–4 **NLW**
Cop ts PR (extracts) C 1770–1897 M 1767–1869 B 1767–1811 **NLW** ts PR M 1814–37 with index **NLW Pemb RO & Soc Gen**

ST NICHOLAS/TREMARCHOG   *SD*
PR 1758– in poor condition in 1933 apparently lost. CB 1793–1803 entered in PR Treopert/Granston. Diocesan records suggest that c1790 the registers went back to 1727
C 1793–1803, 1806–1993 M 1779–1971 (Banns 1780–1817, 1907) B 1793–1803, 1806–1992 **Pemb RO**
BT see Treopert/Granston
Cop ms/ts PR C 1783–1874 M 1782–1899 B 1783–1898 **NLW** ts PR (extracts) C 1810–74 M 1782–1899 B 1799–1898 **Pemb RO** ts PR M 1813–36 with index **NLW Pemb RO & Soc Gen**

* ST PETROX/SAIN PEDROG   *SD*
C 1640–1989 M 1640–1836, 1840–1963 B 1640–1987 **NLW** Mf **Pemb RO**
BT 1685, 1799–1802, 1804–7, 1809, 1811–19, 1821–59, 1861–96 **NLW**
Cop ts PR CMB 1640–1991 arranged alphabetically **NLW & Pemb RO** ts PR M pre-
1813 with index **NLW & Pemb RO** ts PR M 1813–36 with index **NLW Pemb RO &**
Soc Gen

ST TWYNNELLS   *SD*
PR CB 1791–1812 M 1754–71 recorded in 1831 apparently lost
C 1729–91, 1813–1922 M 1729–53, 1774–1835, 1837–1968 B 1729–91, 1814–1991 **NLW**
Mf/Fac **Pemb RO**
BT 1799–1807, 1809–71, 1874–8, 1882, 1889–90, 1899 **NLW**
Cop ts PR CMB 1729–1991 arranged alphabetically **NLW & Pemb RO** ts PR M pre-
1813 with index **NLW & Pemb RO** ts PR/BT M 1813–36 with index **NLW Pemb**
RO & Soc Gen

SLEBETS/SLEBECH   *SD*
C 1788–1806, 1813–1925 M 1762–1957, 1960–71 (Banns 1757–1810, 1874–5, 1941–3) B
1782–1807, 1813–1972 **NLW** Mf **Pemb RO**
BT 1799–1818, 1820–44, 1846–59, 1861–81 **NLW**
Cop ts BT 1799–1820 **Pemb RO & Soc Gen** ts PR M 1813–37 with index **NLW Pemb**
RO & Soc Gen

SOLFACH/SOLVA gweler/see TRE-GROES/WHITCHURCH

SPITAL/SPITTAL   *SD*
C 1754–1991 M 1783–1971 (Banns 1806–79) B 1754–1992 **Pemb RO**
BT 1803, 1813–16, 1818–19, 1823–7, 1849–66 **NLW**
Cop ts PR M 1813–37 with index **NLW Pemb RO & Soc Gen**

STACKPOLE ELIDIR/STACKPOLE ELIDOR   *SD*
C 1724–1930 M 1724–1968 B 1724–1992 **NLW** Mf C 1724–1812 M 1724–1837 B
1724–1983 **Pemb RO**
BT 1685–6, 1799–1802, 1804–37, 1839–43, 1845–74, 1878–96 **NLW**
Cop ts PR/BT M pre-1813 with index **NLW & Pemb RO** ts PR M 1814–37 with index
NLW Pemb RO & Soc Gen ts PR CMB 1724–1991 arranged alphabetically **NLW &**
Pemb RO

STEYNTON   *SD*
C 1637–1917 M 1637–1970 (Banns 1840–75, 1901–91) B 1637–1987 **Pemb RO**
BT 1799–1804, 1806–7, 1809–10, 1812–67 **NLW**
Cop ts PR M 1813–37 with index **NLW Pemb RO & Soc Gen**

TALBENNI/TALBENNY   *SD*
C 1764–1990 M 1764–1958 (Banns 1791–1833, 1905–43) B 1764–1991 **Pemb RO**

BT 1799–1807, 1809–10, 1812–58, 1865, 1874 **NLW**
Cop ts PR M 1813–37 with index **NLW Pemb RO & Soc Gen**

TEMPLETON (TREDEML) *SD*
<Arberth/Narberth 1862
CMB 1862– incumbent
BT 1863, 1865–7 **NLW**

TENBY/DINBYCH-Y-PYSGOD *SD*
C 1711–1930 M 1711–1971 (Banns 1823–66, 1877–1963) B 1711–1971 **Pemb RO** Fac
1711–28 **NLW**
BT 1685, 1762, 1799–1804, 1806–7, 1811–51, 1853–94 **NLW**
Cop ts PR M 1813–37 with index **NLW Pemb RO & Soc Gen**

TREAMLOD/AMBLESTON *SD*
C 1765–1974 M 1776–1968 B 1765–1974 **NLW** Mf **Pemb RO**
BT 1685, 1799–1862, 1864 **NLW**
Cop ts PR M 1813–36 with index **NLW Pemb RO & Soc Gen**

TREFDRAETH/NEWPORT *SD*
PR CMB 1741–62 recorded in 1831 apparently lost
C 1765–71, 1799–1800, 1807–71 M 1765–1940 (Banns 1824–1962) B 1765–71,
1799–1800, 1805–1930 **Pemb RO**
BT 1674–6, 1680–2, 1684–9, 1699, 1702–3, 1800, 1806–73, 1875 **NLW**
Cop ms/ts PR C 1765–1812 M 1778–1895 B 1766–1847 **NLW** ts PR M 1813–37 with
index **NLW Pemb RO & Soc Gen**

TREFELEN/BLETHERSTON *SD*
CB 1653–1812 M 1653–1753 entered in PR Llanhuadain/Llawhaden
C 1653–1980 M 1653–1971 B 1653–1980 **NLW** Mf **Pemb RO**
BT 1772, 1799, 1801–38, 1840–57, 1859–70, 1872–3, 1875–9, 1881–3 **NLW**
Cop ts PR M 1813–37 with index **NLW Pemb RO & Soc Gen**

TREFGARN/TREFFGARNE *SD*
Odd entries CMB 1803–12 with PR Treamlod/Ambleston. C 1984–9 with PR
Spital/Spittal
C 1727–1975 M 1727–1962 B 1727–1990 **Pemb RO**
BT 1799–1804, 1806–9, 1811–19, 1821–56, 1858–9 **NLW**
Cop ts PR M 1814–36 with index **NLW Pemb RO & Soc Gen**

TREFWRDAN/JORDANSTON *SD*
C 1802–13 M 1803–51 (Banns 1812–96) B 1802–13 **NLW** Mf **Pemb RO**
BT 1799–1800, 1802–10, 1812–21, 1823–37, 1839–40, 1843–7, 1857–8, 1866 **NLW**
Cop ts PR (extracts) C 1811–39 M 1834–9 B 1808–97 **NLW** ts PR M 1814–36 with
index **NLW Pemb RO & Soc Gen**

TRE-GROES/WHITCHURCH   *SD*
Diocesan records suggest that *c*1790 the registers went back to 1731
C 1753–1974 M 1772–1969, 1973–89 (Banns 1772–1874, 1877–94) Solfach/Solva 1908–8!
B 1752–1957 **Pemb RO**
BT 1799–1800, 1802–7, 1809–82, 1886, 1889–91, 1898–9, 1902–4 **NLW**
Cop ts PR C 1753–94 M 1772–1812 B 1752–94 (extracts CMB to 1907) **NLW** ts PR M
1813–37 with index **NLW Pemb RO & Soc Gen**

TRELETERT/LETTERSTON   *SD*
The earliest registers reputedly destroyed at the time of the French invasion 1797 (183!
survey). Diocesan records suggest that *c*1790 the registers went back only 36 years
C 1801–1975 M 1801–1982 (Banns 1801–1941) B 1801–1976 **Pemb RO**
BT 1773, 1799, 1802–65, 1886–9, 1891 **NLW**
Cop ts PR (extracts) C 1813–70 **NLW** ts PR M 1813–37 with index **NLW Pemb RO &**
Soc Gen

TREMARCHOG/ST NICHOLAS   *SD*
PR 1758– in poor condition in 1933 apparently lost. CB 1793–1803 entered in PR
Treopert/Granston. Diocesan records suggest that *c*1790 the registers went back to 1727
C 1793–1803, 1806–1993 M 1779–1971 (Banns 1780–1817, 1907) B 1793–1803
1806–1992 **Pemb RO**
BT see Treopert/Granston
Cop ms/ts PR C 1783–1874 M 1782–1899 B 1783–1898 **NLW** ts PR (extracts) C
1810–74 M 1782–1899 B 1799–1898 **Pemb RO** ts PR M 1813–36 with index **NLW**
Pemb RO & Soc Gen

TREOPERT/GRANSTON   *SD*
Diocesan records suggest that *c*1790 the registers went back to 1727
C 1793–1990 M 1778–1970 (Banns 1778–1814, 1828–1908) B 1793–1805, 1813–199!
Pemb RO
BT 1799–1843, 1846, 1865–7 **NLW**
Cop ms PR C 1785–1811 M 1778–1813 B 1784–1813 ts PR (extracts) CB 1785–1902 M
1778–1817 **NLW** ts PR M 1813–35 with index **NLW Pemb RO & Soc Gen**

TREWYDDEL/MOYLGROVE   *SD*
C 1769–1812 M 1770–7, 1781–1837 (Banns 1824–84, 1949–90) B 1769–1988 **NLW** M
Pemb RO
BT 1675–6, 1678–86, 1688–9, 1702–3, 1708, 1799–1801, 1803–19, 1821–75, 1877–9 **NLW**
Cop ts PR (extracts) C 1770–1818 M 1771–1833 B 1770–1815 **NLW** ts PR M 1813–3?
with index **NLW Pemb RO & Soc Gen**

TYDDEWI/ST DAVID'S   *SD*
C 1724–1984 M 1724–1966 (Banns 1808–50, 1878–1963) B 1724–1963 **NLW** Mf **Pem!**
RO
BT 1813–56, 1864, 1866, 1872–4 **NLW**

Cop ts PR C 1724–1858 M 1724–1837 B 1724–1812 (extracts to 1906) **NLW** ts PR M 1813–37 with index **NLW Pemb RO & Soc Gen**

UPTON gweler/see NASH

UZMASTON   *SD*
C 1720–1959 M 1733–79, 1788–1993 (Banns 1827, 1855, 1869–1994) B 1723–1972
  Pemb RO Mf CMB 1720–1812 **NLW**
BT 1799–1810, 1812–16, 1818–70 **NLW**
Cop ts PR M 1813–36 with index **NLW Pemb RO & Soc Gen**

WALTON EAST   *SD*
C 1721–1974 M 1721–1971 B 1721–1974 **NLW** Mf **Pemb RO**
BT 1799–1807, 1809–44, 1846, 1848–52, 1854–5, 1857–69, 1871, 1875 **NLW**
Cop ts PR M 1813–36 with index **NLW Pemb RO & Soc Gen**

WALTON WEST   *SD*
PR M 1755–1812 recorded in 1831 apparently lost. M 1813–37 not recorded in 1933
C 1763–1992 M 1838–1970 (Banns 1824–1946) B 1763–1953 **Pemb RO**
BT 1800–4, 1809–65, 1873–4 **NLW**
Cop ts BT M 1813–35 with index **NLW Pemb RO & Soc Gen**

★ WALWYN'S CASTLE/CASTELL GWALCHMAI   *SD*
C 1767–1920 M 1755–1808, 1812–1962 B 1755–1993 **NLW** Mf **Pemb RO**
BT 1772, 1801–6, 1809–14, 1818–74 **NLW**
Cop ts BT M 1813–37 with index **NLW Pemb RO & Soc Gen**

WARREN   *SD*
PR M 1774–1812 recorded in 1933 apparently lost
C 1760–1968 M 1755–76, 1813–35, 1840–1966 (Banns 1825–1966) B 1760–1990 **NLW**
  Mf **Pemb RO**
BT 1799–1805, 1807–71, 1873–8, 1882, 1888–90 **NLW**
Cop ts PR M pre-1813 with index **NLW & Pemb RO** ts PR M 1813–35 with index
  NLW Pemb RO & Soc Gen

WDIG/GOODWICK   *SD*
<Llanwnda
M 1913–74 (Banns 1923–74) **Pemb RO**

WHITCHURCH/TRE-GROES   *SD*
Diocesan records suggest that *c*1790 the registers went back to 1731
C 1753–1974 M 1772–1969, 1973–89 (Banns 1772–1874, 1877–94) Solfach/Solva 1908–85
  B 1752–1957 **Pemb RO**
BT 1799–1800, 1802–7, 1809–82, 1886, 1889–91, 1898–9, 1902–4 **NLW**
Cop ts PR C 1753–94 M 1772–1812 B 1752–94 (extracts CMB to 1907) **NLW** ts PR M 1813–37 with index **NLW Pemb RO & Soc Gen**

* WHITECHURCH/EGLWYS WEN   *SD*
    C 1704–1992 M 1704–53, 1755–9, 1813–1933, 1948–70 B 1704–1812, 1814–1992 **NLW**
    Mf **Pemb RO**
    BT 1674–5, 1678, 1680–3, 1685–90, 1699, 1701–3, 1799–1800, 1803–39, 1844–6,
    1851–60, 1863, 1865, 1869–70, 1872–80, 1882, 1885, 1890 **NLW**
    Cop ts PR M 1813–37 with index **NLW Pemb RO & Soc Gen**

* WISTON/CAS-WIS   *SD*
    CMB 1653–66 entered in PR Llanhuadain/Llawhaden
    C 1653–66, 1715–1993 M 1653–66, 1715–1970 B 1653–66, 1715–1921 **NLW**   Mf/Fac
    Pemb RO
    BT 1799–1806, 1808–82 **NLW**
    Cop ts PR M 1813–37 with index **NLW Pemb RO & Soc Gen**

YERBESTON   *SD*
PR none before 1813 to be found in 1831, and CB 1791–1812 recorded in 1933 as being in
poor condition now apparently lost. Diocesan records suggest that in 1814 there were
extant PR C 1786–1812 M 1778–1811 B 1787–1812
C 1813–1976 M 1813–1968 B 1813–1976 **Pemb RO**
BT 1799–1831, 1833–5, 1840, 1843–7, 1849, 1851–73, 1875–8, 1880–6, 1888–91, 1893–5,
1898–1902, 1904–9 **NLW**
Cop ts BT 1801–35 **Pemb RO & Soc Gen** ts PR M 1813–36 with index **NLW Pemb**
RO & Soc Gen

TREFALDWYN
MONTGOMERYSHIRE

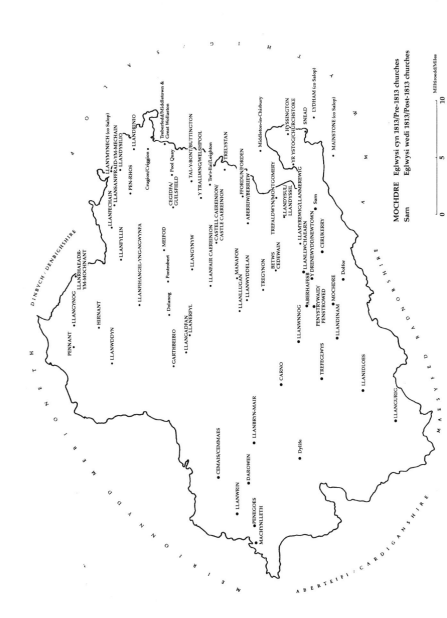

MOCHDRE Eglwysi cyn 1813/Pre-1813 churches

Sarn   Eglwysi wedi 1813/Post-1813 churches

ABERHAFESB *SA*
C 1578–1601, 1623–5, 1630–51, 1721–4, 1726–1993 M 1579–1602, 1623–4, 1628, 1633–42, 1644, 1648, 1721–4, 1726–1970 (Banns 1823–78, 1894–1991) B 1578–82, 1584–7, 1590, 1603, 1619, 1623–6, 1640–6, 1721–4, 1726–1993 **NLW** Mf **PCAO**
BT 1665–8, 1670, 1672–3, 1676–8, 1680–1, 1683–8, 1698–1701, 1703, 1705–17, 1719–1834 **NLW** Mf 1676–1834 **DRO & FRO**

ABERRIW/BERRIEW *SA*
C 1596–1628, 1685–1981 M 1596–8, 1600–3, 1607–9, 1616–26, 1685–1985 (Banns 1834–1986) B 1596–1628, 1683–91, 1693–1923 **NLW** Mf **PCAO**
BT 1662–6, 1668–74, 1676–8, 1681–5, 1687–96, 1698–1700, 1702–10, 1713–1848, 1850–4 **NLW** Mf 1673–1854 **DRO & FRO**

ASTON gweler/see **LYDHAM**

BERRIEW gweler/see **ABERRIW**

BETWS CEDEWAIN *SA*
C 1661–1956 M 1662–1984 (Banns 1809–1993) B 1662–1983 **NLW** Mf C 1661–1956 M 1662–1836 (Banns 1809–1993) B 1662–1983 **PCAO**
BT 1662–8, 1670–4, 1676–83, 1685–8, 1690–6, 1698–1718, 1720–1853 **NLW** Mf **DRO & FRO**
Cop ts PR/BT index M 1662–1837 **NLW**

BUTTINGTON/TAL-Y-BONT *SA*
* PR CMB 1723–35 recorded in 1936 apparently lost
C 1736–1948 M 1736–1971 (Banns 1824–1900) B 1736–1953 **NLW** Mf **PCAO**
BT 1638, 1660–1, 1663–1734, 1736–1833, 1836–48 **HRO** 1849–62 **NLW** Mf 1854–62 **DRO & FRO** Mf 1660–1848 **Soc Gen** Fac 1638–1848 **NLW**
Cop ts PR/Bt index M 1638–1837 **NLW**

CARNO *B*
C 1638–47, 1661–87, 1699–1716, 1718–24, 1736–1809 M 1638–47, 1661–86, 1699–1724, 1736–1837 (Banns 1823–1975) B 1638–47, 1661–86, 1699–1724, 1736–1809, 1813–1916 **NLW** Mf **PCAO**
BT 1677, 1680, 1683, 1685–6, ?1688, 1689–90, 1692–3, 1695–1700, 1703, 1705, 1708–9, 1711–13, 1717–21, 1723–32, 1734, 1737, 1739–56, 1758–80, 1782–1837 **NLW**
Cop ms PR (extracts) M 1757–1809 **NLW**

CARREGHWFA/CARREGHOFA gweler/see **LLANYMYNECH**

CASTELL CAEREINION/CASTLE CAEREINION *SA*
C 1689–1732, 1734–1992 M 1689–1732, 1734–1991 (Banns 1810–1943) B 1689–1732, 1734–1877 **NLW** Mf **PCAO**
BT 1663, 1665–9, 1672–3, 1676–9, 1681, 1685–91, 1693–5, 1698–1709, 1713–14,

1717–23, 1725–7, 1729–31, 1733–5, 1737–1843 **NLW** Mf **DRO & FRO**
Cop ts PR/BT index M 1674–1837 **NLW**

CASTLEWRIGHT gweler/see MAINSTONE

CEGIDFA/GUILSFIELD   *SA*
C 1572–1642, 1696–1960 M 1572–1642, 1696–1991 (Banns 1859–1960) B 1572–1642,
  1696–1994 Fac M 1879–1991 **NLW** Mf C 1572–1895 M 1572–1878 B 1572–1875
  PCAO
BT 1667–8, 1670, 1672–3, 1675–85, 1687–95, 1697–1700, 1702–1859 **NLW** Mf **DRO &**
  FRO
Cop ms PR CMB 1575–1608 **NLW**

CEMAIS/CEMMAES   *B*
C 1711–45, 1751–1927 M 1711–45, 1749–55, 1757–1970 (Banns 1823–1918) B 1711–45,
  1749–1863 **NLW** Mf **PCAO**
BT 1668, 1670–4, 1676–8, 1680–4, 1686–9, 1692, 1694–6, 1700–4, 1706–7, 1709–15,
  1717–18, 1720–3, 1725–32, 1734–5, 1737–1837, 1851 **NLW**
Cop ms PR/BT C 1668–1867 M 1668–1885 B 1668–1863 ms BT (extracts) CMB
  1668–1750 ts PR/BT index M 1668–1837 **NLW**

CERI/KERRY   *SA*
C 1602–6, 1609–1993 M 1602–6, 1609–1993 (Banns 1823–1973) B 1602–6, 1609–1860
  NLW Mf C 1602–1993 M 1602–1961 (Banns 1823–1936) B 1602–1860 **PCAO**
BT 1705, 1707–8, 1710, 1713–40, 1742–95, 1797–1810, 1813–47 **NLW**
Cop PR CMB 1602–1812 *Montgomeryshire Collections,* 39 (1915–20) ts PR CMB 1602–1812
  Soc Gen

* CHURCHSTOKE/YR YSTOG   *H*
Included townships of Brompton and Rhiston, co Salop
C 1558–1853 M 1558–1812 B 1558–1812 **SRR**
BT 1660, 1663–1718, 1720–54, 1756–87, 1789–1833, 1836–53, 1855–8, 1861 **HRO**

CRUGION/CRIGGION   *SA*
<Alberbury (Llanfihangel-yng-Ngheintyn), co Salop 1864. PR for Alberbury C 1564–1908
  M 1564–1958, 1976–1991 (Banns 1824–1953) B 1564–1851 are in SRR. BT for
  Alberbury 1660–1864 with gaps are in HRO. Cop PR for Alberbury CMB 1564–1812 are
  in Shropshire Parish Register Society, Hereford, 6–7 (1902)
C 1829–1923, 1925–93 M 1865–1970 B 1843–1990 **NLW**

DAROWEN   *B*
C 1633–50, 1658–61, 1663–5, 1669–72, 1675–82, 1684–9, 1708–34, 1736–1876 M
  1633–50, 1658–60, 1673, 1675–82, 1684–9, 1708–34, 1736–1837 (Banns 1824–44) B
  1633–50, 1658–60, 1670–1, 1673, 1675–82, 1684–9, 1708–34, 1736–1871 **NLW** Mf
  PCAO
BT ?1669, 1670–2, 1674, 1676–8, 1681–7, 1691–6, 1698, 1700, 1702–6, 1708–13, 1716–17

1719, 1729–31, 1733–8, 1740–1854, 1905 **NLW**
Cop ms PR CMB 1633–1771 (partly indexed) ms BT (extracts) CMB 1670–1757 **NLW**

DOLANOG (PONTDOLANOG) *SA*
<Llanfair Caereinion, Llanfihangel-yng-Ngwynfa, Llanerfyl & Llangynyw 1856
C 1856–1993 M 1862–1970 B 1855–1992 **NLW** Mf M 1862–1970 **PCAO**

DOLFOR *SA*
<Ceri/Kerry 1851. Early entries in PR for Dolfor are copied from those of Ceri/Kerry
C 1852–1991 M 1867–1968 B 1853–1993 **NLW** Mf **PCAO**

DRENEWYDD, Y/NEWTOWN *SA*
C 1660–75, 1679–1971 M 1660–75, 1679–1958 (Banns 1887–1971) B 1660–75,
1679–1993 **NLW** Mf **PCAO**
BT 1662, 1665–8, 1671–4, 1676–84, 1686–96, 1698–1841 **NLW** Mf 1665–1841 **DRO &
FRO**

DYLIFE *B*
<Llanbryn-mair, Darowen, Penegoes & Trefeglwys 1856
C 1856–1926 M 1856–1964 **NLW** B 1857– incumbent Fac B 1857–1980 **NLW** Mf C
1856–1926 **PCAO**
BT 1882, 1890–4 **NLW**

FFORDUN/FORDEN *SA*
C 1598–1748, 1751–1807, 1813–78 M 1598–1748, 1751–1980 B 1598–1748, 1751–1807,
1813–1920 House of Industry C 1795–1863 B 1795–1864 **NLW** Mf **PCAO**
BT 1638, 1660, 1663–1833, 1836–63 **HRO**

GARTHBEIBIO *SA*
PR M 1754–1837 recorded as missing in 1936, although CB 1760–1812 includes M entries
to 1795
C 1710–1925 M 1722–95, 1837–1917, 1919–41 B 1710–1903 **NLW** Mf **PCAO**
BT 1667–76, 1678, ?1680–2, 1684–9, ?1691–4, 1696, 1698–1700, 1702–3, 1705, 1707–8,
1718, 1721–4, 1726–1836, 1850–5 **NLW** Mf **DRO & FRO**
Cop ms PR C 1710–59 M 1722–59 B 1715–59 **DRO** ts PR/BT index M 1667–1837
NLW

GREAT WOLLASTON gweler/see TREBERFEDD/MIDDLETOWN

GUILSFIELD/CEGIDFA *SA*
C 1572–1642, 1696–1960 M 1572–1642, 1696–1991 (Banns 1859–1960) B 1572–1642,
1696–1994 Fac M 1879–1991 **NLW** Mf C 1572–1895 M 1572–1878 B 1572–1875
PCAO
BT 1667–8, 1670, 1672–3, 1675–85, 1687–95, 1697–1700, 1702–1859 **NLW** Mf **DRO &
FRO**
Cop ms PR CMB 1575–1608 **NLW**

HIRNANT   *SA*
C 1600–1, 1614–15, 1620–36, 1640–7, 1651, 1653–7, 1662, 1673–7, 1680–2, 1685–170(
    1720–1992 M 1601, 1614–15, 1620–36, 1640–7, 1653, 1656, 1688–1706, 1720–1971
    1600–1, 1614–15, 1620–36, 1640–7, 1653–7, 1662, 1673–7, 1680–2, 1685–170(
    1720–1990 **NLW** Mf CB 1600–1812 M 1601–1971 **PCAO**
BT 1667, 1670, 1672, 1674, 1682–3, 1685–96, 1698–1702, 1705–7, 1711–14, 171(
    1718–39, 1741–54, 1756–71, 1773–1845, 1851–4 **NLW** Mf 1674–1854 **DRO & FRO**
Cop ms/ts PR C 1720–1912 M 1720–1837 B 1720–1909 **DRO** ts PR/BT index M
    1601–1837 **NLW**

HYSSINGTON   *H*
Included township of Mucklewick, co Salop, transferred to Shelve 1884
CMB 1701– incumbent
BT 1598–9, 1605, 1610, 1613, 1638, 1660–1, 1663–97, 1699–1702, 1704–54, 1756–183:
    1836–47, 1849–63, 1865, 1867, 1869–70 **HRO** Mf 1660–1870 **PCAO & Soc Gen**

* KERRY/CERI   *SA*
C 1602–6, 1609–1993 M 1602–6, 1609–1993 (Banns 1823–1973) B 1602–6, 1609–186(
    NLW Mf C 1602–1993 M 1602–1961 (Banns 1823–1936) B 1602–1860 **PCAO**
BT 1705, 1707–8, 1710, 1713–40, 1742–95, 1797–1810, 1813–47 **NLW**
Cop PR CMB 1602–1812 *Montgomeryshire Collections,* 39 (1915–20) ts PR CMB 1602–181
    Soc Gen

* LEIGHTON/TRE'R-LLAI   *H*
<Worthen, co Salop, 1853. PR for Worthen C 1558–1931 M 1558–1972 B 1558–196(
    are in SRR
C 1854– B 1864– incumbent M 1855–1971 **SRR**

LYDHAM   *H*
Shropshire parish including the detached township of Aston, co Montgomery
C 1596–1660, 1691–1980 M 1596–1660, 1691–1837 (Banns 1823–1978) B 1596–166(
    1679–88, 1691–1981 **SRR**
BT 1638, 1660–1702, 1704–52, 1754–1833, 1836–9, 1845–6, 1850 **HRO**
Cop PR CMB 1596–1812 Shropshire Parish Register Society, Hereford, 3 (1903)

LLAMYREWIG/LLANMEREWIG   *SA*
C 1661, 1663–6, 1670–4, 1676–85, 1688–1993 M 1670–4, 1676–85, 1688–1971 (Ban►
    1825–1982) B 1663–6, 1670–4, 1676–85, 1688–1993 **NLW** Mf **PCAO**
BT 1665, 1667–8, 1670–4, 1676–7, 1679–89, 1691–5, 1699–1703, 1705–25, 1728–5!
    1761–6, 1768–1837 **NLW** Mf **DRO & FRO**
Cop ms PR CMB 1661–1761 ts PR/BT index M 1661–1837 **NLW**

LLANBRYN-MAIR   *B*
C 1663–1899 M 1663–1934, 1938–65 B 1663–1884 **NLW** Fac C 1899–1979
    1884–1981 **NLW** Mf C 1663–1899 M 1663–1934 B 1663–1894 **PCAO**

BT 1670–4, 1676–82, 1685–7, 1689–93, 1695–6, 1699–1702, 1704–23, 1725–1837, 1882, 1905–7 **NLW**
Cop PR CMB (extracts) *Montgomeryshire Collections,* 22 (1888) ms PR CB 1663–1812 M 1663–1837 ms PR (extracts) CMB 1665–1780 **NLW**

LLANDINAM *B*
C 1589–1634, 1636–75, 1678, 1685–6, 1689–90, 1703–6, 1712–71, 1774, 1783–4, 1787, 1789, 1793–6, 1800, 1802–1928 M 1591–1634, 1636–75, 1678, 1685–6, 1689–90, 1703–6, 1712–1970 B 1587–1615, 1636–75, 1678, 1685–6, 1689–90, 1703–6, 1712–71, 1799, 1802–1929 [?Banhadlog chapel] C 1784–1805 Banhadlog chapel C 1840–1965 M 1841–1954 B 1843–1958 **NLW** Mf **PCAO**
BT 1671, 1677–80, 1685–7, 1689–93, 1695–1700, 1703–9, 1711–13, 1716–24, 1726–34, 1737–57, 1759–60, 1762–80, 1782–1839, 1850, 1864 **NLW**
Cop ms PR (extracts) M 1753–1836 **NLW**

LLANDRINIO *SA*
C 1662–8, 1674–1993 M 1664–5, 1675–86, 1688–1971 B 1662–7, 1687–97, 1709–18, 1728–74, 1781–1993 **NLW** Mf C 1662–1898 M 1664–1971 B 1662–1812 **PCAO**
BT 1668, 1674, 1677–96, 1698–1703, 1705–6, 1708–1813, 1815–33 **NLW** Mf **DRO & FRO**
Cop ts PR/BT index M 1664–1837 **NLW**

LLANDYSILIO *SA*
C 1662–1735, 1737, 1740–1963 M 1663–1735, 1740–1971 (Banns 1919–75) B 1662–1733, 1740–1986 **NLW** Mf C 1662–1963 M 1663–1971 (Banns 1919–75) B 1662–1872 **PCAO**
BT 1663, 1668, 1674, 1677, 1680–96, 1698–1701, 1703–9, 1711–43, 1745–51, 1753–1848 **NLW** Mf **DRO & FRO**
Cop ms PR C 1662–1973 M 1663–1837 B 1662–1942 ts PR/BT index M 1664–1837 **NLW**

LLANDYSUL/LLANDYSSIL *SA*
C 1689–1889 M 1689–1971 B 1689–1960 **NLW** Mf **PCAO**
BT 1671–2, 1674, 1677, 1682–90, 1692, 1694–6, 1698–1835, 1850–7 **NLW** Mf **DRO & FRO**
Cop PR/BT index M 1671–1837 **NLW**

LLANERFYL *SA*
C 1626–40, 1643–5, 1648, 1660, 1662–71, 1674–1991 M 1626–36, 1663–70, 1674–1970 B 1626–45, 1652–3, 1660, 1662–71, 1674–1907 **NLW** Mf C 1626–1857 M 1626–1837 B 1626–1812 **PCAO**
BT 1667, 1679, 1682, 1686–94, 1696, 1698–1718, 1720–1837 **NLW** Mf 1667–1836 **DRO & FRO**

LLANFAIR CAEREINION *SA*
C 1608–22, 1624–66, 1669–76, 1680–1702, 1723–1992 M 1608–22, 1624–43, 1662–6,

1670–6, 1680–1702, 1723–1955 B 1608–22, 1624–67, 1670–6, 1680–1702, 1723–1992
NLW Mf **PCAO**
BT 1662, 1665–8, 1678, 1680, 1682–93, 1695–6, 1698, 1700–3, 1705–9, 1711–22, 1724–6,
1728–32, 1734–1852 **NLW** Mf **DRO & FRO**
Cop PR CMB 1644–61 *Montgomeryshire Collections*, 28 (1894)

LLANFECHAIN   *SA*
C 1603–1705, 1707–1993 M 1603–1705, 1707–1970 (Banns 1824–1984) B 1603–1705,
1707–1993 **NLW** Mf C 1603–1863 M 1603–1812 B 1603–1880 **PCAO**
BT 1667, 1671–3, 1678, 1680–7, 1689, 1691–4, 1696, 1698–1703, 1705–15, 1717–19,
1721–1850 **NLW** Mf **DRO & FRO**

LLANFIHANGEL-YNG-NGWYNFA   *SA*
C 1663–7, 1688–98, 1708–1869 M 1663–7, 1688–93, 1708–1968 (Banns 1823–1961) B
1663–7, 1688–98, 1708–1864 **NLW** Mf **PCAO**
BT 1662, 1673, 1676, 1678, 1680–91, 1693, 1703, 1708–10, 1712, 1715–16, 1722,
1724–1857 **NLW** Mf **DRO & FRO**
Cop ts PR C 1663–1761 M 1663–1753 B 1663–1762 **DRO** ts PR/BT index M
1662–1837 **NLW**

LLANFYLLIN   *SA*
C 1654, 1660–1, 1664–1875 M 1669–1708, 1711–1939 (Banns 1871–1963) B 1665–1956
NLW Mf **PCAO**
BT 1667–8, 1672, 1677–81, 1684–92, 1694–5, 1716–19, 1723–1840, 1842, 1846 **NLW** Mf
DRO & FRO

LLANGADFAN   *SA*
PR CMB 1630–41 recorded in 1831 apparently lost. PR B ends in 1873, but burials
1831–1920 are in a separate cemetery register, kept in Welsh, which gives location of grave
as well as dates of death and burial, and deceased's age and abode
C 1673–96, 1700–5, 1717–1879 M 1673–96, 1700–5, 1717–1811, 1813–1970 (Bann
1823–1950) B 1673–96, 1700–5, 1717–1920 **NLW** Mf **PCAO**
BT 1663–5, 1669–72, 1674, 1676–8, 1680–96, 1698, 1703, 1705, 1707–15, 1717–26
1728–1836 **NLW** Mf **DRO & FRO**
Cop ts PR/BT index M 1663–1837 **NLW**

LLANGURIG   *B*
C 1687–91, 1694–1702, 1707–1861 M 1683–1969 (Banns 1827–1958) B 1686–1756
1758–1875 **NLW** Mf C 1687–1861 M 1683–1837 (Banns 1827–1958) B 1686–187
PCAO
BT 1677, 1683, 1685, 1687, 1689, 1691–3, 1695–1713, 1716–28, 1730–5, 1737
1739–1867, 1883–5 **NLW**

LLANGYNOG   *SA*
C 1720–1870 M 1720–61, 1763–1971 (Banns 1824–66) B 1720–1885 **NLW** Mf **PCAO**
BT 1662–5, 1668, 1673, 1676–82, 1684–6, 1691–2, 1694, 1696, 1702, 1704, 1708–1.

1715–16, 1719–26, 1728–1842, 1849–56, 1859 **NLW** Mf **DRO & FRO**
Cop ts PR/BT index M 1662–1837 **NLW**

LLANGYNYW *SA*
C 1584–90, 1593–1683, 1729–1914 M 1584–90, 1593–1649, 1661–83, 1729–1969, 1991 B
1584–90, 1594–1683, 1729–1895 **NLW** Mf C 1584–1914 M 1584–1837 B 1584–1895
PCAO
BT 1662–71, 1673–4, 1676, 1679–96, 1698–1703, 1705–13, 1715–34, 1737–1839 **NLW**
Mf **DRO & FRO**

LLANIDLOES *B*
C 1616–49, 1654–5, 1658, 1660–1830 M 1614–49, 1662–83, 1687–90, 1695–7, 1711–1990
(Banns 1823–47) B 1614–44, 1647–8, 1661–87, 1692–1840 **NLW** Mf C 1616–1830 M
1614–1835 (Banns 1823–47) B 1614–1840 **PCAO & Soc Gen**
BT 1677, 1683, 1685–93, 1695–9, 1703–5, 1707–8, 1711–13, 1716–21, 1724–34, 1737,
1739–56, 1758–1840 **NLW**
Cop ms PR C 1616–1812 (extracts to 1830) M 1614–1812 (extracts to 1836) B 1614–1818
(extracts to 1839) **NLW** ms PR CM 1711–18 with index **Soc Gen**

LLANLLUGAN *SA*
CB 1603–33, 1670, 1672, 1676, 1679–1702, 1731–1991 M 1603–33, 1670, 1672, 1676,
1679–1702, 1731–1971 **NLW** Mf **PCAO**
BT 1663, 1668, 1670, 1672–4, 1676–7, 1679, 1681–4, 1687, 1691–5, 1698–1703, 1705–42,
1744–66, 1768–1807, 1809–50 **NLW** Mf **DRO & FRO**
Cop PR/BT CMB 1603–1790 *Montgomeryshire Collections,* 34–35 (1907–10) ms PR/BT
CMB 1603–1790 **NLW**

LLANLLWCHAEARN *SA*
C 1658–1948 M 1658–1975 (Banns 1823–1932) All Saints M 1891–1971 (Banns
1891–1949) B 1658–1993 **NLW** Mf **PCAO**
BT 1662–8, 1670–4, 1676–9, 1681–96, 1698–1754, 1756–61, 1763–1835, 1837–9, 1850
NLW Mf **DRO & FRO**

LLANMEREWIG/LLAMYREWIG *SA*
C 1661, 1663–6, 1670–4, 1676–85, 1688–1993 M 1670–4, 1676–85, 1688–1971 (Banns
1825–1982) B 1663–6, 1670–4, 1676–85, 1688–1993 **NLW** Mf **PCAO**
BT 1665, 1667–8, 1670–4, 1676–7, 1679–89, 1691–5, 1699–1703, 1705–25, 1728–59,
1761–6, 1768–1837 **NLW** Mf **DRO & FRO**
Cop ms PR CMB 1661–1761 ts PR/BT index M 1661–1837 **NLW**

LLANRHAEADR-YM-MOCHNANT gweler/see SIR DDINBYCH/DENBIGHSHIRE

LLANSANFFRAID-YM-MECHAIN *SA*
C 1582–1615, 1653–4, 1656, 1665, 1680, 1712–50, 1757–1911 M 1582–1615, 1674–1750,
1754–1970 B 1582–1615, 1666, 1668–1750, 1757–1851, 1898–1993 **NLW** Mf C
1582–1911 M 1582–1837 B 1582–1851 **PCAO**

BT 1666–73, 1681–3, 1686–96, 1698–1701, 1705–52, 1754–1844 **NLW** Mf **DRO &** **FRO**
Cop PR B 1759–66, 1772–4, 1780–91 *Montgomeryshire Collections,* 57–59 (1962–6) ts C 1813–1911 M 1789–1837 B 1759–67 **Soc Gen**

LLANWDDYN *SA*
C 1624–44, 1649–59, 1662–3, 1665–80, 1684–91, 1693, 1695–1888 M 1624–30, 1666–79 1683–4, 1695, 1701–1968 (Banns 1823-1928, 1940-91) B 1623–45, 1647, 1649–51 1653–4, 1656–7, 1664, 1666–79, 1681–92, 1695–1881 **NLW** Mf (except Banns) **PCAO**
BT 1669, 1676–80, 1682–8, 1690–2, 1694–6, 1698–9, 1701–2, 1704–5, 1707–19, 1721–33 1735–1851 **NLW** Mf **DRO & FRO**
Cop ts PR C 1624–93 M 1624–95 B 1623–1700 **DRO** ts MB 1624–1700 **NLW**

LLANWNNOG *B*
C 1668–1775, 1783–1873 M 1668–1911 (Banns 1823–49, 1875–99) B 1668–1882 **NLW** Mf **PCAO**
BT 1677, 1679–80, 1685–6, 1690–2, 1695–1700, 1707–13, 1716–21, 1723–37, 1739–56 1758–73, 1775–1852 **NLW**
Cop ms PR C 1668–1812 M 1754–85 B 1668–1850 M (extracts) 1670–1820 **NLW**

LLANWRIN *B*
C 1671–90, 1695–1992 M 1671–90, 1695–1955 (Banns 1824–59) B 1671–90, 1695–199: **NLW** Mf (excluding Banns) **PCAO**
BT ?1667, 1670–2, 1674, 1677, 1680–1, 1683–4, 1686, 1689, 1695–1702, 1704–18, 1720–3 1725–1858, 1906–7, 1910–11 **NLW**
Cop ms BT CMB 1667–1722 **NLW**

LLANWYDDELAN *SA*
PR CMB 1664–1779 recorded in 1936 apparently lost
C 1783–1808, 1813–1944 M 1784–1988 B 1783–1808, 1813–1993 **NLW** Mf C 1783–1944 M 1784–1971 B 1783–1993 **PCAO**
BT 1662–3, 1665–8, 1670–1, 1673, 1676–7, 1679–86, 1688–96, 1698–1727, 1729–184 **NLW** Mf **DRO & FRO**
Cop PR/BT index M 1662–1837 **NLW**

LLANYMYNECH *L*
Parish comprising the townships of Llwyntidman/Llwyntidmon and Treprennal, co Salop and Carreghwfa/Carreghofa (formerly a detached part of Denbighshire), co Montgomery
C 1666–1867 M 1666–1837 B 1666–1898 **SRR**
BT 1676–1857 with gaps **Lichfield RO**
Cop PR CMB 1666–1812 Shropshire Parish Register Society, St Asaph, 8 (1917)

MACHYNLLETH *B*
C 1684–1722, 1731–1993 M 1684–1722, 1731–1971 B 1684–1722, 1731–1993 **NLW** M **PCAO**
BT 1662, 1666–8, 1670–4, 1676–81, 1683–96, 1699–1706, 1711, 1719, 1723, ?1726

1728–1857, 1889–90 **NLW**
Cop ms PR/BT CB 1662–1782 M 1662–1812 B (extracts) 1782–1812 **NLW**

MAINSTONE   H
Shropshire parish including township of Castlewright, co Montgomery
C 1590–1867 M 1590–1956 (Banns 1824–1901) B 1590–1812 **SRR** Mf B 1813–75 **SRR**
BT 1638, 1660–85, 1688–1833, 1836–78 **HRO**

MANAFON   SA
C 1596–1665, 1678–1891 M 1654, 1678–1971 (Banns 1812–38) B 1596–1667, 1678–1930
NLW Mf **PCAO**
BT 1662–3, 1665–8, 1670–4, 1676–96, 1698–1836, 1838–50 **NLW** Mf **DRO & FRO**

MEIFOD   SA
C 1597, 1600, 1602, 1604–22, 1624–6, 1628–32, 1634–42, 1647–1880 M 1602, 1605–18,
1620–6, 1628–31, 1634–7, 1640–2, 1649–1970 (Banns 1838–1917) B 1600, 1602–26,
1628–32, 1634–42, 1647–1922 **NLW** Mf C 1597–1880 M 1602–1837 (Banns 1838-1917)
B 1600–1922 **PCAO**
BT 1662–3, 1665–8, 1670, 1672–3, 1675–7, 1679–82, 1684–96, 1698, 1700–1830, 1832–6
NLW Mf 1667–1822 **DRO & FRO**

MIDDLETON-IN-CHIRBURY   H
<Chirbury, co Salop, & Yr Ystog/Churchstoke, co Montgomery, 1846
C 1846–96 M 1846–1970 B 1847–1972 **SRR**

MIDDLETOWN/TREBERFEDD & GREAT WOLLASTON   H
<Alberbury (Llanfihangel-yng-Ngheintyn) 1864 [see entry for Crugion/Criggion]. Includes
the Montgomeryshire townships of Treberfedd/Middletown and Ucheldre/the Heldre
C 1829–1908 M 1864–1970 (Banns 1864–1976) **SRR** B 1872– incumbent

MOCHDRE   SA
C 1682, 1685–1714, 1717–18, 1722–6, 1729–1993 M 1729–1971, 1984-98 (Banns
1824–1976) B 1695–1715, 1723–4, 1729–1993 **NLW** Mf C 1682, 1685–1714, 1717–18,
1722–6, 1729–1993 M 1729–1971 (Banns 1824–1976) B 1695–1715, 1723–4, 1729–1993
PCAO
BT 1700, 1706–8, 1712–18, 1720–1, 1723–9, 1731–47, 1751–95, 1797–1810, 1813–38,
1840–51 **NLW**
Cop ms PR CMB 1682–1812 **NLW**

MONTGOMERY/TREFALDWYN   SA
C 1574–1641, 1645–8, 1650–3, 1656–91, 1694–1972 M 1575–1641, 1645–7, 1651, 1653,
1656–91, 1694–1981 B 1574–1641, 1645–7, 1652–3, 1656–91, 1694–1966 **NLW** Mf
PCAO
BT 1663–1772, 1774–1826, 1829–33, 1836–72 **HRO**

* NEWTOWN/Y DRENEWYDD   *SA*
C 1660–75, 1679–1971 M 1660–75, 1679–1958 (Banns 1887–1971) B 1660–75
1679–1993 **NLW** Mf **PCAO**
BT 1662, 1665–8, 1671–4, 1676–84, 1686–96, 1698–1841 **NLW** Mf 1665–1841 **DRO &**
FRO

PENEGOES   *B*
C 1679–1993 M 1679–1970 (Banns 1823–77) B 1679–1869 **NLW** Mf C 1679–1812 M
1679–1970 (Banns 1823–77) B 1679–1869 **PCAO**
BT 1667, 1673–4, 1681–4, 1686, 1689–96, 1698–1702, 1704–6, 1715–16, 1718–19, 1721
1726, 1728–36, 1738–9, 1741–3, 1745–1852, 1856–8, 1861–4 **NLW**
Cop ms BT CMB 1667–1743 & PR C 1679–1812 (extracts to 1827) M 1679–1837 B
1679–1865 ts PR/BT index M 1667–1837 **NLW**

PENNANT (PENNANT MELANGELL)   *SA*
C 1680–3, 1685, 1689–1713, 1720–1991 M 1685–6, 1691–1713, 1720–1971 B 1680–6
1689–1713, 1720–1953 **NLW** Mf CB 1680–1812 M 1680–1971 **PCAO**
BT 1662, 1667–8, 1672–3, 1676–8, 1680–2, 1684–7, 1689–96, 1698–1719, 1721–4
1727–1847, 1850–3 **NLW** Mf **DRO & FRO**
Cop ms/ts PR C 1680–1908 M 1680–1837 B 1680–1909 **DRO**

PEN-RHOS (TRINITY CHAPEL)   *SA*
<Llandrinio, Llansanffraid-ym-Mechain, Meifod & Cegidfa/Guilsfield 1844
C 1696–1991 M 1702–54, 1846–1989 (Banns 1846–1935) B 1695–1963 **NLW** Mf C
1805–46 M (Banns 1846–1935) B 1805–1963 **PCAO**
BT see Llandrinio

PENYSTRYWAID/PENSTROWED   *B*
C 1628–47, 1661–1974 M 1628–47, 1661–1968 B 1628–47, 1661–1812, 1814–1994 **NLW**
Mf CB 1628–1812 M 1628–1837 **PCAO**
BT 1676–7, 1679–80, 1683, 1685–7, 1689, 1691–3, 1695–1700, 1703–5, 1707–9, 1712–13
1716–19, 1721, 1724–6, 1728–34, 1737, 1739–50, 1752–6, 1758–65, 1768–80, 1782–93
1795–1837, 1864, 1868–9, 1872 **NLW**

PONTDOLANOG gweler/see DOLANOG

PONTROBERT   *SA*
<Meifod, Llangynyw & Llanfihangel-yng-Ngwynfa 1854
C 1853–1994 M 1853–1970 B 1857–1994 **NLW** Mf M 1853–1970 **PCAO**

POOL QUAY   *SA*
<Cegidfa/Guilsfield & Y Trallwng/Welshpool 1863
C 1863–1978 M 1864–1970 B 1863–1978 **NLW** Mf **PCAO**

RHOS-GOCH gweler/see TRELYSTAN

SARN   *H*
<Ceri/Kerry & Yr Ystog/Churchstoke
C 1860– M 1861– B 1860– incumbent

SNEAD   *H*
C 1665–1988 M 1665–1952 B 1665–1984 **SRR**
BT 1605, 1608, 1614, 1631, 1660–1, 1663–1833, 1836, 1838–9, 1841–60 **HRO**

TAL-Y-BONT/BUTTINGTON   *SA*
PR CMB 1723–35 recorded in 1936 apparently lost
C 1736–1948 M 1736–1971 (Banns 1824–1900) B 1736–1953 **NLW** Mf **PCAO**
BT 1638, 1660–1, 1663–1734, 1736–1833, 1836–48 **HRO** 1849–62 **NLW** Mf 1854–62
    DRO & FRO Mf 1660–1848 **Soc Gen** Fac 1638–1848 **NLW**
Cop PR/BT index M 1638–1837 **NLW**

TRALLWNG, Y/WELSHPOOL   *SA*
C 1634–1703, 1708–1992 M 1634–1703, 1708–1986 (Banns 1960–86) Christ Church
    1965–71 B 1634–1703, 1708–1963 **NLW** Mf C 1634–1992 M 1634–1986 B
    1634–1944 **PCAO**
BT 1662–3, 1681–2, 1684–5, 1690–1, 1693–5, 1698–1705, 1708–1859, 1861–8 **NLW** Mf
    1662–1845 **DRO & FRO**
Cop PR CMB 1634–1736 (extracts) *Montgomeryshire Collections,* 36 (1912)

TREBERFEDD/MIDDLETOWN & GREAT WOLLASTON   *H*
<Alberbury (Llanfihangel-yng-Ngheintyn) 1864 [see entry for Crugion/Criggion]. Includes
the Montgomeryshire townships of Treberfedd/Middletown and Ucheldre/the Heldre
C 1829–1908 M 1864–1970 (Banns 1864–1976) **SRR** B 1872– incumbent

TREFALDWYN/MONTGOMERY   *SA*
C 1574–1641, 1645–8, 1650–3, 1656–91, 1694–1972 M 1575–1641, 1645–7, 1651, 1653,
    1656–91, 1694–1981 B 1574–1641, 1645–7, 1652–3, 1656–91, 1694–1966 **NLW** Mf
    PCAO
BT 1663–1772, 1774–1826, 1829–33, 1836–72 **HRO**

TREFEGLWYS   *B*
C 1625–6, 1630–8, 1660–89, 1695–1957 M 1661–89, 1695–1971 B 1632–9, 1661–91,
    1695–1988 **NLW** Mf **PCAO**
BT 1677, 1680, 1683–7, 1689–93, 1695–1700, 1703–5, 1707–9, 1711–13, 1715–21,
    1723–34, 1737, 1739–43, 1745–56, 1758–1836 **NLW**
Cop PR C 1626–1723 M 1661–1723 B 1632–1722 *Montgomeryshire Collections,* 32–33
    (1902–4) CMB 1695–6 Sir Thomas Phillips, *Register of the Baptisms, Marriages and Burials of
    the Parish of Tref Eglwys ... 1695–6* (Middle Hill Press, *c*1867) ms PR C 1626–1836
    (extracts to 1856) M 1661–1850 (extracts to 1858) B 1632–1812 (extracts to 1873) **NLW**

TREGYNON   *SA*
C 1689–1891 M 1680–4, 1689, 1695–1970 (Banns 1823–1939) B 1677–81, 1685,

1689–1993 **NLW** Mf C 1689–1891 M 1680–1838 (Banns 1823–1938) B 1677–1993
PCAO
BT 1666–8, 1670, 1672, 1674, 1677, 1679, 1681–95, 1699–1724, 1726–97, 1799–1839,
1851–4 **NLW** Mf 1666–1839 **DRO & FRO**

TRELYSTAN (WOLSTONMYND)   *H*
<Worthen, co Salop, 1853. Formerly a chapelry comprising the Montgomeryshire
townships of Trelystan, Tre'r-llai/Leighton and Rhos-goch with Mulsop
C 1660–1961 M 1660–1796, 1815–1955 B 1660–1814 **SRR**
BT 1638, 1660, 1663–1827, 1829–33, 1836–7, 1840–3, 1845–6, 1849–87 **HRO**

TRE'R-LLAI/LEIGHTON   *H*
<Worthen, co Salop, 1853. PR for Worthen C 1558–1931 M 1558–1972 B 1558–1965
are in SRR
C 1854– B 1864– incumbent M 1855–1971 **SRR**

TRINITY CHAPEL gweler/see PEN-RHOS

★ WELSHPOOL/Y TRALLWNG   *SA*
C 1634–1703, 1708–1992 M 1634–1703, 1708–1986 (Banns 1960–86) Christ Church
1965–71 B 1634–1703, 1708–1963 **NLW** Mf C 1634–1992 M 1634–1986 B
1634–1944 **PCAO**
BT 1662–3, 1681–2, 1684–5, 1690–1, 1693–5, 1698–1705, 1708–1859, 1861–8 **NLW** Mf
1662–1845 **DRO & FRO**
Cop PR CMB 1634–1736 (extracts) *Montgomeryshire Collections,* 36 (1912)

WOLSTONMYND gweler/see TRELYSTAN

YSTOG, YR/CHURCHSTOKE   *H*
Included townships of Brompton and Rhiston, co Salop
C 1558–1853 M 1558–1812 B 1558–1812 **SRR**
BT 1660, 1663–1718, 1720–54, 1756–87, 1789–1833, 1836–53, 1855–8, 1861 **HRO**

MYNEGAI : INDEX